LIGAND REACTIVITY
AND CATALYSIS

LIGAND REACTIVITY
AND CATALYSIS

MARK M. JONES

DEPARTMENT OF CHEMISTRY
VANDERBILT UNIVERSITY
NASHVILLE, TENNESSEE

 *1968*

ACADEMIC PRESS   NEW YORK and LONDON

PREFACE

This is a book which has several purposes. The first and most obvious is that of collecting information bearing on the problems of coordination and ligand reactivity. But the mere collection of such data is not really a final goal, so a second purpose has been to attempt to provide an organizational framework into which much of this information could be placed in a logical manner. The principal testing ground for such a framework, however, lies not in the ease with which it can accommodate known information, but its fruitfulness in assisting the application of general principles to completely new situations. This kind of test can only be applied over a period of years. At this point it is necessary to confess that some shortcomings must inevitably be found as new *types* of reactions in this area are being discovered almost continuously.

As the manuscript of this book has grown it has become increasingly obvious that the literature bearing on this subject is not only extensive, but also widely dispersed. Work in this area has been carried out by investigators who have had little interest in many of the broader problems of the field. As a result, some areas have been intensively studied, and other areas with an equivalent intrinsic interest have been largely ignored. A third purpose of this book is then to encourage further work in this field with the goal of making the book itself obsolete.

The enormous extent of the literature has necessitated decisions as to what topics should be covered in great detail, what ones are to be glossed over, and what ones are to be largely omitted. My criterion for these decisions has been a very personal one, namely, my own interest in that particular aspect of the subject. This has had the result that the work on classic types of complexes has been emphasized at the expense of the metallocenes, the metal aromatic complexes, and the organometallic complexes. Since these are covered already in existing treatises the duplication that would have been involved seemed unjustified. The citations given will allow the interested reader to obtain information on these areas from other sources.

I wish to thank the University Research Council of Vanderbilt University for financial assistance in the preparation of the manuscript, and to acknowledge the assistance of my collaborators, with whom investigations in this area have been carried out, especially Drs. W. A. Connor, K. D. Maguire, C. H. Oestreich, and D. G. Lambert. I must also acknowledge a considerable debt to some of my colleagues in the chemistry department at Vanderbilt who have provided me with an enormous amount of very fruitful criticism. Those to whom I have such an obligation include Drs. Thomas M. Harris, John C. D. Brand, and K. Keith Innes. Naturally they cannot be held responsible for any of the mistakes or errors that I have persisted in. I also wish to thank Dr. John H. Craddock of the Monsanto Co. for his careful reading of the manuscript and the many improvements which resulted from his suggestions. I must offer my sincerest thanks to participants in a course based on these notes. Members of the class have given suggestions on many details and points of presentation of the notes. For such help I wish to thank Dr. J. W. Hosking and Messrs. A. E. Gebala, K. P. Lannert, D. T. Livak, R. S. McDow, K. A. Morgan, M. F. Prysak, F. G. Schroeder, C. E. Skinner, II, and M. V. Stevens. Finally, I wish to acknowledge my obligation to my wife, Shirley, who has patiently typed and retyped the various sections of the manuscript.

MARK M. JONES

Nashville, Tennessee
April, 1968

CONTENTS

Chapter IV. **Catalysis via Coordination**

Chapter V. **Theoretical and Physical Studies on Coordinated Ligands**

Chapter VI. **The Prediction of the Effects of Coordination on Ligand Reactivity**

Chapter I INTRODUCTION

1.1. Scope

Metal ions are involved in a very large number of reactions by virtue of their ability to coordinate to simple or polyatomic donor species. In most of these cases, the involvement of the metal results in a modification of either the mechanism of the reaction or its rate, or both. At present, the various types of chemists (organic, inorganic, biochemical, and physical) who study aspects of this have quite different ways of looking at the general problem. It is obvious that it would be very desirable to have some way of predicting the effect of metal ions on the course of *any* ligand reaction. It would be even more desirable to be able to predict when coordination will allow an otherwise impossible reaction to proceed to give reasonable amounts of products. Although this is not yet possible, the mere collection of the work done to date suggests many general patterns and also shows further fruitful lines of investigation. The goal *here* is to present *some* of the physical and chemical evidence that is available on ligand reactivity and to show what meaningful patterns have been revealed. The author's prejudices are inescapable, unfortunately, but the most important one, which may be subject to revision in the light of new facts, is a simple one. It is merely the belief that this field must develop in a manner compatible with its character as a border area between inorganic and organic chemistry. It must ultimately form a smooth bridge from one to the other, and violate the spirit of neither.

1.2. Historical Introduction

The study of the reactivity of ligands in complexes may be traced back over one hundred years. Much of this earlier work was cursory and more was incidental to studies of other aspects of coordination chemistry. The chief reasons for surveying it in any detail are that it shows clearly how some

1

important ideas have been developed and that it presents some problems which have not yet received a satisfactory solution.

The dependence of the ligand reactivity on the nature of the central ion can be seen in data on the reactivity of complex oxalates collected prior to 1860. The corresponding variations in the behavior of cyanide were noted even earlier, as were aspects such as the loss of basicity of coordinated ammonia. The systematic study of this field dates from a much later period, however, and much of this earlier work has not yet been satisfactorily incorporated into later theories.

Over one hundred years ago, Gibbs and Genth[1] noted that the coordination of the oxalate group to cobalt(III) resulted in some striking changes in its reactivity towards oxidizing agents. Such oxalate groups were found to be *less* susceptible to attack by oxidizing agents than free oxalate ions. They also attempted to reduce the nitro group in $[Co(NH_3)_5(NO_2)]Cl_2$ by boiling it with a mixture of acetic acid and iron filings in a conscious effort to see if the reaction were analogous to that found with nitrobenzene. The experiments were not successful.

Since that time an enormous number of observations of this kind have been recorded and it has been established that the pattern of reactivity changes is very complicated. Coordination may result in masking that makes one reaction of a ligand no longer possible, and, at the same time, may allow another reaction to proceed more easily, even one that is otherwise sterically almost impossible. It is obvious that a highly charged metal ion will always polarize a ligand brought into its vicinity, but this may either facilitate a reaction, slow it down, or have no obvious effect depending upon the kind of reorganization required to reach the transition state and the proximity of the cation to the reaction site.

An early example of the appreciation of the differences between free and complexed ligands may be seen in studies of the toxicity of various cyanide complexes. In general, those cyanides that give hydrocyanic acid in the presence of dilute acid (such as is found in the stomach) are poisonous in the same manner as hydrocyanic acid itself.[2] Inert cyanide complexes such as those derived from Fe(II), Au(I), Cr(III), Co(III), and Pt(IV) are either non-poisonous, or much less so than normal cyanides. Much information of this sort was obtained by Pelikan prior to 1860.[2]

The inability of simple complexed anions to undergo their typical precipitation tests was noted very early and formed one of the most convincing chemical proofs for the formation of a new compound. Thus treatment of platinum(II) sulfite complexes with dilute sulfuric or hydrochloric acid results in a solution

1. W. Gibbs and F. A. Genth, *Am. J. Sci.* (2) **23**, 241 (1857); (2) **24**, 89 (1857).
2. A. Heffter, "Handbuch der Experimentallen Pharmakologie," Bd. 1, pp. 776–778. Springer, Berlin, 1923.

from which only a portion of the SO_2 is expelled by gentle heat,[3] and treatment of chloroplatinic acid with silver nitrate solution results in the precipitation of $Ag_2[PtCl_6]$, not AgCl.[4] The inability of barium ion to precipitate more than a fraction of the sulfate in various forms of chromium(III) sulfate[5] was also noted years ago. As a general rule, coordinated anions in inert complexes do not undergo typical precipitation reactions and also their participation in *their* characteristic redox reactions is restricted to a greater or lesser extent. With a *polyatomic* ligand such as thiocyanate, tying up one end in a coordinate bond does not necessarily destroy the ability of the other end to undergo reaction. Thiocyanate coordinated to chromium(III) through the nitrogen, Cr—NCS, can form a coordinate bond with silver through the sulfur to give CrNCSAg.[6] Since this is a characteristic reaction of the sulfur in thiocyanate, it would appear that the changes in reactivity of the ligand atoms become more pronounced as one approaches the coordinate bond.

Examples of more detailed studies of the reactions of coordinated ligands began to appear in the chemical literature before 1900. In 1872, Schutzenberger[7] showed that the alcoholysis of phosphorus trichloride, which is a well-established reaction for the free ligand, also occurs in the complexes $(PtCl_2 \cdot PCl_3)_2$ and $PtCl_2 \cdot 2PCl_3$. These reactions are

$$PCl_3 + 3CH_3OH = P(OCH_3)_3 + 3HCl$$
$$(PtCl_2 \cdot PCl_3)_2 + 6CH_3OH = [PtCl_2 \cdot P(OCH_3)_3]_2 + 6HCl$$
$$PtCl_2 \cdot 2PCl_3 + 6CH_3OH = PtCl_2 \cdot 2P(OCH_3)_3 + 6HCl$$

The alcoholysis reaction follows the same general course in both cases, though differences in the kinetic behavior would be expected. The same kind of reaction is of some generality for complexes of phosphorus trichloride and has been studied by other workers.[8-11]

A very significant advance in studies of ligand reactivity was brought about by the pioneering work of Meerwein. The polarization that the ligand undergoes when brought near a charged ion, or when it donates a share in one of its electron pairs to a cation, leads to a number of changes which Meerwein

3. A. Litton and G. Schnederman, *Ann. Chem. Liebigs* **42**, 319 (1842).
4. C. Claus, "Beitrage zur Chemie der Platinmetalle." Festschrift Universität Kazan, Dorpat, Russia, 1854.
5. A. Recoura, *Ann. Chim. Phys.* **4** (7), 494 (1895). The literature on this topic is collected by I. Koppel, *in* "Handbuch der Anorganischen Chemie" (R. Abegg, ed.), Bd. 4, Abt. 1, Hefte 2, pp. 132–168. Hirzel, Leipzig, 1921.
6. W. C. Waggener, J. A. Mattern, and G. H. Cartledge, *J. Am. Chem. Soc.* **84**, 2958 (1959).
7. P. Schutzenberger, *Bull. Soc. Chim. France* **17**, 482 (1872); **18**, 101 (1872).
8. M. Risler, *Bull. Soc. Chim. France* **18**, 151 (1872).
9. E. M. Pomey, *Jahresberichte* p. 612 (1887).
10. M. L. Lindel, *Ann. Chim. Paris* **11** (6), 190 (1887).
11. A. E. Arbusov and V. M. Zoroastrova, *Bull. Acad. Sci. USSR Div. Chem. Sci.* (*English Transl.*) p. 809, 818 (1952).

showed to be general phenomena. The most important of these is the weakening of the other bonds formed by the donor atom. The example of water is typical; coordination results in a polarization of electrons in the oxygen–hydrogen bond toward the donor atom and as a result the hydrogen atoms of coordinated water molecules are considerably more acidic than water itself. Meerwein showed that the same increase in acidity occurred with coordinated alcohols.[12, 13]

$$B(OC_2H_5)_3 + C_2H_5OH \rightarrow H[B(OC_2H_5)_4] \rightleftarrows H^+ + [B(OC_2H_5)_4]^-$$

Shortly afterward, Meerwein considered the more general problem of the effect of complex formation on ligand properties. In an unusual, but almost completely neglected paper,[14] Meerwein proposed that the effect of coordination of an —OH, —NH$_2$, or —OR group in an organic compound could be estimated from the behavior of the corresponding compound in which a carbonyl group was attached to the particular functional group. This was intended to cover adducts with species such as BF$_3$ and SbCl$_5$ and it is a reasonable procedure. Meerwein ascribed the increased reactivity of coordinated species to the considerably greater dipole moments possessed by the adducts.[15] This presumably provides a path of lower activation energy in a large number of reactions in which a charged or highly polar attacking species is involved *if the orientation of the attacking species* favored by the large dipole moment is the proper one for the given reaction. Meerwein also reasoned that coordination of an unsaturated linkage, such as —C=C—, should increase the ease with which it undergoes addition reactions. This statement was based on the behavior of α,β-unsaturated ketones.

Meerwein studied a number of reactions in which coordination was involved, including the splitting of coordinated ethers,[16]

$$(C_2H_5)_2O + C_6H_5COCl \xrightarrow{ZnCl_2} C_2H_5{-}O\overset{\overset{\displaystyle O}{\|}}{C}{-}C_6H_5 + C_2H_5Cl$$

the methylation of alcohols,[17]

$$C_4H_9OH + CH_2N_2 \xrightarrow{FeCl_3} C_4H_9OCH_3 + N_2$$

$$\underset{H}{\overset{R}{>}}O{\cdots}Al(OR)_3 + CH_2N_2 \longrightarrow \underset{CH_3}{\overset{R}{>}}O{\cdots}Al(OR)_3 + N_2$$

12. H. Meerwein, *Schriften Konigsberger Gelehrten Ges. Naturw. Kl.* **3**, 129–166 (1927).
13. H. Meerwein, *Ann. Chem. Liebigs* **455**, 227–253 (1927).
14. H. Meerwein, *Marburger Sitzber.* **65**, 119–135 (1930).
15. See for example: H. Ulich and W. Nespital, *Angew. Chem.* **44**, 750 (1931).
16. H. Meerwein and H. Maier-Hüser, *J. Prakt. Chem.* **134**, 51–81 (1932).
17. H. Meerwein and G. Hinz, *Ann. Chem. Liebigs* **484**, 1–25 (1931).

the use of boron trifluoride for syntheses,[18]

$$C_6H_5COCH_3 + O(COCH_3)_2 \xrightarrow{BF_3} C_6H_5COCH_2COCH_3 + CH_3COOH \cdot BF_3$$

the migration of aromatic iodo groups in the presence of BF_3 complexes,[19]

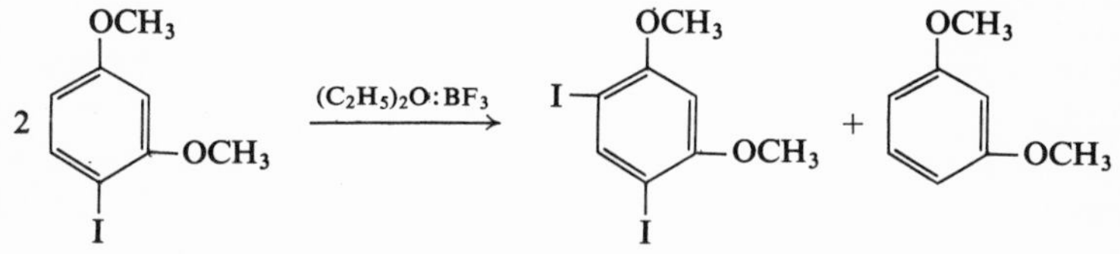

and the addition of diazomethane to anhydrous acetone, which is catalyzed by lithium chloride, presumably via the formation of a complex.[20]

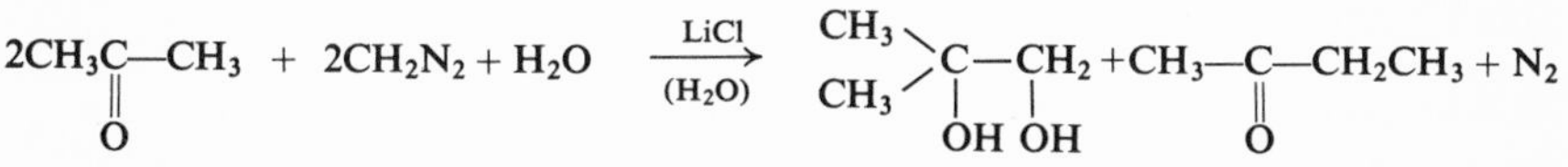

Meerwein also showed that the general principles he had proposed could serve as a valuable guide to the development of new synthetic procedures.

In the years between the First and the Second World Wars, there are to be found a number of studies of ligand reactions of a different type than those examined by Meerwein. Among these, the work of Pfeiffer and of Hölzl are of special interest. Pfeiffer studied several reactions in which the coordination of an ester or an ether to a metallic chloride (such as $SbCl_5$ or $SnCl_4$) gives a product that splits off an alkyl halide when heated. These included complexes formed by oxalic acid esters[21]

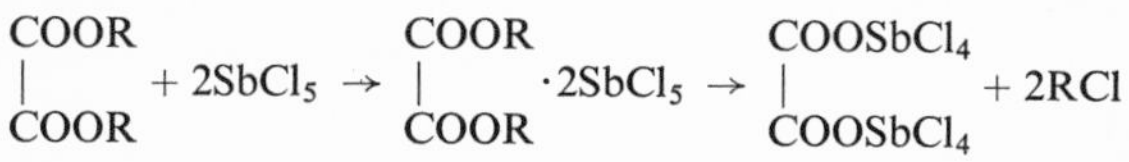

18. H. Meerwein, *Ber. Deut. Chem. Ges.* **66B**, 411–414 (1933).
19. H. Meerwein, P. Hoffman, and F. Schill, *J. Prakt. Chem.* **154**, 266–283 (1940).
20. H. Meerwein and W. Burneleit, *Ber. Deut. Chem. Ges.* **61**, 1840 (1928).
21. P. Pfeiffer, *Z. Anorg. Allgem. Chem.* **133**, 101–106 (1924).

and ethers of alizarin[22]:

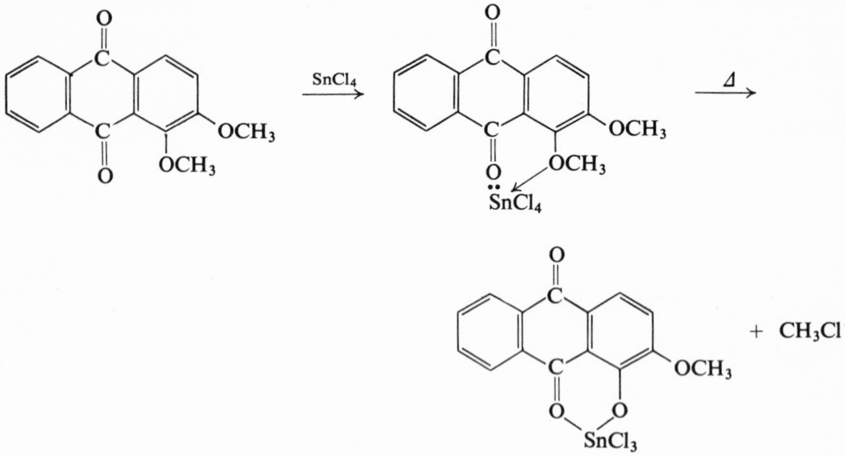

Later work included studies of the complexes formed with ketones by Grignard reagents,[23] and the exchange of amine moieties in inner complex salts of Schiff bases.[24] This last reaction is of the type

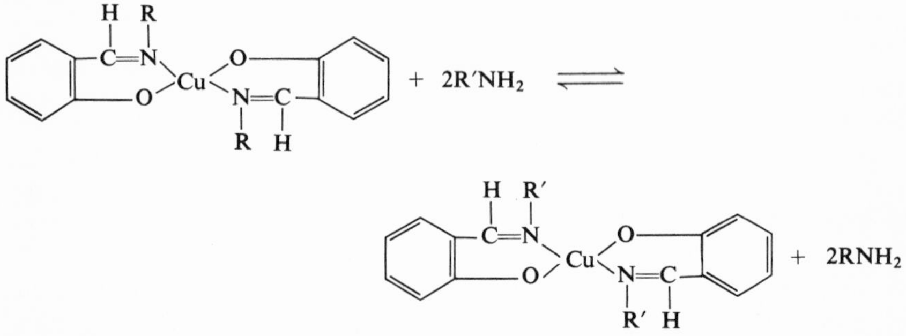

Shortly afterward, Pfeiffer reported that the use of optically active amino acid esters (to furnish the amine) in Schiff base chelates with copper, resulted in the racemization of the asymmetric center.[25] When the attempt was made to prepare the corresponding nickel chelates an oxidative reaction occurred and the nickel chelate of salicylaldimine was obtained.

22. P. Pfeiffer, P. Fischer, J. Kuntner, P. Monti, and Z. Pros, *Ann. Chem. Liebigs* **398**, 137–196 (1913).
23. P. Pfeiffer and H. Blank, *J. Prakt. Chem.* **153**, 242–256 (1939).
24. P. Pfeiffer and H. Glaser, *J. Prakt. Chem.* **153**, 265–284 (1939).
25. P. Pfeiffer, W. Offermann, and H. Werner, *J. Prakt. Chem.* **159**, 313 (1942).

The work of several other investigators, such as that of Hölzl and Baudisch, is roughly contemporaneous with that of Pfeiffer. Hölzl's studies were concerned with the reactions of cyanide complexes. He and his co-workers examined the alkylation of these compounds by the use of a variety of alkylating agents: $(CH_3)_2SO_4$, CH_3I, and alcohols. Examples of these reactions include

$$K_4[Mo(CN)_8] + (CH_3)_2SO_4 \rightarrow [(CN)_4Mo(CNMe)_2(H_2O)_2] \cdot 4H_2O$$

(ref. 26)

$$Ag_4[Fe(CN)_6] + MeI \xrightarrow[\text{MeOH}]{\text{Absolute}} [Fe(CN)_2(CNMe)_4] + 4AgI$$

(ref. 27)

$$H_3[Co(CN)_6] \xrightarrow[\Delta]{\text{EtOH}} \text{Alkylated products}$$

(ref. 28)

Hölzl also carried out similar reactions with $H_4[W(CN)_8]$,[29] cadmium cyanides,[30] and $K_3Cr(CN)_6$.[31] Studies of the reactions of the parent acids of complex cyanides and alcohols showed that the products were often complex and that the degree of alkylation was generally slight. Some related systems examined were

$$H_3[Co(CN)_6] + C_3H_7OH; \qquad H_3[Co(CN)_6] + C_2H_5OH;$$

(ref. 32)   (ref. 33)

$$H_3[Co(CN)_6] + CH_3OH; \quad \text{and} \quad H_4[Fe(CN)_6] + C_2H_5OH$$

(ref. 34)   (ref. 35)

Hölzl's work revealed that reactions carried out on complexes with a number of identical functional groups result in a mixture of products and that such systems are often difficult to characterize thoroughly.

O. Baudisch and his co-workers emphasized the viewpoint that organic ligands that are coordinated to a metal ion become activated and more easily available for oxidative cleavage or chemical replacement.[36–41] Baudisch used

26. F. Hölzl and G. I. Xenakis, *Monatsh. Chem.* **48**, 689–709 (1924).
27. F. Hölzl, *Monatsh. Chem.* **48**, 71–86 (1927).
28. F. Hölzl, T. Meier-Mohar, and F. Viditz, *Monatsh. Chem.* **53/54**, 237–245 (1929).
29. F. Hölzl, *Monatsh. Chem.* **51**, 1–22 (1929).
30. F. Hölzl and S. Kirschmayr, *Monatsh. Chem.* **51**, 397–419 (1929).
31. F. Hölzl and F. Viditz, *Monatsh. Chem.* **49**, 241–264 (1928).
32. F. Hölzl, W. Brell, and G. Schinko, *Monatsh. Chem.* **62**, 349 (1933).
33. F. Hölzl and G. Schinko, *Monatsh. Chem.* **58**, 249 (1931).
34. F. Hölzl and S. Sallmann, *Monatsh. Chem.* **58**, 29–46 (1931).
35. F. Hölzl and J. Krakora, *Monatsh. Chem.* **64**, 97–105 (1934).
36. O. Baudisch, *Biochem. Z.* **232**, 35 (1931).
37. O. Baudisch, *Ber. Deut. Chem. Ges.* **62**, 2699 (1929).
38. O. Baudisch and D. Davidson, *J. Biol. Chem.* **71**, 501 (1927).
39. M. H. Pfaltz, *J. Am. Chem. Soc.* **45**, 2980 (1923).
40. M. H. Pfaltz and O. Baudisch, *J. Am. Chem. Soc.* **45**, 2972 (1923).
41. O. Baudisch, *Ber. Deut. Chem. Ges.* **54**, 406 (1921).

pentacyanoaquoferrate(II) as a catalyst; here the water can be displaced as a ligand by a large variety of organic molecules such as pyridine, nitrosobenzene, p-nitrosodimethylaniline, and pyrimidines. Baudisch also postulated that when this complex functioned as a catalyst for oxidation reactions, it did so by activating molecular oxygen by coordination in the complex $[Fe(CN)_5(O_2)]^{3-}$. Earlier work of Manchot[42] showed that pentacyanoammineferrate(II) absorbed carbon monoxide, nitric oxide, and oxygen from the air but the oxygen oxidizes the iron(II) to iron(III). (Manchot had previously shown that hemoglobin and ethylene form a weak complex.[43]) Baudisch found that the pentacyanoammineferrate catalyzed oxidations by molecular oxygen by a redox process that involved the iron in two different oxidation states, either of which could be added to obtain the catalyst.

Though not concerned directly with the reactions of coordinated ligands, Pfeiffer and Wizinger's paper on the mechanism of aromatic substitution[44] is worthy of note as being the first paper in which the action of halogen carriers, such as $FeCl_3$, was ascribed to the ability of these substances to form co-ordinate bonds with the halogen and to assist the reaction by this process.

A number of other studies of the reactions of coordinated ligands may be found in the literature prior to 1940. Some of those that approach this from the viewpoint of coordination chemistry are listed in Table I.

In addition to these studies there are a very large number that were carried out on systems in which the complex was not characterized at the time. These include many studies of reactions such as the Friedel-Crafts, the Fries, and halogenation reactions carried out with halogen carriers derived from metallic halides. Although the complexes in such systems are often less thoroughly characterized, they are among the most interesting because of their direct involvement in important metal-catalyzed reactions. Many of these will be cited later when the behavior they exemplify is discussed in more detail. It should be noted that the complexes most used in *organic chemistry* are labile ones that rapidly reach equilibrium with their environment as it is altered. This makes their characterization *in the reaction media* often a task of very considerable difficulty. In many cases the exact composition of the complexes present in the multicomponent reaction mixtures is still uncertain and the reactive forms of the complexes are not agreed upon in several *important* reactions.

1.3. Classification Schemes

It is usually found convenient to set up some kind of a classification scheme if one wishes to consider a large number of different reactions in some

42. W. Manchot, *Ber. Deut. Chem. Ges.* **45**, 2869 (1912).
43. W. Manchot, *Ann. Chem. Liebigs* **370**, 241 (1909).
44. P. Pfeiffer and R. Wizinger, *Ann. Chem. Liebigs* **461**, 138–139 (1928).

TABLE I

SOME STUDIES OF THE REACTIONS OF LIGANDS PRIOR TO 1940

Reaction	Reference
Reaction of nickel dimethylglyoxime with acetic anhydride	45
Acetylation of the lead salts of aminothiophenols	46
Esterification of the zinc iodide–ether complex with benzoyl chloride	47
Amination of 3-bromopyridine in the presence of a copper salt	48
Stabilization of aliphatic diazo compounds as CuCl adducts	49
Nonreactivity of carbonyl group of metal acetylacetonates with phenyl-hydrazine	50
Oxygen absorption of manganous acetylacetonate	51
Methyl iodide and the silver salt of o-aminobenzoic acid	52
Reactions of copper enolates	53
Reactions of various complexes	54
Halogenation of cupric ethylacetoacetate	55
Failure of nickel dimethylglyoxime to react with phenyl isocyanide	56
Reaction of copper acetylacetonate and S_2Cl_2	57

systematic fashion. The reactions of coordinated species form such a hetero-geneous group that some such classification scheme is necessary if any order is to be discerned at all. The type of classification scheme may be expected to vary with the viewpoint of its originators and inorganic, organic, or biological chemists may be expected to favor radically different schemes. Another point of choice is whether the classification is primarily to assist in the application of such reactions to new situations or whether the goal is a much deeper theoretical understanding of the basic processes at work.

45. M. F. Barker, *Chem. News* **130**, 99 (1925).
46. H. Bauer and K. Bursshkies, *Ber. Deut. Chem. Ges.* **66**, 1041 (1933).
47. E. Blaise, *Compt. Rend.* **140**, 661 (1905).
48. H. J. Den Hertog and J. P. Wibaut, *Rec. Trav. Chim.* **55**, 122 (1936).
49. O. Diels and W. Kohl, *Ann. Chem. Liebigs* **443**, 262 (1925).
50. R. Emmert and O. Schneider, *Ber. Deut. Chem. Ges.* **69**, 1316 (1936).
51. R. Emmert, H. Gsottschneider, and H. Stanger, *Ber. Deut. Chem. Ges.* **69**, 1319 (1936).
52. P. Karrer, C. Nageli, H. Weidmann, and L. Wilbuschewich, *Helv. Chim. Acta* **2**, 242 (1919).
53. A. Michael and G. H. Carlson, *J. Am. Chem. Soc.* **58**, 353 (1936).
54. H. Reihlen, R. Illig, and R. Wittig, *Ber. Deut. Chem. Ges.* **58**, 12 (1925).
55. B. Schonbrodt, *Ann. Chem. Liebigs* **253**, 171 (1889).
56. L. Chugaev, *J. Chem. Soc.* **105**, 2192 (1914).
57. M. Vaillant, *Compt. Rend.* **119**, 647 (1894).

The first classification scheme was that of Martell and Calvin[58] who restricted their attention to *chelate* catalyst systems. The three kinds of reactions they listed are

(1) Reactions in which the chelate underwent no permanent chemical change (e.g., reversible redox systems such as those found with oxygen-carrying chelates).

(2) Reactions in which the donor group underwent a chemical reaction such as oxidation, halogenation, or rearrangement. An example of this is the catalytic oxidation of oxalates by Mn(III).

(3) Negative catalysis resulting from the removal of catalytically active metals by the chelating agent, for example, the inhibition of hemoglobin by carbon monoxide.

Chaberek and Martell[59] used a similar scheme but modified the second class to include reactions in which either the donor group or the metal ion suffered some permanent chemical change.

A rather different scheme was presented by Beck.[60] He divided the catalytic reactions of coordination chemistry into

(1) Catalysis of the formation of complex compounds, including
    (a) coordination catalysis by either the ligand or the cation;
    (b) catalysis of redox reactions;
    (c) heterogeneous catalysis.
(2) Catalysis by complex compounds.

Another classification scheme, oriented toward a phenomenological classification, was given by Jones and Connor.[61] The classes given by this scheme are

(1) Reactions in which coordination allows the ligand and another reactant to come together more easily for reaction in a mixed complex.

(2) Reactions in which the polarization of the ligand by the positive charge on the central metal ion is the principal source of any change in reactivity.

(3) Instances in which coordination stabilizes a ligand in a form especially suitable for certain reactions.

(4) Reactions in which coordination masks one or more of the reactive

58. A. E. Martell and M. Calvin, "The Chemistry of the Metal Chelate Compounds," p. 336 ff. Prentice-Hall, Englewood Cliffs, New Jersey, 1952.
59. S. Chaberek and A. E. Martell, "Organic Sequestering Agents," p. 378 ff. Wiley, New York, 1959.
60. M. T. Beck, *J. Inorg. Nucl. Chem.* **15**, 250 (1960). A more detailed scheme is presented by this same author in *Record Chem. Progr.* (*Kresge-Hooker Sci. Lib.*) **27**, 37 (1966).
61. M. M. Jones and W. A. Connor, *Ind. Eng. Chem.* **55** (9), 14 (1963).

groups of a ligand so that the reaction occurs at only some of the potential sites.

(5) Reactions in which coordination allows a chelate to be formed from two or more species which do not readily undergo reaction in the absence of a coordination center.

(6) Reactions in which coordination is a prerequisite to the transfer of electrons.

(7) Reactions in which the stereospecificity of the coordination act is utilized.

(8) Instances in which coordination allows a normally unstable ligand to be isolated as a stable complexed species, or makes the thermodynamics of the overall reaction more favorable.

(9) Reactions in which coordination activates a small molecule for reaction usually by assisting its splitting into polar or radical fragments.

It is also possible to set up a classification scheme based upon whether the changes observed result from changes in the *thermodynamic* or *kinetic* factors governing the reactions. Thus, the coordination act can result in a thermodynamically stable complex containing a ligand that is otherwise difficult or impossible to prepare. A number of reactions have been proposed to be of this sort, though detailed data are available on only a few. As an example for which this has been presumed to be the case, one may cite the reaction[62]:

In this case the ligand can be recovered from the complex by careful hydrolysis of the aluminum chloride with ice water.

The ways in which coordination may affect the kinetics of a reaction are quite numerous and can proceed via changes in $\Delta E^{\ddagger}$ or $\Delta S^{\ddagger}$, or both. Coordination usually bonds the ligand into a larger molecule and on this basis alone can be expected to reduce the frequency factor of a reaction involving a typical attacking species. This has been found to occur in the diazo coupling reactions of 8-hydroxyquinoline-5-sulfonic acid and its metal chelates.[63,64] Unfortunately, there is very little comparative data available on the entropies of activation for free and coordinated ligands.

62. E. Ott, *Ann. Chem. Liebigs* **392**, 245 (1912).
63. K. D. Maguire and M. M. Jones, *J. Am. Chem. Soc.* **85**, 154 (1963).
64. J. B. Breinig and M. M. Jones, *J. Org. Chem.* **28**, 852 (1963).

It must be realized that any classification scheme is incomplete in the sense that it can hardly be expected to include all the types of metal-catalyzed reactions to be discovered in the future or all of the reactions of coordinated ligands which will be investigated. Although the reactions known at present can be fitted into present chemical theories, there is no assurance that these are in any way complete. The major problem of the theoretical prediction of electron density patterns in coordinated species has hardly been attacked at all and the ultimate form which such solutions may take is difficult to hazard. One would hope that each succeeding classification scheme would have these advantages over its predecessors:

(1) It will be more nearly all-inclusive of the known types of reaction.

(2) It will come closer to having a *quantitative* theoretical basis.

(3) It will have greater predictive powers for unearthing reactions of previously unknown types.

Such a scheme can be no better than our information on the thermodynamics and kinetics of the reactions on which it is founded.

The principal gaps in our knowledge of ligand reactions and metal-catalyzed reactions are just those needed to form the basis for any *quantitative* theory. There are very few complete kinetic studies of such reactions, and surprisingly, even fewer thermodynamic studies. As a result, the most that can be done at present in the way of predicting when coordination may be used to advantage is by the judicious use of *analogy*. The closer the unknown case is to known examples, the greater the chances of a successful prediction. Since the role of masking in such reactions of coordination compounds is very uncertain, predictions based upon analogy are most difficult to make when considerable steric changes must be taken into account.

Chapter II EQUILIBRIUM SHIFTS RESULTING FROM COORDINATION

An almost inevitable consequence of the coordination act is the alteration of the equilibrium constants for the reactions of the ligand. This is a phenomenon characteristic of both aqueous and nonaqueous systems and is found in complexes of every sort, including those of Lewis acids (such as BF_3 and $AlCl_3$) with a wide variety of organic compounds, aquo complexes of metal ions, and ammine complexes of the platinum elements. The change in equilibrium constant is usually most drastic when the reaction center is close to or coincident with the donor atom of a ligand. As a general rule, such effects fall off in magnitude, as the number of intervening atoms increases, in roughly the same fashion as electrical effects fall off in organic species.

2.1. Increases in the Strengths of Protonic Acids

When a donor atom bearing a hydrogen atom is joined to a Lewis acid in a coordination compound, the resultant displacement of electronic charge toward the Lewis acid should facilitate the ionization of a proton from the ligand. There are numerous examples for which this has been demonstrated unambiguously; aquo complexes were studied early, as were ammines. Werner[1] showed that the acidic properties of such coordinated species decreased as the central ion was changed in the order $Pt^{4+} > Ru^{4+} > Cr^{3+} > Co^{3+}$. Some of the simple aquo complexes are reasonably strong acids: $[Cr(H_2O)_4Cl_2]^+$ has a pK_a of 5.7,[2] and that of $[Co(NH_3)_2(H_2O)_4]^{2+}$ is 3.4.[3]

1. A. Werner, "New Ideas on Inorganic Chemistry," p. 201. Longmans, Green, New York, 1911.
2. A. B. Lamb and G. R. Fonda, *J. Am. Chem. Soc.* **43**, 1154 (1921).
3. J. N. Brønsted and K. Volqvartz, *Z. Physik. Chem.* (*Leipzig*) **134**, 97 (1928). In a compound which has both coordinated water and coordinated ammonia, the acidity of the coordinated water is responsible for the acidity of the complex.

These may be compared to acetic acid which has a pK_a of 4.75. The acid strength of water molecules in the hydrated copper(II) ion is some 10^7 times greater than that of free water.[4] The work of Sillén and his school at Stockholm has introduced a considerable refinement in our understanding of the acidity of such species.[5] Sillén's work has shown that many of the "simple" hydrolytic reactions of aquo ions lead to polymeric products, as

$$2Cu^{2+} + 2H_2O \rightarrow Cu_2(OH)_2^{2+} + 2H^+$$

Some few, however, are simple, as

$$H_2OHgOH_2^{2+} \rightarrow HOHgOH_2^+ + H^+ \quad \log K = -3.70$$

Here it is seen that the coordination of a water molecule to a mercuric ion very drastically increases the acidity of the water. The general acid–base properties of complex ions have been surveyed by Basolo and Pearson,[6] and by Grinberg.[7] The activities of the Russian school of platinum chemists in this area are especially noteworthy and have provided many experimental data.

The ionization of the aquo and ammine complexes is explained on the basis of electronic displacements (polarization) from the bond involving the hydrogen toward the central metal "ion"

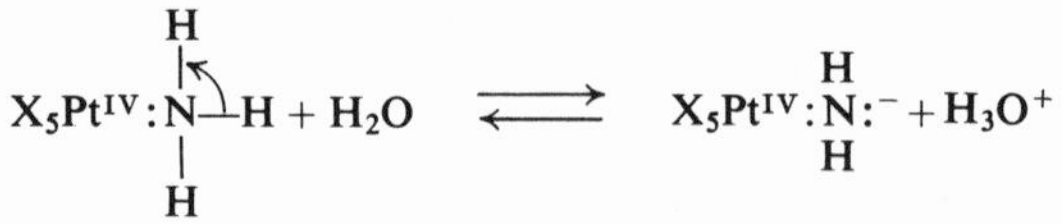

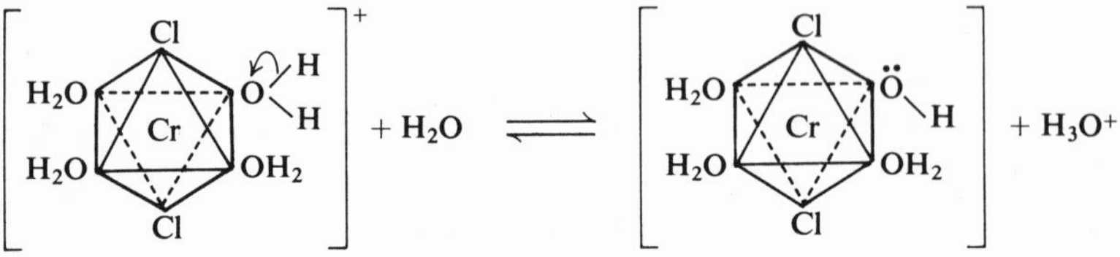

There is a considerable influence of structural and electronic factors on the dissociation constants. The cis and trans isomers of $[Pt(pn)_2Cl_2]Cl_2$ (pn, propylenediamine) show markedly different behavior; the cis isomer is a

4. K. J. Pedersen, *Kgl. Danske Videnskab. Selskab Mat. Fys. Medd.* **22**, No. 12 (1945).

5. L. G. Sillén, *Quart. Rev.* (*London*) **13**, 146 (1959); an older review summarizing much of the early (pre-Sillén) work is F. Reiff, *Z. Anorg. Allgem. Chem.* **208**, 321 (1932). Paper No. 47 from Sillén's group is a study of the hydrolysis of the uranyl ion: S. Hietanen, B. R. L. Row, and L. G. Sillén, *Acta Chem. Scand.* **17**, 2735 (1963).

6. F. Basolo and R. G. Pearson, "Mechanisms of Inorganic Reactions," pp. 386–395. Wiley, New York, 1958.

7. A. A. Grinberg, "An Introduction to the Chemistry of Complex Compounds," transl. by J. R. Leach (D. H. Busch and R. F. Trimble, Jr., eds.), Chapt. IX. Addison-Wesley, Reading, Massachusetts, 1962.

dibasic acid with $K_1 = 6.1 \times 10^{-9}$ and $K_2 = 4.4 \times 10^{-11}$, but the trans isomer is a monobasic acid with $K = 1.8 \times 10^{-11}$.[8] The complex $[Pt(pn)_3]Cl_4$ is a tribasic acid: $K_1 = 3.9 \times 10^{-6}$; $K_2 = 2.5 \times 10^{-10}$; $K_3 = 2.1 \times 10^{-11}$. The acidity of such complexes generally drops off as the oxidation state of the central ion is reduced so that the *upper* limit of the dissociation constants of complex ions such as $[Co(en)_3]^{3+}$, $[Rh(en)_3]^{3+}$, $[Ir(en)_3]^{3+}$, and $[Co(NH_3)_6]^{3+}$ is about 10^{-12}. There is also a relationship between the dissociation constant in compounds of the type *trans*-$[Pt(OH_2)_2(amine)_2]^{2+}$ and the trans effect of the amine, with the dissociation constant of the complex usually increasing as the trans effect of the amine decreases.[9] This relationship is *not* always followed, however, and there are some obvious exceptions such as the fact that *trans*-$[Pt(C_2H_4)(H_2O)Cl_2]$ is a stronger acid than *cis*-$[Pt(NH_3)(H_2O)Cl_2]$.[10]

The behavior of a large number of complexes of tetravalent platinum has been observed, and the more basic ligands tend to give more acidic complexes.[11] The complexes of ethylenediamine are found to be more acidic than the corresponding complexes containing ammonia. Thus one finds increasing acidity in the order $[Pt(NH_3)_6]^{4+} < [Pt(en)(NH_3)_4]^{4+} < [Pt(en)_2(NH_3)_2]^{4+}$.[12]

The behavior of organic ligands is analogous. Early studies of such acids were reported by Meerwein,[13] who showed that the complex of acetic acid and boron trifluoride was a protonic acid whose strength was comparable to that of concentrated sulfuric acid. This effect is also found for a large number of other organic ligands, e.g., chelidamic acid,[14] glycine,[15] pyridine-2-aldoxime,[16] and 2-(2-pyridyl)imidazoline,[17] to cite a few. The example of the ferrous complex of pyridine-2-aldoxime is illustrative. Here thermodynamic data for the ionization of the proton from the oxime —OH group was obtained on both the free ligand and the tris complex with ferrous ion. The pK values for the ionization of the second and third hydrogen ions from the complex

8. A. A. Grinberg, L. V. Vrublevskaya, K. I. Gil'dengershel, and A. I. Stetsenko, *Zh. Neorg. Khim.* **4**, 1018 (1959); *Chem. Abstr.* **60**, 9588.

9. A. A. Grinberg, K. I. Gil'dengershel, and E. P. Panteleeva, *Russ. J. Inorg. Chem.* (*English Transl.*) **8**, 1165 (1963).

10. F. Basolo and R. G. Pearson, *Progr. Inorg. Chem.* **4**, 408 (1962).

11. I. I. Chernyaev and N. T. Kuznetsov, *Zh. Neorg. Khim.* **6**, 81–89 (1961); *Chem. Abstr.* **56**, 12362.

12. I. I. Chernyaev and N. T. Kuznetsov, *Zh. Neorg. Khim.* **7**, 762–768 (1962); *Chem. Abstr.* **57**, 4295.

13. H. Meerwein, *Ges. Befoerd. Ges. Naturwiss. Marburg* **64**, 119 (1930).

14. S. P. Bag, Q. Fernando, and H. Frieser, *Inorg. Chem.* **1**, 887 (1962).

15. A. A. Grinberg, A. I. Stetsenko, and E. N. In'kova, *Dokl. Akad. Nauk SSSR* **136**, 821 (1961); *Chem. Abstr.* **56**, 995. Acid properties of the cis and trans isomers of $[Pt(glycine)_2(NH_3)_2]Cl_2$.

16. G. I. H. Hanania and D. H. Irving, *Nature* **183**, 40 (1959); *J. Chem. Soc.* p. 2745 (1962).

17. G. I. H. Hanania and D. H. Irving, *J. Chem. Soc.* p. 2745, 2750 (1962).

(from the 3:1 complex) were about 3 and 7, respectively, compared with 10.2 for the free ligand.

Coordinated ammines in complexes of the first row transition elements have hydrogen atoms that are only weakly acidic, though these do undergo complete exchange with D_2O when dissolved in water containing D_2O.[18,19] More detailed studies have shown that the rate of this exchange decreases with increasing atomic number of the metal in a family of elements and that square planar complexes exchange more rapidly than octahedral complexes of neighboring metals in the periodic table.[20] The rate decreases with decrease in the charge of the cation and increases with increasing trans effect of the trans group in a complex such as $[Pt(dien)X]^+$, where dien is diethylene-triamine.[21]

It is also known that multidentate chelating agents may be attached to a metal ion by some of the donor groups and yet have other donor groups which are protonated. The theoretical treatment of such equilibria has been developed.[22] For ligands such as malonate and succinate, coordination of HA^- to a metal ion such as cadmium(II) results in a very pronounced increase in the acid dissociation constant.

Another family of examples of a somewhat different sort may be seen in the complexes of inorganic oxyacids with polyols. The best known of these is the mannitol–boric acid complex, which has been widely studied. Here it is a hydroxy group of the boric acid which has its acidity increased when the complex

| Mannitol | Boric acid | Complex |

is formed. The same general behavior occurs with polyol complexes with other inorganic acids such as molybdic, arsenic, or tungstic acids. Complexes with simple alcohols show a very much reduced tendency to form in these cases.[23]

18. H. Erlenmeyer and H. Gartner, *Helv. Chim. Acta* 17, 1008 (1934).
19. H. Erlenmeyer and H. Lobeck, *Helv. Chim. Acta* 18, 1213 (1935).
20. J. W. Palmer and F. Basolo, *J. Inorg. Nucl. Chem.* 15, 279 (1960).
21. J. W. Palmer and F. Basolo, *J. Phys. Chem.* 64, 778 (1960).
22. G. Schwarzenbach and I. Szilard, *Helv. Chim. Acta* 45, 1222 (1962).
23. A. Chretien, *in* "Nouveau Traite de Chimie Minerale" (P. Pascal, ed.), Vol. VI, p. 215. Masson, Paris, 1961. P. Pascal, *ibid.*, p. 305. M. F. Lappert, *Chem. Rev.* 56, 976–980 (1956).

Meerwein[24] showed that zinc chloride adducts with water had pronounced acidity and catalytic activity because of this acidity. As measured by the effect on the rate of inversion of sucrose, an 11.2 M $ZnCl_2$ solution in water has the same acidity as 1 M HCl. Similarly the adduct with acetic acid, obtained as the oxonium salt with ether, $[ZnCl_2OCOCH_3]HO(C_2H_5)_2$, is a sufficiently strong acid that it self-catalyzes its addition to the double bonds of compounds such as camphene. Brubaker and his co-workers[25] have carried out quantitative studies of the acidity of systems such as the $HCl–AlCl_3$ system in water. Other examples of analogous compounds widely used as catalysts are the $H_3PO_4 \cdot BF_3$ adduct and the species "$HF \cdot BF_3$," which is capable of protonating aromatic hydrocarbons in a suitable environment.

The coordination of 2-(2-pyridyl)benzimidazole and 2-(2-pyridyl)imidazoline with various divalent metals was found to increase the acidity of the imino hydrogen of the imidazole group. The increase in this acidity was different for different metal ions.[26]

The influence of the charge on the iron atom and the other coordinated groups, on the acidity of heme-linked histidine components of hemo- and hemiglobin was first explained by Coryell and Pauling.[27] The general arrangement of the atoms is

where the position designated D may be occupied by O_2, or CO, or it may be empty. When the oxidation state of the central iron is increased from +2 to +3, the pK_a value of the acid dissociation of the imidazole system changes to a lower value (more strongly acidic). When the sixth coordination position is emptied the acidity of the coordinated imidazole ring will decrease. This can be explained either on the basis of the older valence bond theory[27] or on the basis of the removal of the opportunity for the iron to back-donate a pair of electrons to D and so reduce its attraction for the positively charged proton.

24. H. Meerwein, *Schriften Konigsberger Gelehrten Ges.* 3, 129–166 (1927).
25. C. H. Brubaker, Jr., P. G. Rasmussen, and D. C. Luehrs, *J. Chem. Eng. Data* 7, Pt. 2, 563–564 (1962).
26. T. R. Harkins and H. Freiser, *J. Am. Chem. Soc.* 78, 1143 (1956).
27. C. D. Coryell and L. Pauling, *J. Biol. Chem.* 132, 769 (1940).

The study of a number of complexes of 4-(2-pyridylazo)resorcinol showed that the acid strength of the 1-hydroxy group varied with the metal complexed. There is an increase in this acid strength in the order Mn(II) < Zn(II) ≈ Ni(II) < Cu(II) < Co(II).[28]

In summary, it can be stated that many of the general features that affect protonic ionizations of ligands have been investigated, though it is obvious that most of the data collected cannot be adequately represented by a simple theory. Although the electrostatic interaction of the metal ion charges and the ligand dipoles is the most important single factor, in most cases the effect of the other ligands on any given acidic group will be significant. With transition metal ions for which back-donation may be important, these interactions can result in qualitative differences between predicted and observed changes in acidity.

2.2. Tautomeric Shifts

When *one* of a pair or group of tautomers forms complexes with metal ions much more readily than any of the others, this form will be preferentially stabilized by coordination. A good example of this is found with acetylacetone, which normally consists of about 72% of the enol form and 28% of the keto form.

$$CH_3—C—CH_2—C—CH_3 \; \rightleftarrows \; CH_3—C=CH—C—CH_3$$

$$\underset{O}{\overset{\|}{}} \qquad \underset{O}{\overset{\|}{}} \qquad\qquad \underset{O—H}{\overset{|}{}} \qquad \underset{O}{\overset{\|}{}}$$

Keto, 28%   Enol, 72%

In the presence of copper(II) ion and a weak base, a copper complex is formed with the enolate anion and the acetylacetone can be transformed completely into its *coordinated enol form* by coordination to copper(II). Ethyl acetoacetate is an even more striking example, as it normally contains only 7% of the enol form, yet it can be transformed completely to the coordinated enolate in complexes with copper(II) and nickel(II). This preferential stabilization of one form in a complex is also found in various derivatives of β-diketones, such as β-ketoimines.

A direct result of the stabilization of one tautomeric form in the complex is to be found in the types of reactions undergone by the complexes. These are found to be largely reactions characteristic of the particular tautomeric form of the ligand present in the complex. In the case of acetylacetone it is known that the enolic form undergoes a variety of electrophilic substitution reactions

28. A. Corsini, Q. Fernando, and H. Freiser, *Inorg. Chem.* **2**, 224 (1963).

at the 3-position,[29] e.g., bromination and thiocyanation. The complexes also undergo the same reactions. Tris(acetylacetonato)chromium(III) reacts with bromine to give the corresponding complex of 3-bromoacetylacetone.[30] In such systems there is evidence that substitution on one of the chelate rings

affects the ease of reaction for other chelate rings in the complex. Collman has reported cases in which the complete substitution reaction of a tris(acetyl-acetonato)metal complex cannot be effected and only one or two of the three reactive positions undergo substitution.

The exact course of this kind of substitution reaction is not known. For the free ligand, the reaction of the enol form with bromine was formerly considered to result in the initial formation of the vicinal dibromide, by the *addition* of bromine to the double bond. This was presumed to be unstable at ambient temperatures and split out HBr to give the 3-bromo-β-diketone. The intermediate dibromo compound has never been isolated and at the present time there is no proof for either the formation of an unstable intermediate in the bromination of the free ligand, or for the alternative claim that the bromination of the free complex proceeds by a typical aromatic mechanism.[30] The mechanisms available to the coordinated species are more restricted in number than those available to the free species. One apparently available to both is the following:

29. K. H. Meyer, *Ann. Chem. Liebigs* **380**, 212 (1911). A survey of these reactions is given by H. Henecka, "Chemie der Beta-Dicarbonylverbindungen." Springer, Berlin, 1950.
30. J. P. Collman, *Advan. Chem. Ser.* **37**, 78 (1963).

This mechanism, which proceeds through a diketo intermediate, is of a sort which can be used for the free ligand in the following way:

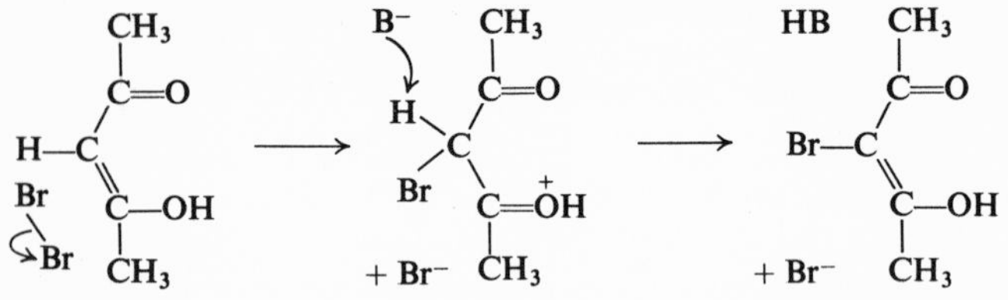

In the usual "salt" of a β-diketone, the reactive sites are the double bond or the 3-carbon atom. Examples include the copper(II)-catalyzed bromination of ethyl acetoacetate[31]

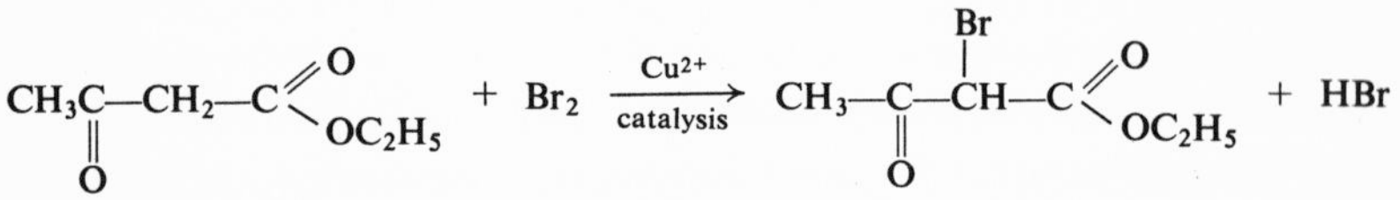

the preparation of 3-substituted β-diketones from the copper(II) complexes and nitrobenzoyl chlorides[32]

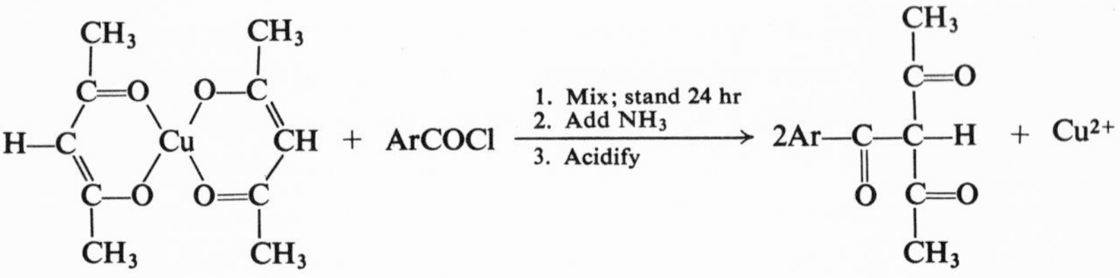

as well as various substitution reactions on acetoacetic acid[33] and a large number of related reactions studied by Collman and his co-workers.[34]

When salts of these compounds with a variety of metals are examined it is obvious that the reactivity pattern depends strongly upon the nature of the

31. K. J. Pedersen, *Acta Chem. Scand.* **2**, 252 (1948).
32. W. J. Barry, *J. Chem. Soc.* p. 670 (1960).
33. A. Michael and G. H. Carson, *J. Am. Chem. Soc.* **57**, 159 (1935); **58**, 353 (1936).
34. J. P. Collman, *Angew. Chem. Intern. Ed. English* **4**, 132 (1965).

cation involved. This can be appreciated more readily from the resonance forms for the anion derived from a β-diketone. These are

$$\text{R—C=CH—C—R'} \longleftrightarrow \text{R—C—CH—C—R'} \longleftrightarrow \text{R—C—CH=C—R'}$$

There are thus three regions of relatively high electron density that represent favorable sites for the attack of electrophilic species: the two oxygen atoms and the 3-carbon position. Such species can and do undergo reactions such as alkylation at *any* of the reactive centers.[35] A rule that helps to put such reactions on a systematic basis was proposed by Kornblum and his co-workers[35]:

> The greater the S_N1 character of the transition state the greater is the preference for covalency formation with the atom of higher electronegativity and, conversely, the greater the S_N2 contribution to the transition state the greater the preference for bond formation to the atom of lower electronegativity.

As an example, the reaction of sodio derivatives of acetoacetic ester with primary alkyl halides goes via carbanion attack and gives only carbon alkylation. When the attacking reagent is CH_3—O—CH_2—Cl the reaction goes via carbonium ion attack to give *oxygen* alkylation. In essence this rule states that when a reaction proceeds via a carbonium ion, it will simply attack the substrate atom of highest electronegativity and hence highest electron density. With this as a basis, the role of the different metal ions in the complex can be seen to be based upon the way in which they affect the electron density pattern of the substrate (ligand). A summary of much of the earlier literature on this kind of reaction, together with important new data, has been given by Brandstrom.[36] One point that must be emphasized is that ions such as Ag(I) and Cu(II), which may be coordinately unsaturated in these complexes, can interact with the attacking alkyl halide via coordination to the halide and assist in the generation of the carbonium ion. In many cases, alkali metal salts seem to favor carbon alkylation over oxygen alkylation, with the reverse holding for compounds of copper or silver. This factor seems to be related to the ability of the transition metal ions to increase the electron density at the oxygen atom by back-donation of electron pairs from their filled d orbitals. It must be remembered that two alternative reaction paths are available for these reactions: one that is S_N1 in character and one that is S_N2. As the conditions are varied slightly, one can favor one mechanism over the other, yet have *both* operating simultaneously.

35. N. Kornblum, R. A. Smiley, R. K. Blackwood, and D. C. Iffland, *J. Am. Chem. Soc.* **77**, 6269 (1955).
36. A. Brandstrom, *Arkiv Kemi* **6**, 155 (1953); **7**, 81 (1954).

A number of other types of chelating groups can also exist in tautomeric forms having different chemical properties. Two examples of this are α-nitroso-β-naphthol

and dithizone

The differing reactivity of the two forms of dithizone can be seen in the studies of H. Irving and his collaborators on the reactions of dithizone with reagents such as methyl sulfate.[37] Silver dithizonate, which had been previously formulated as a complex of the first tautomer, was shown by these investigators to react with methyl iodide to give S-methyldithizone. The observation is consistent with the formulation of the silver complex as a salt of the second tautomer. The S-alkylated dithizones were found *not* to form complexes with Ag(I), Hg(II), and Cu(II). Such complexation reactions are characteristic of the thiol form of dithizone.

In summary, one can predict most of the reactions of such a tautomeric ligand from a knowledge of which tautomeric form is present in the complex and of the reactivity pattern of that form in the uncomplexed state.

2.3. Equilibria Favoring Product Formation

When a molecule forms a metal chelate complex it also forms two or more additional bonds which should help to hold the molecule together if it has a tendency to break up into monodentate species or smaller molecules with fewer donor atoms per molecule. If the metal complex is insoluble, the formation of the solid complex results in an additional relative stabilization of the ligand through factors that are essentially thermodynamic in nature.

An example of this was demonstrated over a hundred years ago—the stabilization of the Schiff base, formed between salicylaldehyde and ammonia,

37. H. Irving and C. F. Bell, *J. Chem. Soc.* p. 4253 (1954).

that resulted when the insoluble nickel complex was formed. This reaction is represented by the following equations [38,39]:

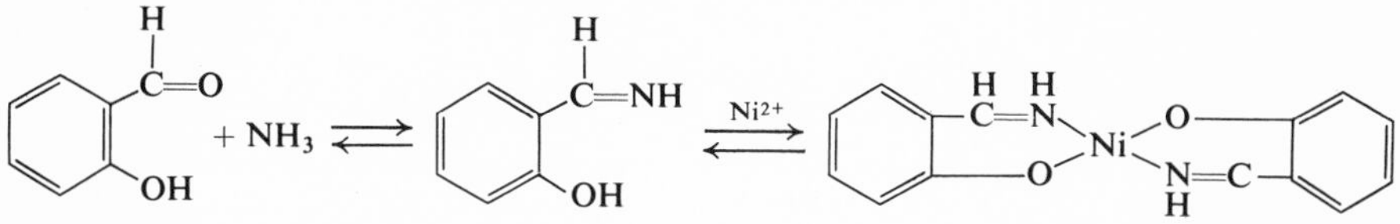

Similar stabilization of other Schiff bases has been reported, for example, that of salicylaldehyde and glycine.[40]

This stabilization of products by chelation is found in many other situations and has been exploited by Stiles and his co-workers in very ingenious studies.[41] In these the chelation process furnishes the basis for the displacement of equilibria in favor of desired products. An example is furnished by carboxylation reactions of the sort

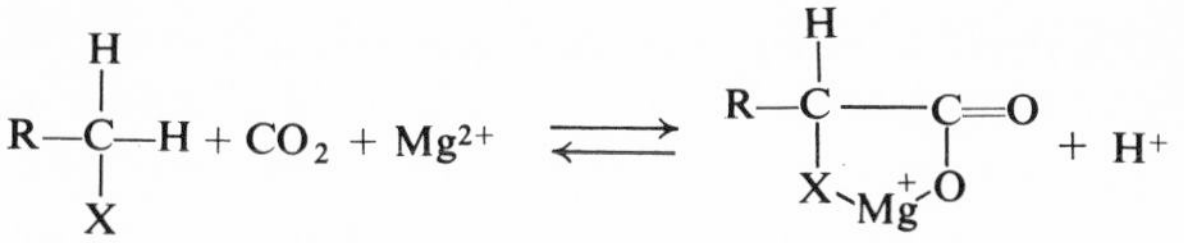

Here X is an electron-withdrawing group which can also form coordinate bonds to magnesium(II). Examples of X groups are the nitro group and the carboxyl group. The procedures developed use magnesium methyl carbonate,

$$Mg(O{-}\underset{\underset{O}{\|}}{C}{-}OCH_3)_2$$

(obtained by saturating a magnesium methoxide suspension with carbon dioxide) as the source of both the magnesium ion and carbon dioxide. This can be treated with a suitable compound, such as an α-nitro hydrocarbon, to obtain the magnesium chelate of the α-nitrocarboxylic acid. Decomposition of the chelate by cold acid leads to the desired product, the α-nitrocarboxylic acid. Stiles has extended these studies to a number of analogous reactions.[42]

38. C. Ettling, *Ann. Chem. Liebigs* **35**, 265 (1840).
39. F. R. Duke, *Ind. Eng. Chem. Anal. Ed.* **16**, 750 (1944).
40. G. L. Eichhorn and N. D. Marchand, *J. Am. Chem. Soc.* **78**, 2688 (1956); see also D. L. Leussing and C. K. Standfield, *J. Am. Chem. Soc.* **88**, 5726 (1966).
41. H. L. Finkbeiner and M. Stiles, *J. Am. Chem. Soc.* **85**, 616 (1963); H. L. Finkbeiner and G. W. Wagner, *J. Org. Chem.* **28**, 215 (1963), and the literature cited therein.
42. M. Stiles, *Ann. N.Y. Acad. Sci.* **88** (2), 332 (1960).

The magnesium chelate formed as an intermediate in this reaction also undergoes an addition reaction with $CH_2\!=\!CH\!-\!COOH$ as follows[43]:

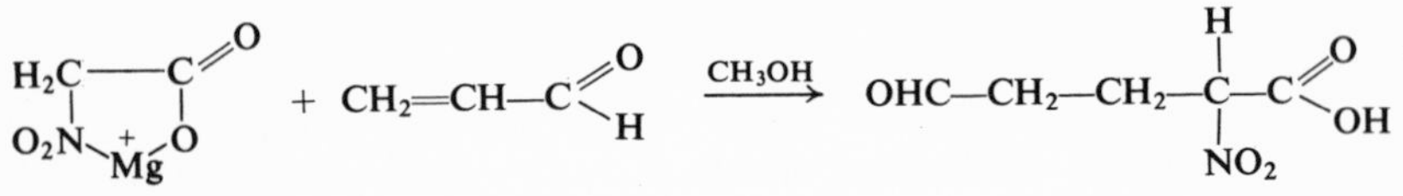

$$
\underset{\substack{| \\ O_2N \overset{+}{\,\,}O \\ \diagdown Mg}}{H_2C\!-\!C} \overset{O}{\diagup} \quad + \quad CH_2\!=\!CH\!-\!C \overset{O}{\underset{H}{\diagdown}} \quad \xrightarrow{CH_3OH} \quad OHC\!-\!CH_2\!-\!CH_2\!-\!\underset{\underset{NO_2}{|}}{\overset{\overset{H}{|}}{C}}\!-\!C \overset{O}{\underset{OH}{\diagdown}}
$$

Finkbeiner[44] has developed a synthesis of amino acids that proceeds by the carboxylation of 3-phenylhydantoin by means of magnesium methyl carbonate, followed by the alkylation of the resulting diketone. The reactions involved for phenylalanine are as follows:

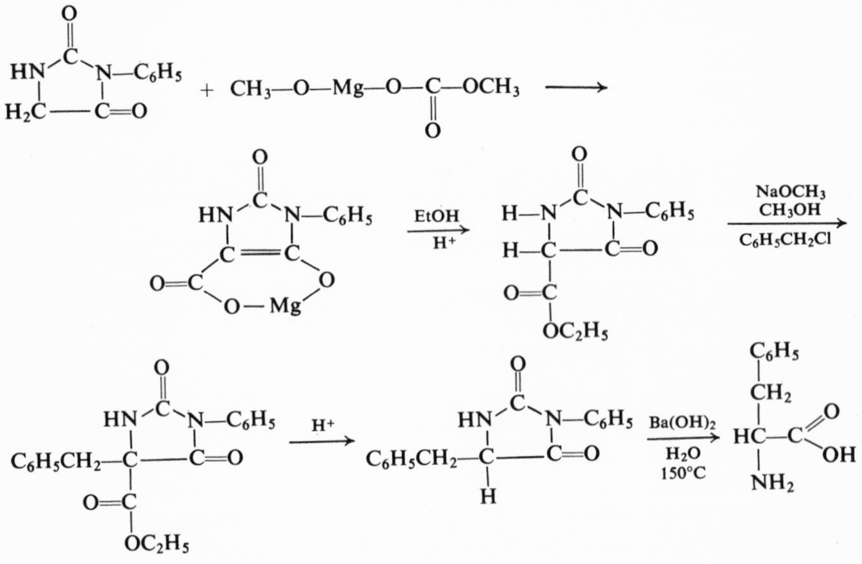

An analogous situation has been found in a study of the Gatterman-Koch synthesis of aldehydes, where Dilke and Eley[45] showed that the coordination of the product was important in making the over-all reaction thermodynamically more favorable for product formation. In this case the stabilizing reaction is that of the carbonyl oxygen of the aldehyde and aluminum chloride.

43. V. M. Belikov and Y. N. Belokon, *Izv. Akad. Nauk SSSR Ser. Khim.* p. 1134 (1964); *Chem. Abstr.* **61**, 7094.
44. H. L. Finkbeiner, *J. Am. Chem. Soc.* **86**, 961 (1964).
45. M. H. Dilke and D. D. Eley, *J. Chem. Soc.* p. 2613 (1949).

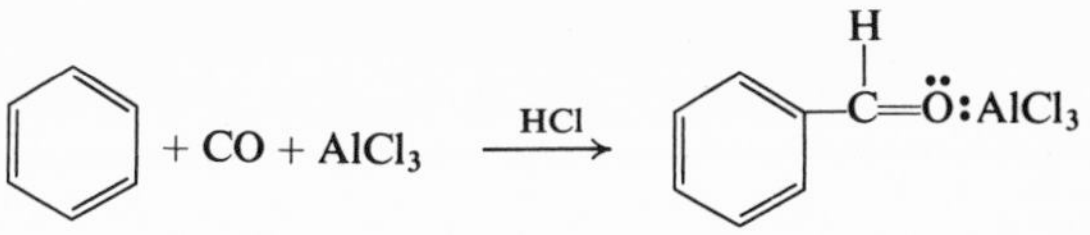

Another example is seen in the way coordination modifies the reaction of α-diketones and β-mercaptoethylamine.[46] In the presence of nickel(II), the nickel complex with the Schiff base is formed; when no nickel is present a heterocyclic organic compound (a thiazolidine) is formed:

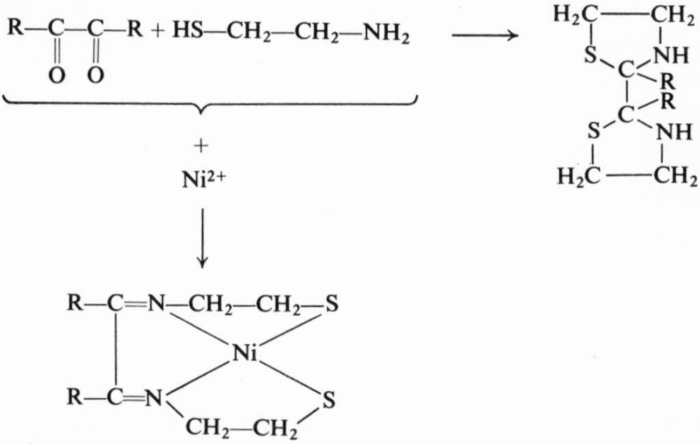

An additional factor, which is especially important in many aromatic systems, is the dependence of the equilibrium constants of isomerization reactions on the nature and the amounts of "catalyst" present. This behavior is strikingly exhibited in systems of aromatic compounds bearing halo, alkyl, and some related groups as substituents. Small amounts of BF_3 in HF will convert any of the xylenes to the equilibrium mixture of ortho, meta, and para isomers. However, when a great deal of BF_3 is present, the product is almost exclusively the meta isomer. Here a sigma complex is formed and the isomer distribution in such a system containing an excess of Lewis acid is characteristic of the equilibria involving the complexes, rather than the hydrocarbons themselves. Examples of this sort have been collected by Olah.[47] In many cases where only ortho- or para-directing substituents are present on a ring, equilibration in a system containing large amounts of

46. M. C. Thompson and D. H. Busch, *J. Am. Chem. Soc.* **84**, 1762 (1962); D. H. Busch, *Record Chem. Progr.* (*Kresge-Hooker Sci. Lib.*) **25**, 107 (1964).

47. G. A. Olah, "Friedel-Crafts and Related Reactions," Vol. I, p. 71. Wiley (Interscience), New York, 1963.

hydrogen halide and a Lewis acid (such as BF_3 or $AlCl_3$) leads to an isomerization reaction that produces meta-substituted derivatives in relatively large amounts. The presumable course of such processes involves the protonation of the aromatic system followed by the loss of a carbonium ion (in the case of the xylenes). The subsequent repeated gain and loss of the carbonium ion occurs under conditions that soon give an equilibrium mixture of the products. When large amounts of the Lewis acid and protonic acid are present, there are probably large amounts of a carbonium ion intermediate present and in such cases the most stable carbonium ion intermediate will be the product favored by the equilibration process (rather than the most stable hydrocarbon). In many of these cases the more stable *meta* carbonium ion is formed to the exclusion of the ortho and para forms. There is some selectivity in these reactions, as in the equilibration of mixtures of 2-, 3-, and 4-fluorobiphenyl in the presence of $AlCl_3$ promoted with a catalytic amount of H_2O. Here the fluoro groups do not migrate, but the phenyl groups do.[48]

2.4. Steric Interactions

In many cases the *steric* interactions between the species participating in the coordination act play a very obvious role. Because many coordinate bonds, especially those between uncharged species, have relatively low bond energies, such steric interactions can often prevent the formation of a coordinate bond. This was recognized years ago in such situations as the inability of hindered β-diketones to form complexes with iron(III).[49] The donor ability of amines such as tri(*tert*-butyl)amine is obviously dependent upon steric factors as they are with amines such as $N(CH_2CH_2NH_2)_3$, which require a certain arrangement of the coordinate bonds if they are to exert their full coordinating power. In this case the four bonds of $N(CH_2CH_2NH_2)_3$ can be to a tetrahedrally bonded species, or to four of six octahedral positions.

The study of the vapor-phase behavior of complexes between boron acceptors (such as trimethylboron) and nitrogen donors (such as trimethylamine), led H. C. Brown and his collaborators to recognize various types of steric interactions which could arise in such cases.[50] In cases where the donor and acceptor centers bear bulky substituents, steric hindrance to the formation of the coordinate bonds arises by the mutual confrontation of these attached groups. This is called front strain or F strain.

48. G. A. Olah and M. W. Meyer, *J. Org. Chem.* **28**, 1912 (1963).
49. J. Marshall, *J. Chem. Soc.* **107**, 518 (1915) (dibenzoylethane).
50. H. C. Brown and R. B. Johannesen, *J. Am. Chem. Soc.* **75**, 16 (1953), and the literature cited therein. G. S. Hammond, *in* "Steric Effects in Organic Chemistry" (M. S. Newman, ed.), p. 454 ff. Wiley, New York, 1956. J. Hine, "Physical Organic Chemistry," 2nd Ed., p. 165, 281. McGraw-Hill, New York, 1962.

When the formation of an additional bond by an acceptor center (say, boron) that carries bulky substituents results in a reorganization of these groups in such a way that they interfere with each other as they are pushed back to make way for the additional bond, one speaks of back strain or B strain. It is now commonly accepted that this is not very important for the *donor* center, as the presence of the lone pair requires that spatial accommodation be provided for it. This results in a hybridization pattern and steric arrangement which is not too different in the free ligand from that found in the complex. This kind of strain can then be expected to be found primarily with acceptor species.

The third kind of strain introduced by Brown is internal strain or I strain.[51,52] This concept has been used to explain the reduced reactivity of cyclopropyl halides in reactions in which a carbonium ion intermediate is formed. It is based on ideas related to the old Bayer theory of strain in ring systems. In cyclopropane the bond angles are close to $60°$ and are $49.5°$ short of the normal tetrahedral bond angle ($109.5°$). If such a system forms a carbonium ion it should then have sp^2 hybridization and a bond angle of $120°$ at the carbon on which the positive charge is centered. This would lead to a state in which there was an even greater divergence between the actual bond angles, which are fixed at $60°$, and the "strainless" state. This makes the attainment of the carbonium ion *more* difficult and is the reason for the slowness of such reactions. The internal strain here represents an additional contribution to the energy required to reach the transition state or a reactive intermediate. The angles of such bonds are *not* necessarily measures of the "strain" as such, but only of the relatively low strength of such bonds because of poor overlap.

In principle all of these factors may affect ligand reactivity. F strain will be important in either preventing coordination or in making the coordinate bonds that do form either longer or weaker or both. For example, one would expect that the metal-ion-catalyzed hydrolysis of glycine ethyl ester would be much more pronounced than that of *N,N*-dimethylglycine ethyl ester. B strain would be most plausibly present in governing the effectiveness of various Lewis acids as catalysts. It should also be present in reactions in which an octahedral complex with a replaceable sixth group functions as a catalyst. Such is the case with various heme derivatives. I strain should be demonstrable with chelate rings, but in ways quite different from that used with the organic systems for which it has been invoked. Thus chelate rings of carbonato complexes are less stable than those of oxalato complexes. The reduced stability seems to be found with other three- and four-membered chelate rings such as those involving peroxide or sulfite groups. The usual result of I strain in complexes is thus a lower stability of the chelate rings themselves, rather than

51. H. C. Brown, R. S. Fletcher, and R. B. Johannesen, *J. Am. Chem. Soc.* **73**, 212 (1951).
52. H. C. Brown and M. Bockowski, *J. Am. Chem. Soc.* **74**, 1894 (1952).

any slight changes in reactivity. In some related cases the various donor groups of a chelating agent are so far removed from each other that the formation of a ring with two donor groups bonded to the same metal ion is a statistically improbable event, and the usual fate of those rings that do form is a rather rapid disruption. It must be noted that the occurrence of I strain (of the sort found in organic systems) in chelate rings will be rather uncommon (except for organometallic compounds) because processes analogous to carbonium ion formation will be rare, but those analogous to carbanion formation will be more common. Since I strain was originally formulated in terms of the consequences of an ionization process involving a small ring compound, it is possible to study the steric consequences of such processes in chelate rings. The development of a negative charge on a chelate ring, the most fruitful case for examination, is one of the sort

$$
\begin{array}{ccc}
\text{H} & & \text{H} \\
| & & | \\
:\text{N}-\text{CH}_2 & & :\ddot{\text{N}}-\text{CH}_2 \\
| & & | \\
\text{M} \diagdown \; \text{H} \; | & \longrightarrow & \text{M} \diagdown \; \text{H} \; | \\
\text{H} \; | & & \text{H} \; | \\
| & & | \\
:\text{N}-\text{CH}_2 & & :\text{N}-\text{CH}_2 \\
| & & | \\
\text{H} & & \text{H}
\end{array}
$$

For the nitrogen atom carrying the negative charge we *do not* have a change in hybridization of the sort that gives rise to I strain in organic compounds. We do have an altered sequence of repulsion energies among the electron pairs that surround it. We must now accommodate the fact that the non-bonding pair on the nitrogen will take up more space than when it was part of an N—H bond. Consequently it will tend to lead to a closed up M—N—C angle. This is a change in the opposite direction to that found with organic cyclic carbonium ions. As a result, changes of this sort will *facilitate* the formation of the charged intermediate and assist reactions that must pass through such an intermediate. There should thus be instances in which the charged form of such a chelate ring undergoes reactions more readily than the uncharged form—simply because of the decrease in ring strain energy.

It must also be noted that when a positive charge (with a corresponding decrease of coordination number) is put on a member of a chelate ring, consequences analogous to those found for alicyclic compounds may be expected.

The sorting out of steric factors in the reactions of complexes is often rendered difficult by the fact that the variation of steric factors *independently* of electronic factors is rarely achieved.

When the conformations of the coordinated groups are examined it is found that chelate rings usually result in a situation in which one of the conformations is preferred. With straight chain organic donor systems this results in a stabilization of one form in the complex, but in no usable reactivity difference. With cycloaliphatic donors the situation is quite different.

With (−)2,3-butanediol, the reaction with boric acid results in a larger change in the conductivity than is found with the meso diol. This could be caused by the fact that the meso diol is more stable than the levo form in water or because the levo complex is more stable than that of the meso isomer.[53] By analogy with the conformational preferences in the cases of other ligands one would expect that the second explanation is the correct one.[54] An analysis of the conformational forms possible in chelate rings has been given by Corey and Bailar.[54] For both the dextro and levo forms of an ion such as $[Co(en)_3]^{3+}$, four conformational forms are possible that differ in stability and are in equilibrium. Of these forms, one, called the "lel" form by Corey and Bailar, is the most stable. The procedure developed by Corey and Bailar allows the predictions of the differences in reactivities of isomers, based upon their relative energies.

The use of the complex-forming ability of ligands to solve stereochemical problems is not without its difficulties.[55] In some cases the relative donor abilities of a series of very closely related aliphatic systems is very difficult to explain. Thus ethylene glycol, with free rotation of the two donor groups, does not form a complex with boric acid, as evidenced by the absence of any change in the electrical conductivity of such mixtures. Catechol and cis-1,2-cyclopentanediol do form such complexes. Here the hydroxy groups are not only on the same side of the carbon atoms, they are constrained to be coplanar. In addition to boric acid complexes, those with the cuprammonium ion have been used in the conformational analysis of sugars.[56] Most of these complexes are quite labile. The differences in reactivity of the complexing and non-complexing isomers in such cases have not been exploited.

53. E. L. Eliel, "Stereochemistry of the Carbon Compounds," pp. 142–143. McGraw-Hill, New York, 1962. Related material is discussed in E. L. Eliel, N. L. Allinger, S. J. Angyal, and G. A. Morrison, "Conformational Analysis," pp. 428–429. Wiley (Interscience), New York, 1965.
54. E. J. Corey and J. C. Bailar, Jr., *J. Am. Chem. Soc.* **81**, 2620 (1959).
55. J. P. Sickels and H. P. Schultz, *J. Chem. Educ.* **41**, 343 (1964); D. C. Kubler and R. G. Zepp, *Furman Univ. Bull. Furman Studies* **11** (1), 1 (1963).
56. R. E. Reeves, *J. Am. Chem. Soc.* **72**, 1499 (1950).

Chapter III LIGAND REACTIVITY

The variety of known ligand reactions that has been explored is impressive from two points of view. The first of these is the recognition of the enormous number of such reactions that have already been studied. The second is the inescapable and overwhelming recognition of the very incomplete state of our knowledge and of the innumerable reactions that have not yet been examined in a comprehensive fashion. It is also apparent that new *types* of such reactions, which do not fit into our present conceptual framework, are yet to be discovered. The material in the present chapter is thus incomplete, in the sense that it must be altered greatly in both organization and content as the field expands.

3.1. The Effect of Polarization on Ligand Reactivity

3.1.1. GENERAL REMARKS

One result to be anticipated from the coordination of a ligand to a positively charged metal ion is a distortion of the electronic distribution of that ligand toward the metal ion. This should result in a facilitation of attack on the ligand by nucleophiles and a retardation of attack by electrophiles. Since oxidizing agents are generally electrophiles* we would expect that coordination would slow down the reactions of ligands with most oxidizing agents. Reducing agents, which are generally nucleophiles, would be expected to react more rapidly with species after they are coordinated. Such a view places an *overemphasis* on the polarization of the ligand. Other factors, such as steric

* A very few nucleophilic oxidizing agents are known, such as OOH^-, which can act as in the following case:

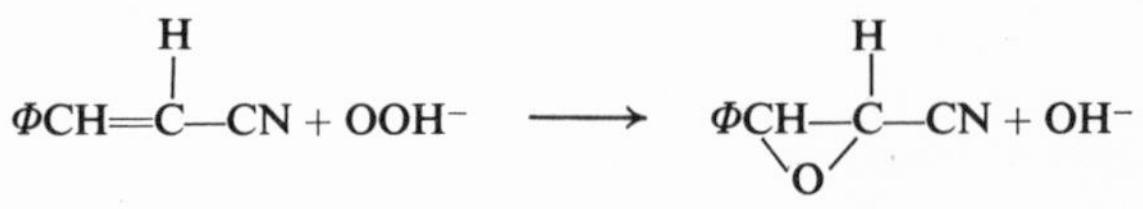

$$\phi CH{=}\overset{\overset{\displaystyle H}{|}}{C}{-}CN + OOH^- \longrightarrow \phi CH\overset{\overset{\displaystyle H}{|}}{\underset{\underset{\displaystyle O}{\diagdown\diagup}}{C}}{-}CN + OH^-$$

requirements of the reaction, the *change* in the *charges* of the reactants, and the distance of the reactant center from the donor part of the ligand, can all play a part in profoundly modifying the rates of such reactions.

In any discussion of polarization and ligand reactivity, it is imperative to remember that the different kinds of coordinate bonds can have very different effects on the charge density patterns of the ligands. When a typical σ-type coordinate bond is formed there is a drift of electrons toward the metal ion. The extent of this drift is determined roughly by the differences in the electronegativity of the bonded species, but it is always in the same direction, *away from the ligand*. When π-bonds are formed, they may have an effect which will actually *reverse* the usual changes in charge density. If a π-bond is formed by the back-donation of electrons from filled d_{xz}, d_{xy}, or d_{yz} orbitals of the metal to empty molecular orbitals of the ligand, a certain degree of compensation of the σ-bond charge shift occurs. If the π-component of the bond is much more important that the σ-component, the net transfer of charge may be from the metal to the ligand. This may proceed to such a point that an electron is transferred to the ligand from the metal and a redox process occurs. It is also possible to have a π-bond in which the electrons, originally on the ligand, are shared with suitable empty orbitals of the central metal. In this case, π-bonding accentuates the shift of electronic charge from the ligand. The problem of *a priori* prediction of changes in the ligand electron density patterns is a very difficult one. It is usual to rely on various types of physical data for such estimates (e.g., infrared spectra). In any event the experimental data on reactivity are more directly relevant, and it is to this subject that attention should be turned initially.

The role of the coordination center in a large number of reaction systems was very obviously established by the early 1930's. At this time, however, the amount of structural information (from X-ray studies) was very limited so the microscopic formulations of the processes involved were often imperfect. One such example may be seen in a discussion of the role of coordination in assisting the decomposition reactions of boron trichloride adducts and alcohols. It was suggested[1] that the migration of protons in such a system occurred in accordance with the rule[2] that the protons moved from atoms of greater positive charge to those of lesser charge. Thus the hydrolysis of $BCl_3 \cdot ROH$ was written as

$$
\begin{array}{ccc}
\overset{\displaystyle Cl}{\underset{\displaystyle R-O^{+}-H}{Cl-B^{-}Cl}} & \longrightarrow & \overset{\displaystyle Cl}{\underset{\displaystyle R-O}{Cl-B\!\!<\!\!{}^{Cl}_{H}}} \longrightarrow \overset{\displaystyle Cl}{\underset{\displaystyle R-O}{Cl-B}} + HCl
\end{array}
$$

1. E. Wiberg and W. Sutterlin, *Z. Anorg. Allgem. Chem.* **202**, 1, 22, 31, 37 (1931).
2. E. Wiberg, *Z. Phys. Chem.* (*Leipzig*) **A143**, 97 (1929).

Although the five-coordinate boron intermediate is unrealistic, the rule is an interesting early attempt to explain such reactions. Ethers in such adducts undergo a similar reaction to produce RCl and $ROBCl_2$. Reactions of BCl_3 with dimethylamine proceed via loss of HCl to give a product analogous to that obtained with alcohols.

Meerwein[3] has given an account of the use of coordination to BF_3 or $SbCl_5$ to assist the reactions of ethers, acetals, esters, and ortho esters. These reactions are of the general type

$$\frac{R}{R}{>}O + MX_n \longrightarrow \left\{ \begin{array}{c} \overset{+\delta}{R}\cdots \overset{-\delta}{\underset{R}{\cdot}}{:}O{-}MX_n \\ \text{or} \\ R^+,\ ROMX_n \end{array} \right\} \longrightarrow \text{Products}$$

Electrical conductivity studies[4] show that such ether and ester complexes may undergo a slight amount of ionization as a result of ligand polarization. Thus, $CH_3COOC_2H_5 \cdot BF_3$ is dissociated to the extent of about 0.09%,[5] at least part of which can be attributed to an ionization of the type written above. The reactions of such complexes are often those expected of a less highly polarized form. Meerwein found the reaction of ethylene oxide and the boron trifluoride–ethyl ether complex to proceed as

$$\begin{array}{c} CH_2 \\ | \\ CH_2 \end{array}{>}O + (C_2H_5)_2O{:}BF_3 \longrightarrow \begin{array}{c} CH_2{-}OBF_3{}^- \\ | \qquad\quad C_2H_5 \\ CH_2{-}\overset{+}{O}{<}_{C_2H_5} \end{array}$$

In the case of acetals or ortho esters, the initial coordination with BF_3 is followed by a fairly rapid reorganization so that the over-all reactions are

$$3 \;{>}C{<}^{O{-}R}_{O{-}R} + 4BF_3 \longrightarrow 3\left[{>}\overset{+}{C}{-}O{-}R \right]BF_4{}^- + B(OR)_3$$

and

$$3\;\overset{\displaystyle OR}{\underset{\displaystyle OR}{-C-OR}} + 4BF_3 \longrightarrow 3\left[-\overset{+}{C}{<}^{OR}_{OR} \right]BF_4{}^- + B(OR)_3$$

3. H. Meerwein, *Angew. Chem.* **67**, 374 (1955).
4. N. N. Greenwood, R. L. Martin, and H. J. Emeleus, *J. Chem. Soc.* p. 3030 (1950); p. 1472 (1953).
5. N. N. Greenwood and R. L. Martin, *Quart. Rev.* (*London*) **8**, 13 (1954).

The intermediate salts can be isolated in good yields in a number of cases. Meerwein and his co-workers also examined the behavior of complexes of oxime ethers and found a number of interesting reactions. For example,

$$\underset{C_6H_5}{\overset{C_6H_5}{\diagdown}}C{=}N{-}O{-}CH_3 + SbCl_5 \longrightarrow \left(\underset{C_6H_5}{\overset{C_6H_5}{\diagdown}}C{=}N{-}\overset{\overset{\displaystyle SbCl_5}{\displaystyle |}}{O}{-}CH_3\right)$$

$$\underset{C_6H_5}{\overset{C_6H_5}{\diagdown}}C{=}N{-}\overset{\overset{\displaystyle SbCl_5}{\displaystyle |}}{O}{-}CH_3 \longrightarrow \left[\underset{C_6H_5}{\overset{C_6H_5}{\diagdown}}C{=}N\right]^+ + [CH_3OSbCl_5]^-$$

$$5\left[\underset{C_6H_5}{\overset{C_6H_5}{\diagdown}}C{=}N\right]^+ + 5CH_3OSbCl_5^- + SbCl_5 \longrightarrow 5[C_6H_5{-}C{\equiv}N{-}\overset{+}{C_6H_5}] + 5SbCl_6^- + Sb(OCH_3)_5$$

The reaction with BF_3 is similar.

$$\underset{C_6H_5}{\overset{C_6H_5}{\diagdown}}C{=}N{-}OH + BF_3 \longrightarrow \underset{C_6H_5}{\overset{C_6H_5}{\diagdown}}C{=}N{-}\overset{\overset{\displaystyle BF_3}{\displaystyle \uparrow}}{O}{-}H \longrightarrow \left[\underset{C_6H_5}{\overset{C_6H_5}{\diagdown}}C{=}N\right]^+ + HOBF_3^- \longrightarrow$$

$$[C_6H_5{-}C{\equiv}N{-}C_6H_5]^+ \xrightarrow{HOBF_3^-} C_6H_5{-}\overset{\overset{\displaystyle F_3B{-}OH}{\displaystyle |}}{C}{=}N{-}C_6H_5$$

A related reaction, the isomerization of aldoximes to amides, is catalyzed by a number of metals and metal salts. This can be carried out homogeneously by the use of a solution of nickel acetate in refluxing xylene.[6] The yields are quite high. This system can be used to effect the isomerization of benzaldoxime to benzamide which can be obtained in a yield of 87% when 0.05 mole of benzaldoxime and 1.2 millimoles of nickel acetate tetrahydrate are refluxed in 50 ml of xylene for 5 hours. The over-all equation is

$$C_6H_5{-}\overset{\overset{\displaystyle H}{\displaystyle |}}{C}{=}NOH \xrightarrow[\text{xylene, } \Delta]{Ni(C_2H_3O_2)_2 \cdot 4H_2O} C_6H_5{-}\overset{\overset{\displaystyle O}{\displaystyle \|}}{C}{-}NH_2$$

6. L. Field, P. B. Hughmark, S. H. Shumaker, and W. S. Marshall, *J. Am. Chem. Soc.* **83**, 1983 (1961).

This kind of reaction is a "typical" trans Beckman rearrangement.[7] It has been shown to be a reaction of some generality.

3.1.2.   HYDROLYTIC AND SOLVOLYTIC REACTIONS OF AMINO ACID ESTERS

The metal-ion-catalyzed hydrolysis of amino acid esters was discovered by Kroll.[8] He examined this hydrolysis in the pH range 7.5–8.5 at 25.4°C, and established a number of salient features of such reactions including

(1) the fact that the 1:1 complex undergoes hydrolysis more rapidly than complexes containing two or more molecules of ester per metal ion;

(2) the participation of the hydroxide ion in the process; and

(3) the relative order of effectiveness of several divalent metal ions, which is $Cu^{2+} > Co^{2+} > Mn^{2+} > Ca^{2+} \sim Mg^{2+}$.

Kroll wrote the velocity of the hydrolysis at constant pH as

$$v = k_1[MeB^{2+}] + k_2[MeB_2^{2+}] + \cdots + k_n[MeB_n^{2+}]$$

and suggested the following mechanism, which emphasizes the polarization produced upon coordination as the source of catalytic action:

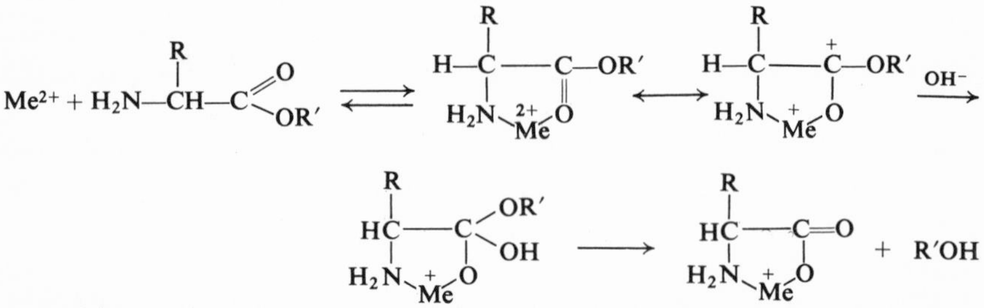

Subsequently, this reaction was studied by Li and his co-workers,[9] but under different conditions. They studied the hydrolysis of ethyl glycinate and methyl cysteinate in strongly alkaline solution. The ratio of amino acid ester, sodium hydroxide, and metal ion was $1:1:\frac{1}{3}$. As a result, their hydrolysis data refer to higher complexes in which two or three amino acid ester molecules are coordinated to a single metal ion.

---

7. A. Bryson and F. P. Dwyer, *J. Proc. Roy. Soc. N. S. Wales* **74**, 455, 471 (1940). Only the β-aldoximes form metallic complexes and α-aldoximes must of necessity undergo isomeriza-tion prior to complexation. The normal Beckman rearrangement *is* a trans migration. Other coordination centers can also effect this isomerization, e.g., BF_3: D. S. Hoffenberg and C. R. Hauser, *J. Org. Chem.* **20**, 1496 (1955).

8. H. Kroll, *J. Am. Chem. Soc.* **74**, 2036 (1952).

9. J. M. White, R. A. Manning, and N. C. Li, *J. Am. Chem. Soc.* **78**, 2367 (1956).

White, Manning, and Li proposed the following mechanism for the hydrolysis of ethyl glycinate in their systems:

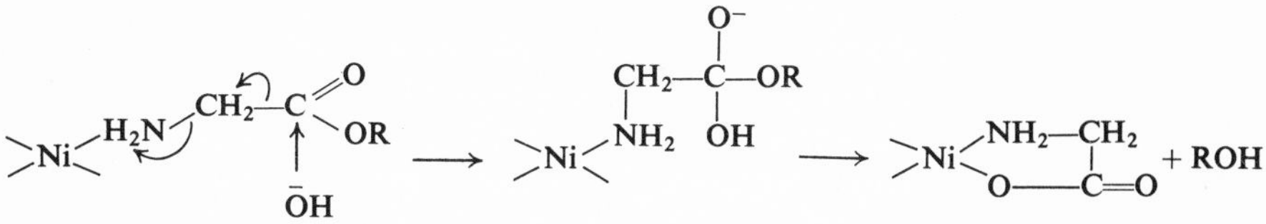

The reaction studied here is observed only at high concentrations of hydroxide. The pseudo first-order rate constants of Kroll are actually $k_2[OH^-]$, so the k_2 values for the reactions he studied are about 10^6 larger than the values given in his paper. The k_2 values for the reactions in strongly basic solution are composite rate constants as they include the base-catalyzed hydrolysis of both the free and the coordinated ester. The total rate can be broken down into its composite parts as follows:

$$\text{Rate} = k_2{}^0[\text{Complex}][OH^-] + k_2[\text{Ligand}][OH^-] + k_1[\text{Complex}]$$
$$= [OH^-]\{k_2{}^0[\text{Complex}] + k_2[\text{Ligand}]\} + k_1[\text{Complex}]$$

The value of k_2 can be determined from the rates of hydrolysis of solutions which do not contain metal ions. The value of $k_2{}^0$ can only be determined rigorously if the stability constants are known for the complexes involved. In some cases it is possible to study the reaction with an excess of ligand under conditions in which only one complex is present.

Li et al.[10] measured the rate of hydrolysis of histidine methyl ester in strongly basic solutions in the presence and absence of metal ions. The ratio of ester to sodium hydroxide to metal cation was $1:1:\frac{1}{3}$ in each case. The results obtained at 25°C are as shown in the following tabulation.

Ester concentration	Metal ion	k_r (liter mole^{-1} sec^{-1})	$\log k_{\text{stability}}$
0.00478 M	None	0.62	—
0.00382 M	Ni^{2+}	1.57	6.73
0.00382 M	Cu^{2+}	2.84	9.10

These authors point out that coordination to nickel increases the rate of hydrolysis of ethyl glycinate by only 25 % (from 0.73 to 0.92 liter mole^{-1} sec^{-1}), but the analogous process in the case of the methyl ester of histidine results in

10. N. C. Li, Br. E. Doody, and J. M. White, *J. Am. Chem. Soc.* **79**, 5859 (1957).

an increase of 250 % (from 0.62 to 1.57 liter mole^{-1} sec^{-1}). This is attributable to the probability that the complex with the histidine ester involves coordination with one more donor site than is the case with the glycine ester.

A different system was used by Bender and Turnquest[11] to study the cupric-ion-catalyzed hydrolysis of amino acid esters. These authors used glycine as a buffer. They found that this buffer and the buffer system used by Kroll [tris(hydroxymethyl)aminomethane] form complexes with the copper and are involved in the transition state. The hydrolysis reaction in the presence of glycine is written to involve the following steps:

$$[(Glycine)_2Cu] + Ester \rightleftharpoons Glycine + [(Glycine)Cu(Ester)]^+$$

$$[(Glycine)Cu] + Ester \underset{k_2}{\overset{k_1}{\rightleftharpoons}} [(Glycine)Cu(Ester)]^+$$

$$[(Glycine)(Ester)Cu]^+ + H_2O \overset{k_3}{\longrightarrow} [Cu(Glycine)_2] + ROH$$

The main steps of the reaction involve the second and third reactions given. These authors found that when ^{18}O was present in the initial ester as the carbonyl oxygen, this ^{18}O ended up, in part, in the water resulting from the hydrolysis, with the rate of hydrolysis about four times greater than the rate of exchange. The mechanism of the hydrolysis in the glycine buffer system was given by Bender and Turnquest as

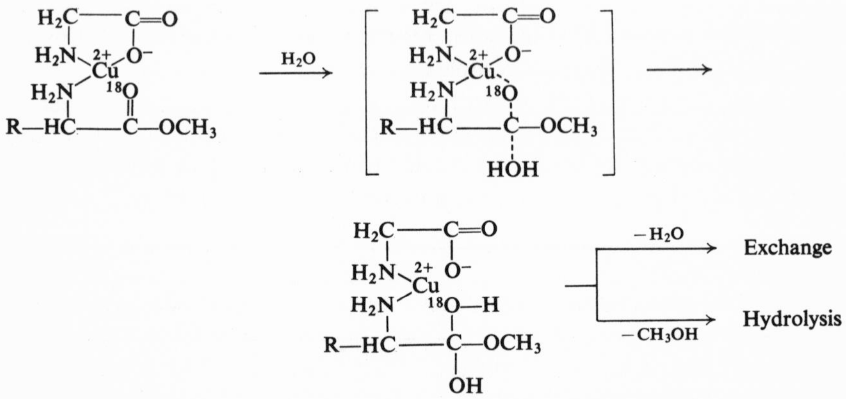

This reaction scheme can be modified to take into consideration the dependence of the rate of hydrolysis of the complex on the pH (directly proportional to [OH$^-$]), by the use of OH$^-$ as the attacking species rather than water, followed by the protonation of the carbonyl oxygen by water or by a tautomeric shift of the hydrogen of the attacking ion.

11. M. L. Bender and B. W. Turnquest, *J. Am. Chem. Soc.* **79**, 1889 (1957).

The studies described above were almost all carried out at 25°C. None of them contains information on the temperature dependence of these reactions. The rate of the copper-catalyzed hydrolysis has a rather unusual temperature dependence with the $\log k$ vs. $1/T$ plot showing two extrema.[12] Since the gross rate of this reaction and others of its type are dependent upon the complexation equilibria and the rate of hydrolysis of the ligand in each kind of complex, it is necessary to obtain experimental data to sort out these factors. This is made difficult by the relatively low precision of most methods for determining stability constants in such systems and the critical dependence of the rate upon the manner in which the ligand is distributed among the various complexes.

More detailed studies of the rate laws for the metal-ion-catalyzed hydrolysis of amino acid esters have shown that attack by both water and hydroxide ion are important over the pH range 7–9.[13–15] The hydroxide ion attack can be separated from the attack of water by determining the rate as a function of pH. The over-all rate is

$$\text{Rate} = k_{OH}[ME^{2+}][OH^-] + k_{HOH}[ME^{2+}][HOH],$$

where ME^{2+} is the 1:1 metal:ester complex. If the measured rate is expressed in terms of a pseudo first-order rate constant this becomes

$$\text{Rate} = k_1[ME^{2+}] = (k_{OH}[OH^-] + k_{HOH}[HOH])[ME^{2+}],$$

and a plot of k_1 vs. $[OH^-]$ will have a slope of k_{OH} and an intercept of $k_{HOH}[HOH]$.[15] The intercomparison of the rate of hydroxide ion attack on the protonated esters with those of complexed esters allowed Conley and Martin[13] to obtain a more detailed insight into the occurrence of "super-acid" catalysis due to metal ions. An initial, very thorough, study of the kinetics of the hydrolyses of free amino acid esters allowed development of detailed rate laws involving the species carrying various charges (i.e., protonated and unprotonated forms). The comparison of these rates with the rates observed for the metal complexes showed that the formation of the complexes had roughly the same effect *per unit charge added* as protonation *when chelation via the carbonyl group did not take place*. This has been confirmed in part by other workers.[16] A correlation of the rate with the concentration distribution of the various forms of complexed ester was carried out. For the conditions used, one (or two) complexed form(s) often predominated and it was possible to obtain characteristic rate constants for the complexes involved. For those

12. W. A. Connor and M. M. Jones, *Nature* **201**, 1122 (1964).
13. H. L. Conley, Jr., and R. B. Martin, *J. Phys. Chem.* **69**, 2914 (1966).
14. H. L. Conley, Jr., and R. B. Martin, *J. Phys. Chem.* **69**, 2923 (1966).
15. J. E. Hix, Jr., and M. M. Jones, *Inorg. Chem.* **5**, 1863 (1966).
16. R. W. Hay and P. J. Morris, *Chem. Commun.* p. 23 (1967).

complexes in which chelation to the carbonyl of the ester did not occur, the hydrolysis rates generally increased with the formation constants. The rates for complexes containing two or more esters per metal ion were found to be the same as, or slightly less than, the rates for the 1:1 complex. This work is the first in which an analysis was attempted for a system containing more than one reactive complex. In the pH ($\sim$ 9) region examined, the principal attacking species was the hydroxide ion, though evidence for attack by water was obtained at lower pH values.

The examination of the "super-acid" effect by Conley and Martin is especially revealing. An example is seen in the copper(II)-catalyzed hydrolysis of ethyl glycinate, where the copper(II) forms a transient bond to the carbonyl oxygen. In this case, protonation puts a charge on the ester at a site further removed from the point of attack of the hydroxide ion. The promotion of the hydrolysis of histidine methyl ester by divalent metal ions is similar to that found for the diprotonated form of the ester and represents a case for which the "super-acid" effect of coordination does not occur.[14]

Glycine amide and phenylglycine amide also undergo a hydrolysis subject to pronounced metal ion catalysis by copper(II), nickel(II), and cobalt(II).[17] This type of reaction was examined over a considerable range of temperature, though most of the studies were carried out at 65.5°–75°C. Here the mechanism must be similar in its gross aspects to that of the ester hydrolysis. It was also found that the hydrolyses of phenylalanylglycine, glycylphenylalanine, and the mixed diketopiperazine were only slightly promoted by Ni^{2+} or Cu^{2+}.

The ability of cobalt(III) complexes (of suitable composition) to effect the hydrolyses of both peptides[18] and amino acid esters[19] has been clearly demonstrated. In the hydrolysis of peptides, it has been found that cis-hydroxyaquo-triethylenetetraminecobalt(III) causes the selective hydrolysis of the N-terminal amino acid. The amino acid that is split off in this reaction is retained as a chelated group in the product complex. The type of reaction is illustrated by the example

$$[Co(trien)(OH)(H_2O)]^{2+} + \text{glycylglycylglycine} \xrightarrow[\substack{pH\ 7.5, \\ 12\ min}]{65°C} [Co(trien)(gly)]^{2+} + \text{glycylglycine}$$
$$\hspace{2.8cm} 0.03\ M \hspace{2.4cm} 0.03\ M$$

The specificity of this reaction for the free N-terminal amino group was indicated by the failure of the reagent to assist the hydrolysis of molecules which did not possess such a group, for example, N-carbobenzoxyglycyl-phenylalanylamide. The mechanism proposed for the process involves the

17. L. Meriwether and F. H. Westheimer, J. Am. Chem. Soc. 78, 5119 (1956).
18. J. P. Collman and D. A. Buckingham, J. Am. Chem. Soc. 85, 3039 (1963); D. A. Buckingham, J. P. Collman, D. A. R. Hopper, and L. G. Marzelli, J. Am. Chem. Soc. 89, 1082 (1967).
19. D. H. Busch and M. D. Alexander, J. Am. Chem. Soc. 88, 1130 (1966).

initial replacement of the coordinated water by the amino group of the peptide followed by the attack on the peptide carbonyl by either the coordinated hydroxy group or an external one.

The examination of the assistance of the hydrolysis of glycine esters by cobalt(III) revealed some similar features.[19] In this case the starting materials were complexes of the general composition $[Co(en)_2(glycinate\ ester)X]^{2+}$ in which X is a halogen and the glycine ester is coordinated to the cobalt via its amino group. The hydrolytic reaction was initiated by the addition of Hg^{2+}, which resulted in the removal of the halogen in the coordination sphere and its replacement by water or the carbonyl group of the ester. The formation of the intermediate complex

was detected by the appearance of an absorption band at $1610\ cm^{-1}$ that then slowly disappeared as the ester hydrolyzed. As this band decreased in intensity, another band at $1640\ cm^{-1}$, which results from the corresponding complex with glycine, was found to increase in intensity. The hydrolysis of the chelated ester thus appears to be much more rapid than that of an ester linked to the cobalt only through the nitrogen of its amino group. The rate data obtained by the use of the intensity of the infrared band at $1610\ cm^{-1}$ were found to be in agreement with analogous data obtained previously by different methods.

The stereospecificity of such reactions has been clearly established by the work of Murakami and his co-workers.[20] They used dichlorobis(propylene-diamine)cobalt(III) as the catalyst with either D-propylenediamine or L-propyl-enediamine as the ligand. The rate of hydrolysis of L(−)-phenylalanine ethyl ester with D-propylenediamine as catalyst was greater than when the L-propyl-enediamine complex was the catalyst. They also found that the intermediate complex formed in the hydrolysis of L(−)-valine ethyl ester was more stable than that formed during the hydrolysis of the D ester.

The proton magnetic resonance of amino acid esters in the presence of metal ions shows that such resonances are shifted to a greater extent for those

20. M. Murakami, H. Itatani, K. Takahashi, J. W. Kang, and K. Suzuki, *Mem. Inst. Sci. Ind. Res. Osaka Univ.* **20**, 95 (1963); *Chem. Abstr.* **60**, 15978.

protons closest to the site at which the metal ion is bound.[21] The same paper reports a conductivity study of the rate of the basic hydrolysis of cysteine ethyl ester in the presence of Cd^{2+} (as nitrate) at 25°C. $Ca(NO_3)_2$ was added to maintain a constant ionic strength. Under such conditions good second-order rate constants are obtained. The rate data can be treated as follows:

$$\text{Rate} = k_{obs} T_{ester} C_{OH^-}$$

$$= k(C_{ester} + k' C_{Cd\text{-}ester}) C_{OH^-}$$

where T_{ester} is the total concentration of ester, C_{OH^-} is the concentration of hydroxide ion, and k_{obs} is the observed pseudo rate constant based on T_{ester}. If the ratio of cadmium to ester is low, all of the cadmium is tied up in a complex and T_{Cd}, the total concentration of cadmium, can be set equal to $C_{Cd\text{-}ester}$. One can then rearrange the expression for k_{obs} to obtain

$$k_{obs} = k\{(T_{ester} - T_{Cd}) + k' T_{Cd}\}/T_{ester}$$

or

$$k_{obs} = k + [k(k' - 1)/T_{ester}] T_{Cd}$$

so a plot of k_{obs} vs. T_{Cd}/T_{ester} should be a straight line of intercept k and slope $k(k' - 1)$. Here k' is not a rate constant, but the factor by which the rate constant of the free ester must be multiplied in order to obtain the rate constant of the coordinated ester.

The rates of the base-catalyzed hydrolyses of the calcium complexes of some acylated α-amino acid esters have been determined by the use of a pH stat. Since this is an instrument that monitors the pH and adds base to neutralize the hydrolytic products formed, these studies were carried out at a constant pH in the absence of any buffer.[22] For the system of ester (S), calcium ion (M), and hydroxide ion, the reactions that give the acid (P) are

$$S + M \underset{k_2}{\overset{k_1}{\rightleftarrows}} MS$$

$$MS + OH^- \xrightarrow{k_3} M + P$$

$$S + OH^- \xrightarrow{k_4} P$$

and the rate of formation of P is

$$v' = d[P]/dt = k_3[MS][OH^-] + k_4[S][OH^-]$$

21. R. Mathur and N. C. Li, *J. Am. Chem. Soc.* **86**, 1289 (1964).
22. R. B. Martin and C. Niemann, *J. Am. Chem. Soc.* **79**, 5828 (1957).

Studies carried out under conditions such that $[M] \gg [MS]$ allowed the establishment of the relation

$$v' = k_3[MS][OH^-] + k_4[\sigma][OH^-] - k_4[MS][OH^-]$$

where $[\sigma] = [S] + [MS]$. For a steady state process for MS,

$$v' - k_4[\sigma][OH^-] = v = \frac{\{(k_3 - k_4)[OH^-][M][\sigma]\}}{[M] + \{(k_2 + k_3[OH^-])/k_1\}}$$

Since $k_4[\sigma][OH^-]$ was determined experimentally and the reactions were first order in hydroxide ion, $k_2 \gg k_3[OH^-]$ and

$$\frac{k_2 + k_3[OH^-]}{k_1} \approx \frac{k_2}{k_1} = K = \frac{[M][S]}{[MS]}$$

If one now sets

$$k_3' = k_3[OH^-]; \quad k_4' = k_4[OH^-]; \quad \text{and} \quad k_3'' = k_3' - k_4' = (k_3 - k_4)[OH^-],$$

then one can write

$$\frac{[M]}{v/[\sigma]} = \frac{[M]}{k_3''} + \frac{K}{k_3''}$$

and a plot of the quantity $[M]/(v/[\sigma])$ vs. $[M]$ will give a straight line of slope $1/k_3''$ and intercept K/k_3''. Such was indeed found to be the case. Data obtained in this way for aqueous solutions at 25°C led to the constants in the following tabulation:

Ester	pH	K	k_3
Benzoylglycine methyl ester	7.90	25 ± 2	680 ± 30
	8.40	25 ± 2	670 ± 30
Acetyl-L-valine methyl ester	7.90	2.8 ± 0.1	7.2 ± 0.2

These results constitute one of the few such systems for which a reasonably complete kinetic analysis (other than the temperature effect) has been carried out. It should be noted that the ester giving the most stable complex undergoes hydrolysis at the highest rate.

The behavior of ester groups in multidentate chelating agents such as ethyl glycinate N,N-diacetic acid is similar in that they are subject to a metal ion catalyzed hydrolysis.[22a]

22a. R. J. Angelici and B. E. Leach, *J. Am. Chem. Soc.* **89**, 4605 (1967).

The nature of the various reactions possible in these systems, and the conditions under which they become accessible to experimental study, becomes apparent only when the work as a whole is considered. In this case the reactions found can be divided into two main classes:

(1) The first type of reaction involves a coordination center that bears only one amino acid ester as a ligand. The hydrolysis reaction of this species becomes appreciable at rather moderate pH, as soon as the 1:1 complex is formed. This is usually the most rapid of the possible catalytic hydrolyses and its rate is found to increase very markedly with pH. Here the polarizing effect of the coordination center is operative on only one reactive ligand. Under conditions in which this reaction has a slow or moderate rate, the hydrolysis reaction can often be suppressed completely by adding a sufficient quantity of amino acid ester to convert all the metal to a 2:1 or higher complex. The nucleophile under these circumstances is probably hydroxide ion. A reaction path via an intermediate in which the amino acid ester ligand acts as a chelating agent with the carbonyl oxygen bound to the metal, as well as the amino group, is more easily attained in such a complex.

(2) The second type of reaction involves a coordination center that bears two (or more) amino acid ester molecules as ligands. The hydrolyses of species of this sort usually become appreciable only at higher pH values. This reaction is often a slower one than that which proceeds through the 1:1 complex. Of course it occurs in steps in which first one ester group is hydrolyzed and then this is followed by a reaction in which the second one is hydrolyzed.

3.1.3. HYDROLYSES OF PEPTIDES AND OTHER NITROGEN-CONTAINING COMPOUNDS

An extensive series of studies of the metal-catalyzed hydrolyses of peptides and related compounds, including both homogeneous and heterogeneous reactions, has been carried out by Bamann and his collaborators. They[23] were able to show that highly charged ions, such as Th^{4+} that undergo hydrolysis rather readily are able to catalyze the decomposition of leucylglycylglycine at pH values as low as 5. The thorium(IV) species is very extensively hydrolyzed at this pH and the reaction is presumably a heterogeneous one. Such readily hydrolyzed metallic ions are also able to catalyze the hydrolysis of peptides at relatively low temperatures (e.g., 37°C), and ions such as Cu^{2+}, which will form stable complexes with this type of substrate, catalyze the hydrolysis in a noticeable manner only at much higher temperatures ($\sim 70°C$). It was also found that metal ions were capable of catalyzing the hydrolytic splitting of the C—N bond in N-acetylated amino acids.

23. E. Bamann, J. G. Haas, and H. Trapmann, *Arch. Pharm.* **294**, 569 (1961).

The catalytic hydrolysis of dipeptides by rare earth salts has been examined also.[24] In the case of Ce(IV) and Ce(III) in an alkaline medium, the C—N bond in dipeptides is hydrolyzed at temperatures as low as 37°C. The same reaction with lanthanum(III) as the catalyst is much slower and reaches an appreciable rate only at 70°C. The peptides which were most susceptible to such catalytic hydrolysis were glycylglycine, glycylalanine, and alanylglycine. The catalytic hydrolysis exhibits an optimum rate at pH values between 8.0 and 8.6. At pH values much greater than this the basic hydrolysis of the peptide (uncatalyzed) becomes important.

The hydrolytic splitting of the amides of dibasic acids was found to be catalyzed by roughly the same metal ions under analogous conditions.[25] Malonamide, (H_2NOC—CH_2—$CONH_2$) was found to undergo the most marked catalytic hydrolysis in the presence of Ce(IV) at 37°C. For Ce(III) and La(III) the effect was notable only at a higher temperature (70°C). As the chain of carbon atoms between the two amide groups becomes longer the catalysis becomes much less pronounced. Thus succinamide (H_2NOCCH_2-CH_2CONH_2) reacts much more slowly and the higher analogs are essentially unaffected unless the catalyst concentration is increased considerably. This was ascribed to the formation of a chelate ring as an intermediate. In this same paper the catalytic deamination of L-aspargine is also reported.

The hydrolysis of esters of carboxylic acids in the presence of various lanthanon metal ions has also been examined.[26] Here again, La^{3+}, Ce^{3+}, and Ce^{4+} were used as catalysts in a medium which was slightly alkaline (pH 8). When the ethyl esters of acetic or propionic acid were examined, the catalytic effect was either absent or very small. When the acid contained a second functional group capable of acting as an electron pair donor, the catalysis was fairly pronounced. Thus ethyl glycinate, N,N-dimethylglycine ethyl ester, ethyl α-aminopropionate, and ethyl α-hydroxypropionate showed pronounced increases in their rates of hydrolysis in the presence of added La^{3+}, Ce^{3+}, or Ce^{4+}. In these cases the order of effectiveness of the ions is $La^{3+} > Ce^{3+} > Ce^{4+}$. Esters of malonic acid and its derivatives were examined also and catalytic effects were found in some of these cases. The importance of the second donor group can be seen in a comparison of the results obtained with ethyl phenyl-acetate and ethyl mandelate. The first of these has a single functional group and shows only a slightly increased rate of hydrolysis in the presence of metal ions. The second has a hydroxy group in a position where it can form a chelate

24. E. Bamann, H. Trapmann, and A. Rother, Chem. Ber. 91, 1744 (1958); Naturwissen-schaften 43, 326 (1956).
25. E. Bamann, H. Trapmann, and H. Munstermann, Arch. Pharm. 296, 47 (1963).
26. E. Bamann, M. Winkler-Steber, and H. Trapmann, Arch. Pharm. 293, 175 (1960). See also J. I. Hoppe and J. E. Prue, J. Chem. Soc. p. 1775 (1957); E. Jäger, Z. Anorg. Allgem. Chem. 349, 139 (1967).

ring. The result is a much greater increase in the rate of hydrolysis when metal salts are added.

A comprehensive review of the work of Bamann and his co-workers is available which covers their work up to 1959.[27] Most of these studies have been concerned with the catalytic hydrolysis of various linkages by hydrolyzed rare earth ions. The types of reactions that have been found to undergo a catalytic process in the presence of the rare earth species include the following:

(a) The hydrolysis of esters of phosphoric acid

$$—P—O—C— + H_2O \rightarrow —P—OH + HO—C—$$

(b) The hydrolysis of pyrophosphates

$$—P—O—P + H_2O \rightarrow —P—OH + HO—P—$$

(c) The hydrolysis of amides of phosphoric acid

$$—P—\overset{|}{N}— + H_2O \rightarrow —P—OH + H—\overset{|}{N}—$$

(d) The hydrolysis of peptides

$$—\overset{\overset{\textstyle O}{\|}}{C}—N— + H_2O \rightarrow —\overset{\overset{\textstyle O}{\|}}{C}—OH + H—N—$$
$$\quad\;\; \underset{H}{|} \qquad\qquad\qquad\qquad\qquad \underset{H}{|}$$

(e) The hydrolysis of esters

$$—\overset{\overset{\textstyle O}{\|}}{C}—O—C— + H_2O \rightarrow —\overset{\overset{\textstyle O}{\|}}{C}—OH + HO—C—$$

The mechanistic basis for all these catalyzed processes appears to be the same. The extensively hydrolyzed ions [such as La^{3+}, present as $LaOH^{2+}$ or $La(OH)_2{}^+$] form a complex with the substrate through its available donor atoms. This results in an electronic polarization of the substrate which facilitates the attack of water and hence the hydrolysis. It is not certain whether the reactions examined by Bamann are homogeneous or heterogeneous, though the basic mechanism can be invoked in either case.

The hydrolysis of 8-acetoxyquinoline is catalyzed by copper(II) by a process similar to those described for the amino acid esters.[28] The over-all rate expression is quite complicated:

$$\text{Rate} = k[\text{8-acetoxyquinoline}]$$

27. E. Bamann and H. Trapmann, *Advan. Enzymol.* **21**, 169 (1959).
28. C. R. Wasmuth and H. Freiser, *Talanta* **9**, 1059 (1962); R. H. Barca and H. Freiser, *J. Am. Chem. Soc.* **88**, 3744 (1966).

where

$$k = \frac{1}{[H^+] + K_a} \{k_1[H^+]^2 + K_a(k_2[H^+] + k_3 + k_4[OH^-] + k_5[OH^-][Cu^{2+}])\}$$

The reactions occurring include the hydrogen-ion-catalyzed hydrolysis of the ester and the protonated ester, the hydroxide-ion-catalyzed hydrolysis of the ester, the hydrolysis not involving either proton or hydroxide ion catalysis, and a hydroxide-ion-catalyzed reaction of the 1:1 copper:ligand complex. K_a is the acid dissociation constant for the protonated ester and the remaining k's are the rate constants for the particular hydrolyses in the order mentioned.

The role of metal ions and their hydrolytic products in catalyzing the hydrolysis of peptide linkages has been studied.[29] These reactions were carried out in an alkaline medium where the peptide chains are open. In an acidic medium, where they are present in a helical form, the peptide linkages are more resistant to hydrolysis and to the catalytic effects of metal ions. In studies at a pH of 8.4, a large number of metal ions were found to be effective. At a temperature of 37°C, the effective species were found to be Th^{4+}, Zr^{4+}, Y^{3+} and others that undergo very extensive hydrolysis. At higher temperatures (70°C), the catalytically active ions include those which would form complexes with the peptide (e.g., Zn^{2+}, Cu^{2+}, Ni^{2+}) as well as those effective via hydrolytic products. For the systems examined, an optimum pH for the reaction generally occurred at some intermediate value of the pH. In addition to the effect resulting from coordination, the rates of these reactions are dependent upon the steric interactions with the peptide chain and the electrostatic effects of negative carboxy groups.

The use of the carbo(8-quinoloxy) group for the protection of amino nitrogen has been developed, together with a subsequent metal-catalyzed hydrolysis of the protective group.[30] The sequence of reactions here can be summarized as

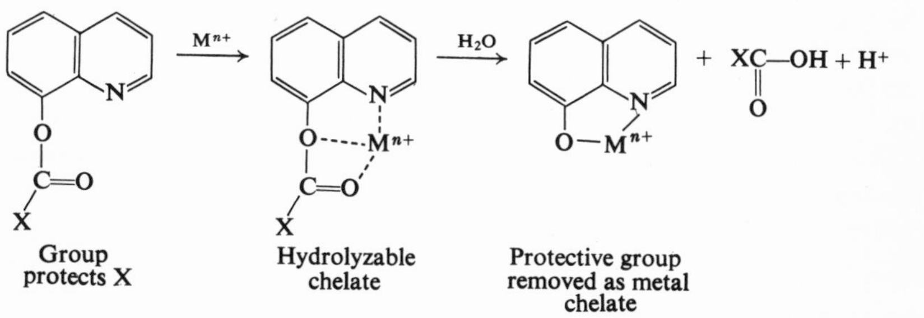

| Group
protects X | Hydrolyzable
chelate | Protective group
removed as metal
chelate |

29. E. Bamann, J. G. Haas, and H. Trapmann, *Arch. Pharm.* **294**, 569 (1961).
30. E. J. Corey and R. L. Dawson, *J. Am. Chem. Soc.* **84**, 4899 (1962).

For some complexes that undergo hydrolysis by an addition reaction of water across the double bond, it has been found possible to isolate the intermediate hydrated form. The isolation of complexes in which the Schiff base ligand is partially hydrolyzed was reported for the β-form of the copper(II) derivative of bis(pyridinal)ethylenediimine.[31] Here the structure of the complex was given as

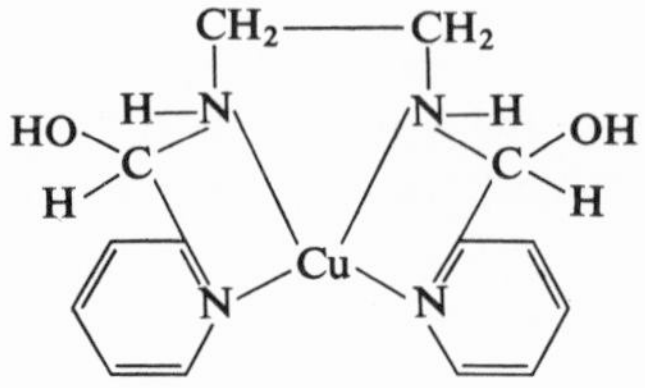

The complex tris[bis(acetyl)bis(methylimine)]iron(II) forms a similar product.

The Schiff base formed between 2-pyridinealdehyde and ethylenediamine forms copper complexes in boiling methanol or ethanol in which one molecule of alcohol has added across one of the —C≡N— bonds.[32]

Hoyer and his co-workers have studied a number of related complexes, including the intermediate bis chelates in which the aldehyde groups have been hydrolyzed from the nitrogen donor atoms[33]:

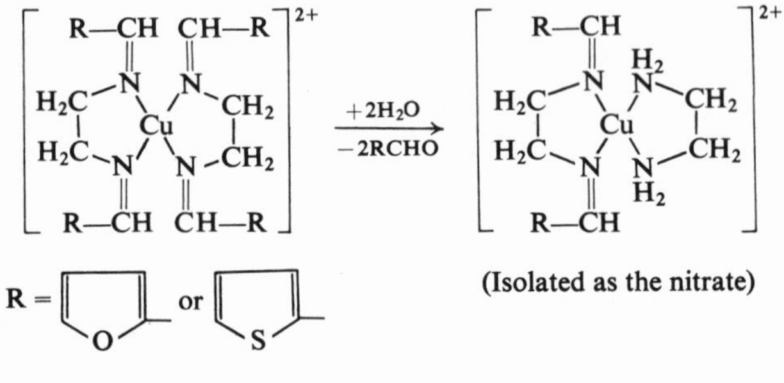

This group of workers has isolated and characterized the copper(II) derivative of bis(pyridinal)ethylenediamine, which has added on one molecule of water.[34]

31. D. H. Busch and J. C. Bailar, Jr., *J. Am. Chem. Soc.* **78**, 1141 (1956).
32. C. M. Harris and E. D. McKenzie, *Nature* **196**, 670 (1962).
33. E. Hoyer, *Naturwissenschaften* **46**, 14 (1959); L. Wolf, G. Kozlowski, and E. Hoyer, *Z. Chem.* **3**, 68 (1963).
34. D. Kutscher and E. Hoyer, *Z. Chem.* **3**, 68 (1963).

Copper(II) catalyzes the addition of alcohols to the nitrile group of dicyandiamide to give the corresponding N-alkylguanylureas.

$$\underset{\substack{| \\ H_2N-C=N-C\equiv N}}{\overset{NH_2}{}} + ROH \xrightarrow{Cu^{2+}} \underset{\substack{| \\ H_2N-C=N-C-NHR}}{\overset{NH_2 \quad O}{}}$$

This reaction proceeds to give the adduct as the copper(II) complex. When copper(II) acetate is used as the catalyst, the product is the complex copper guanylurea acetate.[35] The same reaction is catalyzed by nickel(II), though this is not so effective as copper(II).[36] Copper(II) catalyzes the addition of water to dicyandiamide to give guanylurea[37].

$$\underset{\substack{| \\ H_2N-C=N-C\equiv N}}{\overset{NH_2}{}} + HOH \xrightarrow{Cu^{2+}} \underset{\substack{| \\ H_2N-C=N-C-NH_2}}{\overset{NH_2 \quad O}{}}$$

In this case the reaction is slow enough to allow the copper(II) complex of dicyandiamide to be isolated as its sulfates: $[Cu(dicyandiamide)_2]SO_4 \cdot 5H_2O$ (blue) or, on drying $[Cu(dicyandiamide)_2]SO_4 \cdot 2H_2O$ (green). Both of these complexes produce bis(N'-methylguanylurea)copper(II) sulfate when refluxed in methanol.[36]

3.1.4. HYDROLYSES OF PHOSPHATE ESTERS

The role of metal ions in catalyzing the hydrolysis of a wide variety of derivatives of phosphoric acid has long been recognized. This is especially important in the metal-ion-activated enzymes that carry out such reactions in biological systems.

The catalytic (nonenzymic) hydrolysis of acetyl phosphate has been studied in some detail.[38,39] This reaction

$$CH_3COOPO_3^{2-} + H_2O \rightarrow CH_3COO^- + HPO_4^{2-} + H^+$$

is catalyzed by both calcium and magnesium ions. At pH 7.7 the catalysis by the magnesium ion is very pronounced and the catalyzed reaction is first order in acetyl phosphate. The transition state for the catalyzed reaction may be assumed to contain one magnesium ion and one acetyl phosphate. The pseudo first-order rate constant for this reaction at 39°C can be expressed as:

$$k_{obs} = k_u + k_{Mg^{2+}}[Mg^{2+}]$$

where k_u is the rate constant for the uncatalyzed reaction. The value of $k_{Mg^{2+}}$ under these conditions was found to be 0.70 liter mole min^{-1}. The magnesium

35. R. L. Dutta and P. Ray, *J. Indian Chem. Soc.* **36**, 499 (1959).
36. W. A. Baker, Jr., and M. Daniels, *J. Inorg. Nucl. Chem.* **25**, 1194 (1963).
37. P. Ray, *Chem. Rev.* **61**, 313 (1961).
38. D. E. Koshland, Jr., *J. Am. Chem. Soc.* **74**, 2286 (1952).
39. F. Lipman and L. C. Tuttle, *J. Biol. Chem.* **153**, 571 (1944).

ion does not catalyze the reaction at a pH of 2.7. Under conditions where the catalysis is pronounced, the acetyl phosphate exists in the form of a doubly charged negative ion, $CH_3C(O)OPO_3^{2-}$, and this is presumably the species involved in the metal-ion-catalyzed reaction. At a pH of 2.7, the singly charged negative ion predominates and is apparently not subject to a metal-ion-catalyzed hydrolysis.

More comprehensive studies of the rate of this reaction have subsequently revealed that it shows many similarities to other metal-ion-catalyzed hydrolyses.[40-42] There is attack by both water and hydroxide ion, and $k_{Mg^{2+}}$ is actually a composite term of some complexity. The catalytic route proceeds via complexes of the dianion $CH_3COOPO_3^{2-}$, and is facilitated ·by a wide variety of divalent ions. An analogous situation is found in the catalysis of the reaction

$$NH_2COOPO_3^{2-} \rightarrow NCO^- + HPO_4^{2-} + H^+$$

the elimination reaction of carbamyl phosphate, which is also catalyzed by Ca^{2+} and Mg^{2+}.[43]

The hydrolysis of salicyl phosphate in the presence of metal ions and metal complexes has been studied by Martell and his co-workers.[44,45] For this compound the hydrolyzed polynuclear form of Zr(IV) was found to be the best catalyst. For species that are presumably not hydrolyzed, the order of the catalytic power was found to be $VO^{2+} > UO_2^{2+} > Cu^{2+}$. In the first study, a large number of chelating agents were added to solutions containing metal ions to determine the possible catalytic activity of metal chelate complexes. It was found that many of these compounds did possess a catalytic activity which could be ascribed to mixed complexes, though the actual delineation of the catalytically active species was not attempted.

A more detailed study of the catalytic action of the 1:1 complex of hydroxyethylethylenediamine and copper(II) in the hydrolysis of salicyl phosphate was carried out.[45] It was found that this complex was *not* very active and a similar result was drawn from studies of the 1:1 dipyridine–copper(II) complex. In systems which contain these complexes, one has a metal ion buffer system that allows studies to be made at total metal ion concentrations which would result in considerable hydrolysis if the chelating agent were not present. Thus the study of metal-ion-catalyzed reactions is possible in systems where

40. J. L. Kurz and C. D. Gutsche, *J. Am. Chem. Soc.* **82**, 2175 (1960).
41. G. DiSabato and W. P. Jencks, *J. Am. Chem. Soc.* **83**, 4393 (1961).
42. C. H. Oestreich and M. M. Jones, *Biochemistry* **5**, 2926 (1966).
43. C. H. Oestreich and M. M. Jones, *Biochemistry* **5**, 3151 (1966).
44. R. Hofstetter, Y. Murakami, G. Mont, and A. E. Martell, *J. Am. Chem. Soc.* **84**, 3041 (1962).
45. Y. Murakami and A. E. Martell, *J. Phys. Chem.* **67**, 582 (1963).

a direct transfer of the metal ion from the complex to the substrate obviates the necessity for the presence of hydrolyzable free metal ions.

The alkaline hydrolyses of pyrophosphate, polyphosphate, metaphosphate, ethyl phosphate, and ethyl pyrophosphate are all catalyzed by the calcium ion.[46] In these cases, strontium was found to have a much reduced catalytic action, and barium had practically no effect at all. The action of the calcium ion in these cases vanishes in an acid medium, presumably because the calcium ion is unable to compete effectively against the hydrogen ion for the electron pairs of the donor sites on the substrates.

The catalytic effect of a large number of metal ions and metal chelate compounds on the basic (pH = 6.29) hydrolysis of pyrophosphate at 70°C was shown by Hofstetter and Martell.[47] The order of increasing catalytic effectiveness was found to be as follows: Ce(III) salts, MoO_2(VI)–2,4-disulfopyrocatechol < UO_2(VI)–2,4-disulfopyrocatechol < Zr(IV)–EDTA < Zr(IV)–NTA (nitrilotriacetic acid) < ZrO(IV)–2,4-disulfopyrocatechol, Zr(IV)–2,4-disulfopyrocatechol < ZrO(IV)–EDTA. Salts and chelates of Cu(II), Mn(II), Pb(II), and Th(IV) had no catalytic activity under the same conditions. It is quite possible that these catalysts are polymeric complexes generically related to those studied by Bamann and his co-workers.[27]

The hydrolysis of pyrophosphate and organic di- and triphosphates, such as adenosinediphosphate (ADP) and adenosinetriphosphate (ATP), have been examined in considerable detail by many biochemists. In some cases such as the pyrophosphatase enzyme (which catalyzes the hydrolysis of inorganic pyrophosphate), the literal substrate for the enzyme is the magnesium pyrophosphate complex, $MgP_2O_7^{2-}$. In this complex the magnesium still has readily accessible coordination positions for attachment to the enzyme. The catalytically active complex is thus the mixed chelate complex: enzyme–magnesium–pyrophosphate.[48] The same kind of a catalytically active substrate has been suggested for a magnesium-activated enzyme that splits ATP.[49]

The importance of metal complexes as substrates for enzymes was first emphasized by Najjar.[50] These he designated as metallosubstrates. The reaction of the metallosubstrate with the enzyme would be expected to exhibit the same kind of stereospecificity as is found in the formation of complexes with simple chelating agents only if the metal is at the site where the substrate is bonded to the enzyme and acts as a bridge between the two. When the

46. E. Cherbuliez, J.-P. Leber, and P. Stucki, *Helv. Chim. Acta* **36**, 537 (1953).
47. R. Hofstetter and A. E. Martell, *J. Am. Chem. Soc.* **81**, 4461 (1959).
48. E. A. Robbins, M. P. Stulberg, and P. D. Boyer, *Arch. Biochem. Biophys.* **54**, 215 (1955).
49. S. V. Perry and T. C. Grey, *Biochem. J.* **64**, 190 (1964).
50. V. A. Najjar, *in* "Phosphorus Metabolism" (W. D. McElroy and B. Glass, eds.), Vol. I, pp. 500–516. Johns Hopkins Press, Baltimore, Maryland, 1951.

metal is bound to the substrate at some distant site this may not influence the stereospecificity of the enzyme. There are a reasonably large number of enzyme systems for which it has been established that the enzyme reacts with a previously formed metallosubstrate.[51]

The role of various metal cations in accelerating the hydrolysis of ATP and ADP have been studied in considerable detail by Lowenstein and his co-workers.[52-56] These metal ions also catalyze the nonenzymic transfer of phosphate from adenosine triphosphate to a variety of substrates including orthophosphate, acetate, glycine, and β-alanine. In these reactions, different divalent metal ions may show quite different catalytic behavior. For example, the products of the hydrolysis of ATP include ADP, AMP, pyrophosphate, and orthophosphate and the relative amounts of these vary with the metal ion. At a pH of 5, the relative order of the catalytic effectiveness of divalent metal ions is $Cu^{2+} > Zn^{2+} > Cd^{2+} > Mn^{2+} > Be^{2+}$. At a pH of 9 the order is quite different: $Ca^{2+} > Mn^{2+} > Cu^{2+} > Cd^{2+} > Zn^{2+} > Co^{2+}$. The magnesium ion is quite ineffective as a catalyst under these conditions. The manganous ion is also seen to fall out of a sequence based upon the general order of magnitude of the stability constants of complexes of these metal ions. Lowenstein ascribed these differences, as well as the variation in the relative amounts of ADP and AMP produced in the hydrolysis, to the variety of mechanisms that exist by virtue of the different kinds of binding sites for metals in the phosphate chains of ATP and ADP.

The splitting of phosphate esters under the influence of gels of metal hydroxides was first reported and examined by Bamann and his co-workers.[57,58] This work developed in a rather direct manner from Bamann's studies of the activation of enzymes which split phosphate bonds (phosphatases) by magnesium and other metal ions. The hydrolytic reactions which were found to be catalyzed by such gels (especially by gels of the rare earth hydroxides), include the hydrolysis of phosphate esters, pyrophosphate, polyphosphate, and metaphosphate.

The catalytic influence of these gels on hydrolytic reactions is very clearly differentiated from the corresponding activity of most enzymes by the lack of specificity of the gels (but it must be noted that many phosphatases show a

51. M. C. Dixon and E. C. Webb, "The Enzymes," 2nd Ed. Longmans, Green, New York, 1964. For a more complete discussion of the different kinds of interactions which can arise in these systems, see M. Cohn, *Biochemistry* **2**, 623 (1963).

52. M. Tetas and J. Lowenstein, *Biochemistry* **2**, 350 (1963).

53. J. M. Lowenstein, *Biochem. J.* **70**, 222 (1958).

54. J. M. Lowenstein, *Biochim. Biophys. Acta* **28**, 206 (1958).

55. J. M. Lowenstein, *Nature* **187**, 570 (1960).

56. J. M. Lowenstein and M. N. Schatz, *J. Biol. Chem.* **236**, 305 (1961).

57. E. Bamann, *Angew. Chem.* **52**, 186 (1939).

58. E. Bamann and M. Meisenheimer, *Chem. Ber.* **71**, 1711, 1980, 2086, 2233 (1938).

very low specificity).[51] Thus a gel made from lanthanum chloride at a pH of 8.5 catalyzes *all* of the reactions cited. The relative order of the rates of these reactions in the presence of such a gel is

metaphosphate hydrolysis $\approx$ triphosphate hydrolysis > pyrophosphate
hydrolysis > glycerophosphate hydrolysis

The effect of the pH and the ester structure on the rate of hydrolysis of aliphatic phosphate esters in the presence of such gels has been examined.[59] These reactions (the catalyzed hydrolyses of ethyl phosphate, *p*-cresyl phosphate, and glycerin β-phosphoric acid) show two maxima when their rates are plotted against the pH. The first occurs in weakly basic media at pH values between 7 and 9, and the second at higher pH values, around 10. The interpretation given these by Bamann is in terms of two different catalytic species. The species active at the lower pH is the first hydrolysis product of the ion, e.g., $La(OH)^{2+}$, but the one at the higher pH is a more completely hydrolyzed species such as $La(OH)_2^+$.

The role of the ester structure in determining the hydrolysis rate is determined by those factors which govern the ease of coordination and the polarization of the ester linkage. The diesters undergo hydrolysis more slowly than the monoesters. The presence of electron-attracting substituents in the esters leads to a more rapid hydrolysis and a displacement of the pH of the optimum rates to lower pH values. It should be noted that glucose-1-phosphate was found to undergo a more rapid hydrolysis than glucose-2-phosphate, presumably because of the closer proximity of the polarizing groups, though two different mechanisms may be involved.

In a study of the rates of hydrolysis of aromatic esters:

$$X-\langle\text{C}_6\text{H}_4\rangle-O-\underset{\underset{OH}{|}}{\overset{\overset{OH}{|}}{P}}=O + H_2O \longrightarrow X-\langle\text{C}_6\text{H}_4\rangle-OH + HO-\underset{\underset{OH}{|}}{\overset{\overset{OH}{|}}{P}}=O$$

it was found that the rate increased as X was varied in the following way:

$$CH_3 < H < COO^- < Cl < Br$$

It is probable that such groups can affect the hydrolysis by both inductive and electromeric effects. For this series the Hammett σ constants increase in the order given. Although La(III), Ce(III), Ce(IV), Zr(IV), and Th(IV) are effective catalysts in alkaline solution, with their activity increasing from La(III) to Th(IV), only Zr(IV) and Th(IV) appear to be effective catalysts in acid solutions (pH < 4). This is directly related to the fact that these ions

59. E. Bamann and W.-D. Mütterlein, *Chem. Ber.* **91**, 471, 1322 (1958).

undergo extensive hydrolysis even in weakly acid solutions and can form the catalytically active hydroxy complexes at low pH values.

The mechanisms of nucleophilic substitution in phosphate esters in the absence of metal ions have been comprehensively reviewed.[60]

3.1.5. The Hydrolyses of Fluorophosphate

The hydrolyses of Sarin [the isopropyl ester of methylphosphonofluoridic acid (or isopropoxymethylphosphoryl fluoride)] and DFP (isopropylphosphorofluoridate or diisopropoxyphosphoryl fluoride) have been shown to be catalyzed by acids, bases, and a wide variety of ions.[61] The reaction is the splitting of a P—F bond.

This is catalyzed by metal salts and complexes, especially copper(II) complexes with dipyridyl and histidine,[62] by chromate, molybdate, and tungstate ions,[63] and by a large variety of metal chelate complexes.[64] The study of the effect of CrO_4^{2-}, MoO_4^{2-}, and WO_4^{2-} is rather complete and a detailed consideration of this shows some important factors.

Larsson[63] examined the catalysis of the hydrolysis of Sarin by chromate, molybdate, and tungstate and determined the rate either by the direct titration of the acid generated using a pH stat or, when the reaction was carried out in a bicarbonate buffer, the rate was determined by measurement of the amount of gaseous carbon dioxide evolved. From the data, it was apparent that chromate, molybdate, and tungstate ions were true catalysts and were not consumed during the course of the reaction. The pseudo first-order rate constants obtained were sorted out by using the rate expression

$$-d[S]/dt = k_{obs}[S]_t = k_s[S] + k_c[C][S]$$

60. J. R. Cox, Jr. and O. B. Ramsay, *Chem. Rev.* **64**, 317 (1964).

61. M. Kilpatrick and M. L. Kilpatrick, *J. Phys. Colloid Chem.* **53**, 1371, 1385 (1949).

62. T. Wagner-Jauregg, B. E. Hackley, T. A. Lies, O. O. Owen, and R. Proper, *J. Am. Chem. Soc.* **77**, 922 (1955).

63. L. Larsson, *Acta Chim. Scand.* **11**, 1138 (1957); **12**, 1226 (1958).

64. (a) R. C. Courteney, R. L. Gustafson, S. J. Westerback, H. Hyytainen, S. C. Chaberek, Jr., and A. E. Martell, *J. Am. Chem. Soc.* **79**, 3030 (1957); (b) R. L. Gustafsen, S. C. Chaberek, and A. E. Martell, *J. Am. Chem. Soc.* **85**, 598 (1963).

where k_{obs} is the observed pseudo first-order rate constant, k_s is the rate constant for the spontaneous hydrolysis, k_c is that for the catalyzed reaction, [C] is the concentration of the catalyst, [S] is that of the substrate, and $[S]_t$ is the total concentration of substrate, i.e., $[S] + [CS]$. From this

$$k_c = (k_{obs} - k_s)/[C]$$

The catalytic constants are found to be independent of the pH when the pH is above 8.5. From the data obtained on the temperature variation of k_s and k_c, the activation energies and entropies of activation were obtained. These are listed in the following tabulation:

Catalyst	E_a (kcal/mole)	$\Delta S^{\pm}$ (eu)
None	9.1 ± 0.3	-24 ± 1
CrO_4^{2-}	14.0 ± 0.4	-18 ± 1
MoO_4^{2-}	12.3 ± 0.4	-23 ± 1
WO_4^{2-}	11.5 ± 0.3	-26 ± 1

It is obvious that the catalytic reaction appears to have both a higher E_a and, in one case, a higher $\Delta S^{\pm}$, than the uncatalyzed one. This strange situation results from the fact that $k_c[C][S]$ is a composite term. In this case the reaction is presumably catalyzed by a path which goes through CS. Thus there is a pre-equilibrium

$$C + S \rightleftarrows CS$$

$$K_1 = [CS]/[C][S] \quad \text{so} \quad [CS] = K_1[C][S]$$

The rate expression then has the form

$$-d[S]/dt = k_{obs}[S]_t = k_s[S] + k_c'[CS] = k_s[S] + k_c' K_1[C][S]$$

As a result, the temperature variation ascribed solely to k_c actually includes that from k_c' and K_1. In a situation of this sort, k_c' and K_1 can sometimes be separated by using the procedure of Martin and Niemann.[22]

The examination of the hydrolysis of Sarin and DPF in the presence of a large number of metal complexes showed that the most effective catalysts were those derived from copper(II), though metal chelates of UO_2^{2+}, ZrO^{2+}, Th^{4+}, and MoO_2^{2+} were also effective.[64(a)] From an examination of a large number of complexes, the following feature was found to be required for catalytic activity:

The chelating agent must *not* occupy all the coordination sites of the metal ion. At least some must be occupied by water or oxo groups.

For the complexes of copper(II) it was found that maximum catalytic activity was favored by (1) the presence of aquo groups in two of the coordination positions, (2) a low stability constant for the complex, and (3) increased positive charge on the complex. The catalytic effects of these metal chelates increased with increasing pH. This study[64(a)] is of especial importance because of the large number of complexes examined, though the detailed rate laws were not developed.

A rather thorough study of the hydrolysis of diisopropylphosphorofluoridate (DFP) in the presence of copper ion and its chelates, normal and basic, presents some very interesting results.[64(b)] The study extended over the pH range 6.9–8.90. The reaction was found to be first order in the substrate and observed (composite) first-order rate constants were calculated from $k_{obs} = 0.693/t_{1/2}$. In the absence of metal ion there is a base-catalyzed reaction so

$$k_{obs} = k_{OH}[OH] + C'$$

It was found that C' was negligibly small. In the presence of a metal ion such as Cu^{2+}, and chelating agent (L) the observed rate constant is the composite

$$k_{obs} = k_L[CuL^{2+}][OH^-] + k_B[Cu(OH)_2L] + k_M[Cu^{2+}][OH^-] + k_{OH}[OH^-]$$

In this expression k_L is given as the rate constant representing catalysis by both the diaquo chelate and the monohydroxo complex or either one alone, and k_B, k_M, and k_{OH} are the rate constants assigned to the dihydroxo chelate species, free Cu^{2+}, and the hydroxyl ion, respectively. When the concentration of [Cu(OH)₂L] is very small and the term in k_B can be neglected, the equation in k_{obs} can be rearranged to give

$$\frac{k_{obs}^*}{[Cu^{2+}][OH^-]} = k_L \frac{[CuL^{2+}]}{[Cu^{2+}]} + k_M$$

where $k_{obs}^* = k_{obs} - k_{OH}[OH]$ (this assumes that a negligible amount of DPF is complexed). Using this equation, a plot of the left-hand side against $[CuL^{2+}]/[Cu^{2+}]$ should be a straight line of slope k_L and intercept k_M. In this system, k_M was about 1×10^7 liter² mole⁻¹ sec⁻¹ at 25°C and the value of k_L was dependent upon the chelating agent used and was 7.4×10^6 for dipyridyl. The activation parameters for the hydrolysis of DFP are as follows:

Rate constant	$\Delta H^{\ddagger}$	$\Delta S^{\ddagger}$
k_L (L = dipyridyl)	5.1 ± 0.6 kcal/mole	−9.8 e.u. 25°C

3.1.6. DECARBOXYLATION REACTIONS

Decarboxylation reactions of organic substrates can be catalyzed by the coordination of the substrate to a suitable metal ion when appropriately oriented donor groups are present. The types of compounds which may be found to undergo such a catalytic decarboxylation can be judged from the structures which appear to be susceptible to such a process. These include the following:

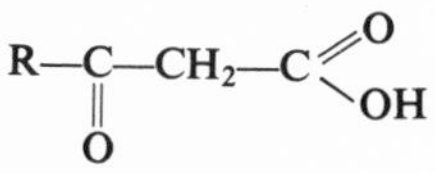

β-Keto acids

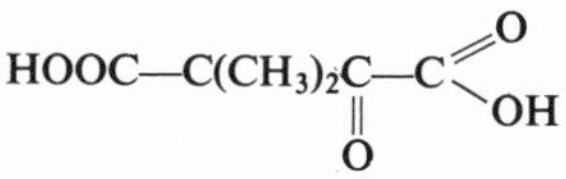

α,α-Dimethyloxaloacetic acid

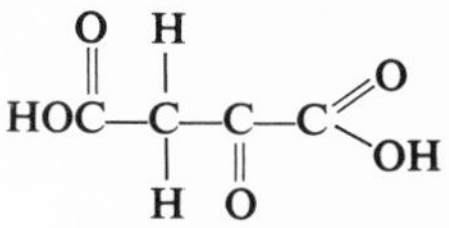

Oxaloacetic acid

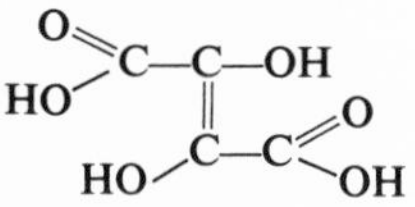

Dihydroxyfumaric
acid

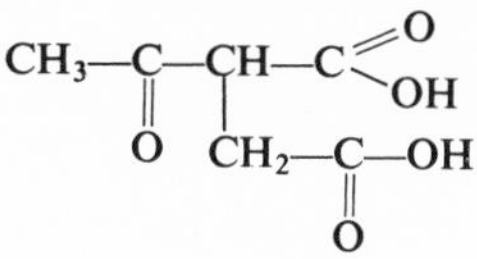

Acetosuccinic
acid

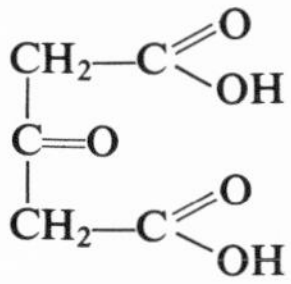

Acetonedicarboxylic
acid

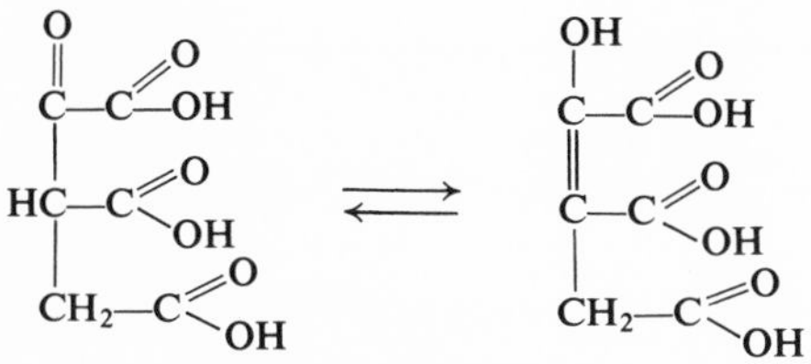

Tautomeric forms
of
oxalosuccinic acid

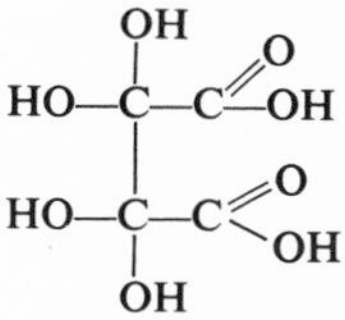

Dihydroxytartaric acid
(also called diketosuccinic acid)

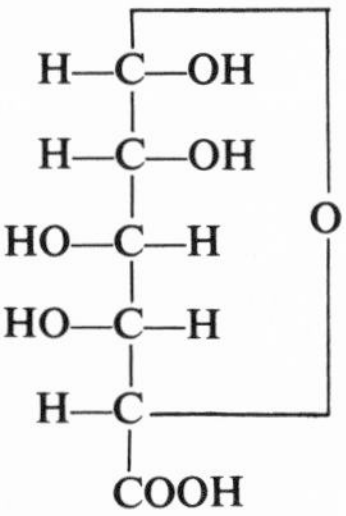

Galacturonic acid

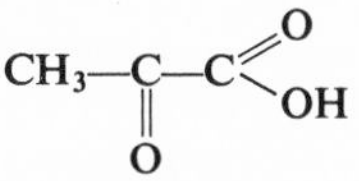

Pyruvic acid
(1-ketopropionic acid)

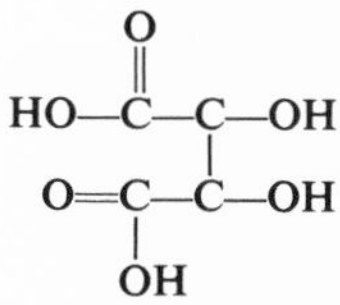

Dihydroxymaleic
acid

The one structural feature common to all of these compounds is the occurrence of multiple donor sites capable of forming chelating rings with suitable metal ions.

The decarboxylation of β-keto acids is catalyzed by metal ions, metal complexes, and metal activated enzymes. It has been subjected to a very wide variety of kinetic studies, but is still incompletely understood. The reaction in the absence of metal ions goes through a hydrogen-bonded intermediate[65]:

$$
\underset{\text{(A)}}{R-C\overset{\overset{\displaystyle H_2}{C}}{\underset{\underset{H}{O}}{\underset{|}{\overset{||}{C}}}}C=O} \longrightarrow \underset{\text{(B)}}{R-C\overset{CH_2}{\underset{\underset{H}{O}}{|}}} \quad + \quad CO_2
$$

The enol intermediate (B) has been detected and found to have an appreciable half-life.[66] Compounds of this sort which occur in biological systems are subject to enzymatic decarboxylation by metal-activated enzymes that have a negligible activity in the absence of the metal.[67] The metals themselves, however, do possess such catalytic powers.[68] The enzymes that catalyze these reactions are activated by a variety of di- and trivalent metal ions, and the manganous ion is about ten times more effective for this purpose than the nickel(II) ion.[69,70] The nonenzymatic decarboxylation reaction has been studied with α,α-dimethyloxaloacetic acid,[66,71,72] oxaloacetic acid,[68,69,73-79] dihydroxyfumaric acid,[80] acetosuccinic acid,[81] acetonedicarboxylic acid,[82-85]

65. F. H. Westheimer and W. A. Jones, *J. Am. Chem. Soc.* **63**, 3283 (1941).
66. R. Steinberger and F. H. Westheimer, *J. Am. Chem. Soc.* **73**, 429 (1951).
67. L. O. Krampitz and C. H. Werkman, *Biochem. J.* **35**, 595 (1941).
68. H. A. Krebs, *Biochem. J.* **36**, 303 (1942).
69. J. F. Speck, *J. Biol. Chem.* **178**, 315 (1949).
70. D. F. Herbert, in "Methods of Enzymology" (S. P. Colowick and N. O. Kaplan, eds.), Vol. I, p. 753. Academic Press, New York, 1955.
71. R. Steinberger and F. H. Westheimer, *J. Am. Chem. Soc.* **71**, 4158 (1949).
72. J. V. Rund and R. A. Plane, *J. Am. Chem. Soc.* **86**, 367 (1964); J. V. Rund, Ph.D. Thesis, Cornell Univ., Ithaca, New York, 1962. Univ. Microfilms, Ann Arbor, Michigan, Order No. 63-2816.
73. E. Gelles and R. W. Hay, *J. Chem. Soc.* p. 3673 (1958).
74. E. Gelles and K. S. Pitzer, *J. Am. Chem. Soc.* **77**, 1947 (1955).
75. E. Gelles and J. P. Clayton, *Trans. Faraday Soc.* **52**, 353 (1956).
76. E. Gelles, *J. Inorg. Nucl. Chem.* **8**, 625 (1958).
77. M. Nassal, *Nature* **163**, 405 (1949).
78. F. Westheimer, *Trans. N.Y. Acad. Sci.* **18**, 15 (1955).
79. R. J. P. Williams, *Nature* **171**, 304 (1953).
80. R. W. Hay and S. J. Harvey, unpublished results cited in *Rev. Pure Appl. Chem.* **13**, 158 (1963), a review.
81. K. J. Pedersen, *Acta Chem. Scand.* **12**, 919 (1958).
82. J. E. Prue, *J. Chem. Soc.* p. 2331 (1952).
83. S. Fallab, *J. Inorg. Nucl. Chem.* **8**, 631 (1958).
84. S. Fallab and H. Erlenmeyer, *Helv. Chim. Acta* **42**, 1152 (1959).
85. O. Toyama, Y. Kubokawa, and Y. Yoshida, *Nippon Kagaku Zasshi* **74**, 955 (1953); **75**, 879 (1954).

oxalosuccinic acid,[86] dihydroxypyruvic acid, galacturonic acid,[87] and pyruvic acid.[88-91]

Most of the compounds studied have had a structure that allowed the formation of a chelate ring that does not involve the carboxyl group lost by decarboxylation. Thus in oxaloacetic acid the reaction is depicted as proceeding via the following mechanism[73]:

Keto form, loses CO_2

Enol form, does not lose CO_2

The metal ion polarizes the ligand and facilitates the movement of electrons towards itself. The rate constants for this reaction in the presence of a number of transition metal ions as well as the stability constants for the complexes with those ions have been determined.[92] Somewhat unexpectedly, *no* correlation was found between the rate constants for the decarboxylation reaction and the stability constants of the corresponding oxaloacetate complexes. Such a relationship *was* found between these rate constants and the stability constants of the corresponding *oxalate* complexes. This finding was interpreted on the basis that the transition state of the decarboxylation reaction resembled the oxalate complexes more closely than it did the oxaloacetate complexes, i.e., bond breaking was extensive. For the catalysis of this reaction by the lanthanide ions, a linear free energy relationship between the rate and the stability constants (both for oxaloacetate) was found.[75]

86. A. Kornberg, S. Ochoa, and A. H. Mehler, *J. Biol. Chem.* **174**, 159 (1948).
87. G. Zweifel and H. Deuel, *Helv. Chim. Acta* **39**, 662 (1956).
88. C. Flesch, W. Schuler, and R. Meier, *Helv. Chim. Acta* **43**, 2014 (1960).
89. A. Schellenberger and E. Podany, *Chem. Ber.* **91**, 1781 (1958).
90. A. Schellenberger and K. Winter, *Chem. Ber.* **92**, 793 (1959).
91. A. Schellenberger, *Z. Physiol. Chem.* **309**, 16 (1957).
92. E. Gelles and A. Salama, *J. Chem. Soc.* p. 3684, 3689 (1959).

Seltzer *et al.*[93] proposed the following mechanism for the decarboxylation of dimethyloxaloacetic acid:

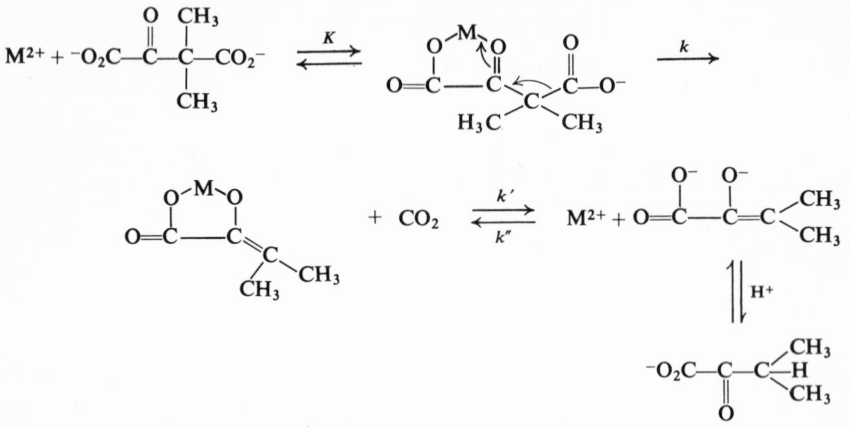

This mechanism and the one cited earlier for β-keto acids provide explanations for the fact that the carboxyl group lost as carbon dioxide may or may not be involved in a chelate ring. In the case of pyruvic acid a similar mechanism involving a smaller ring can be invoked.

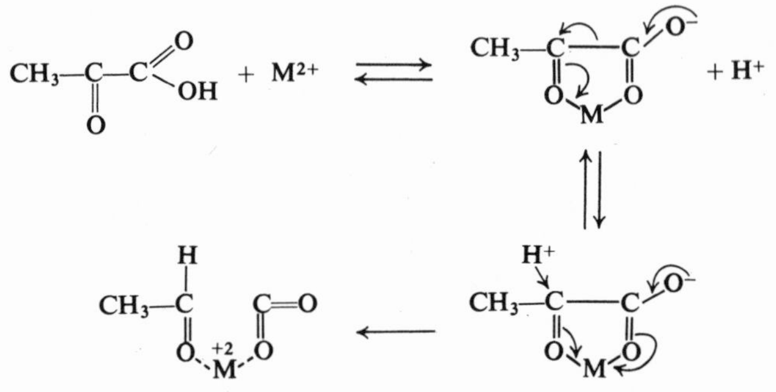

The mechanisms cited incorporate all of the essential features of such metal-catalyzed decarboxylation reactions but one: their inhibition by high concentrations of metal ions.[69, 94] This inhibition has been attributed to the presence

93. S. Seltzer, G. Hamilton, and F. H. Westheimer, *J. Am. Chem. Soc.* **81**, 4018 (1959).
94. K. J. Pedersen, *Acta Chem. Scand.* **3**, 676 (1949).

of chelate structures that are not decarboxylated; these are formulated as

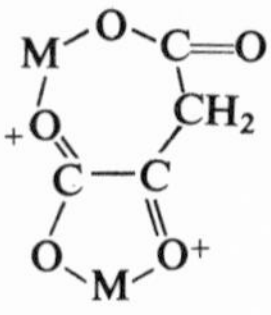

and

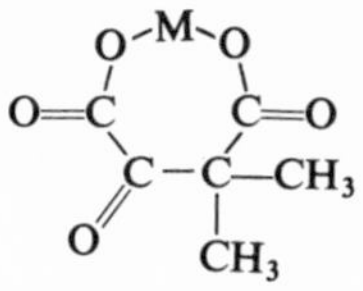

Also, if the substrate functions as a tridentate chelating agent, stabilization of the substrate could occur in the form

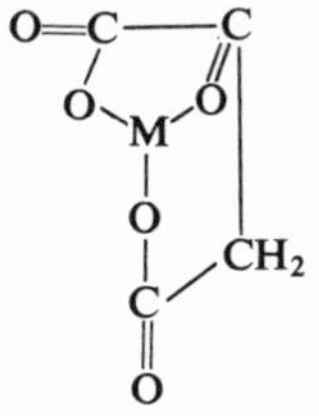

Although these intermediates have not been adequately differentiated, a mechanism incorporating the second (or third) of these has been presented in more detail.[72] The kinetic path has been described in outline as

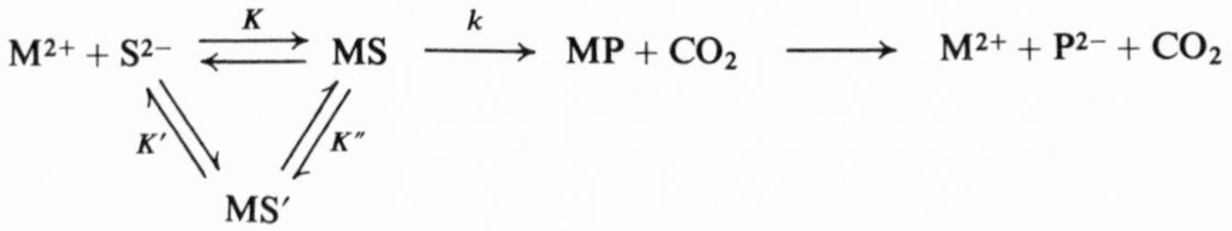

where M^{2+} is a divalent metal ion, S^{2-} is the dimethyloxaloacetate ion, MS is the reactive complex, MS' is the unreactive complex, and MP is the decarboxylated complex. The rate constant characteristic of the catalyzed reaction, k_{cat}, is given by

$$\frac{1}{k_{cat}} = \frac{1 + K_a[H^+]}{kK[M^{2+}]} + \frac{K' + K}{kK}$$

where K_a is the second ionization constant of dimethyloxaloacetic acid and the other terms are defined in the reaction scheme given. Because the data seem consistent with both an active and an inactive complex containing only one metal ion, it seems reasonable to postulate that the inactive complex is one in which the dimethyloxaloacetate functions as a *tridentate* ligand. In the case of similar reactions catalyzed by a metal-activated *enzyme*, it seems

probable that one of the functions of the organic moiety of the holoenzyme*
is to prevent the formation of such unreactive complexes by sterically hinder-
ing the formation of more than two coordinate bonds between the metal ion
and the substrate. The enzymes which catalyze decarboxylation reactions
have been reviewed.[95] Not all of these have an established metal ion
requirement.

A rather thorough study of the uncatalyzed and the nickel(II)-catalyzed
decomposition of dihydroxyfumaric acid has revealed a number of similarities
to other reactions of this type.[96] This decarboxylation is a two-step process

$$HO_2CCOCH-CO_2H \xrightarrow{k_1} \{HO_2CCOCH_2OH + HO_2CCH(OH)CHO\} + CO_2$$
$$\underset{OH}{|}$$

$$HO_2CCH(OH)CHO \xrightarrow{k_2} HOCH_2CHO + CO_2$$

This reaction is markedly accelerated in the presence of small concentrations
of nickel(II), but the presence of nickel(II) concentrations greater than 0.15 M
was found to decrease the rate of decarboxylation. This was explained by Hay
and Harvie on the basis of two different nickel complexes, a 1:1 complex (A)
that was catalytically active and a 2:1 complex (B) that was less active. The
reaction scheme given was

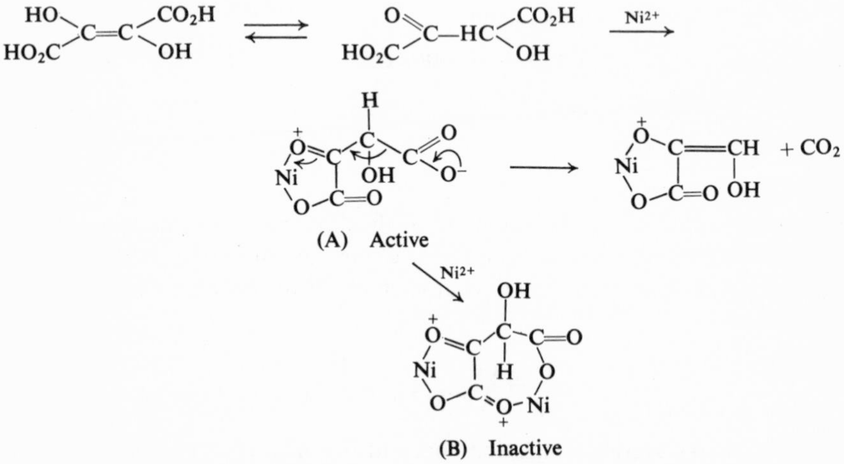

(A)   Active

(B)   Inactive

---

* The holoenzyme consists of all the parts necessary for complete functioning; the apo-
enzyme is the enzyme less the metal.

95. M. Dixon and H. C. Webb, "Enzymes," p. 195, 760. Longmans, Green, New York, 1962.
96. R. W. Hay and S. J. Harvie, *Australian J. Chem.* **18**, 1197 (1965).

It should be noted that the mechanisms of most of the metal-ion-catalyzed reactions of this type are quite different from those proposed for the reactions in which hydrogen furnishes the polarizing center for the uncatalyzed reaction.[65] In this connection it is interesting to find that in many systems in which the metal ions are forced to function in an analogous manner (e.g., with acetoacetic acid[68]) they do not catalyze the decarboxylation. The decarboxylation of acetosuccinic acid, which involves a carboxyl group one carbon further from the polarizing action of the metal ion than in the other examples,

$$
\begin{array}{c}
CH_2{-}COOH \\
| \\
CH \\
O{=}C \diagup \quad \diagdown C{-}CH_3 \\
| \quad \quad \| \\
O \diagdown \quad \diagup O^+ \\
M
\end{array}
$$

is only weakly catalyzed by copper(II).[81]

From the evidence collected to date it is obvious that β-keto acids themselves have *not* been the subject of most of these studies. The majority of the work has been carried out with γ-carboxyl-β-keto acids and the γ-carboxy group plays a very fundamental role in the process, although it could conceivably be replaced by another suitable donor group.

A complication may arise in some of these reactions if the metal ion used as catalyst is capable of acting as an oxidation catalyst also.[97] Thus citrate, in the presence of Mn^{2+} in a basic media, gives acetone dicarboxylic acid

$$
\begin{array}{ccc}
CH_2COO^- & & CH_2COO^- \\
| & \underset{pH \sim 11}{\overset{Mn^{2+} (air)}{\longrightarrow}} & | \\
{}^-O{-}C{-}COO^- & & C{=}O \quad \quad + CO_2 + 2e \\
| & & | \\
CH_2COO^- & & CH_2COO^-
\end{array}
$$

A large number of other α-hydroxypolycarboxylic acids were examined and the formation of keto acids was established as a reaction of some generality. The type of reaction found here is proposed to be

$$
\begin{array}{ccc}
COO^- & & \\
| & \underset{pH \sim 10{-}12}{\overset{Mn^{2+}, Co^{2+}, \text{ or } Cu^{2+} (air)}{\longrightarrow}} & \\
R{-}C{-}O^- + \tfrac{1}{2}O_2 & & R{-}C{=}O + CO_3^{2-} \\
| & & | \\
COO^- & & COO^-
\end{array}
$$

The occurrence of such oxidative decarboxylations introduces an additional complicating factor in determining the mechanisms of these reactions.

97. S. P. Datta, A. K. Grzybowski, and S. S. Tate, *Nature* **207**, 1047 (1965).

3.2. Electrophilic Reagents

3.2.1. GENERAL ASPECTS

Since the coordination act binds a ligand to either a positively charged or an electron-deficient species, it would be anticipated that this would render ligand attack by another positively charged electrophilic species more difficult. This situation is often complicated by the fact that the metal ion has replaced a proton in the process of forming the complex. Based upon the analogous way in which protonation and coordination usually are assumed to tie up a pair of electrons, one would expect that neutral ligands that coordinate without losing a proton should be deactivated by coordination in much the same way that they are deactivated by protonation. An examination of the available evidence shows that the analogy between protonation and coordination is often a poor one. Coordination does *deactivate* ligands towards *electrophilic* reagents, but not nearly so drastically as protonation does. Although coordination compounds have been used as catalysts in organic reactions for almost a century, there is still very little specific information on how the coordination process, per se, compares with typical substituent groups in varying the reactivity of an aromatic ligand.

The coordination of aniline to chromium(III) in the neutral complex, $[CrCl_3 \cdot (C_6H_5NH_2)_3]$, does not have the deactivating effect anticipated from valence bond considerations. This complex reacts with bromine in glacial acetic acid and the ultimate product is 2,4,6-tribromoaniline.[98] This result is unexpected because the valence bond explanation of ortho–para orientation for electrophiles in aniline (and phenols) is based upon the involvement of the normally unshared electron pair in important resonance structures in which it *is* shared with the aromatic ring. In the ground state formulation, the accumulation of negative charge at the ortho and para positions of aniline is based upon the importance of structures (II), (III), and (IV). In these, the

(I)   (II)   (III)   (IV)

unshared electron pair is not available for coordination.[99] In the transition state formulation of electrophilic attack on such systems, the same problem arises, but in a slightly different manner. Here the number of canonical forms

98. J. C. Taft and M. M. Jones, *J. Am. Chem. Soc.* **82**, 4196 (1960).
99. L. Pauling, "The Nature of the Chemical Bond," 3rd Ed., pp. 277–280. Cornell Univ. Press, Ithaca, New York, 1960.

and their estimated relative energies are used to predict the ease of attainment of the transition states for ortho, para, and meta attack. These are shown below for attack by a positively charged reagent Y$^+$.

Para attack

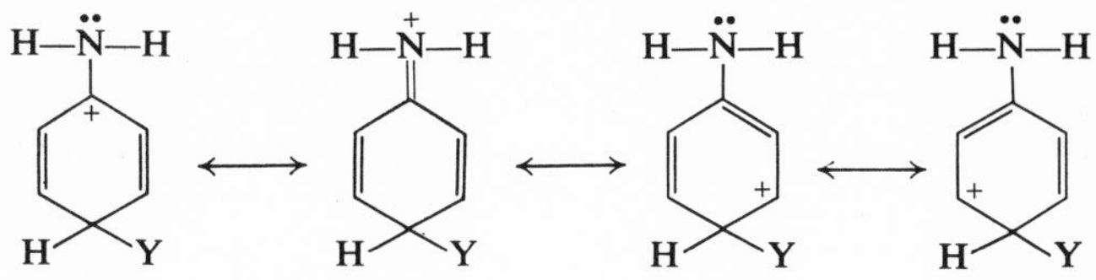

(V)   (VI)   (VII)   (VIII)

Ortho attack

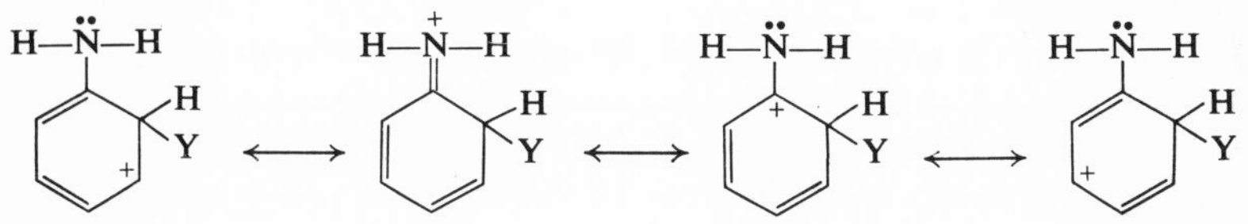

(IX)   (X)   (XI)   (XII)

Meta attack

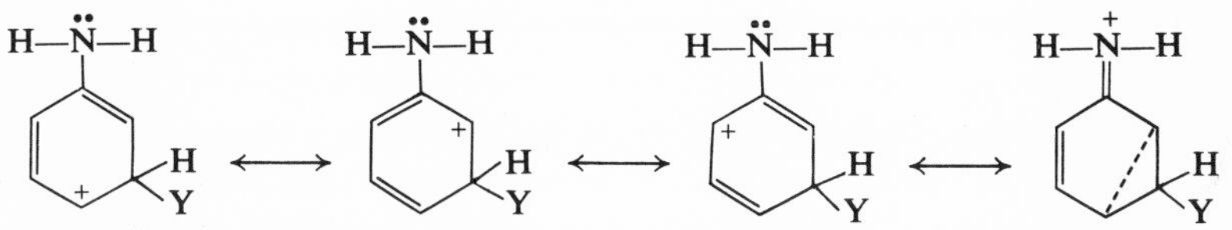

(XIII)   (XIV)   (XV)   (XVI)

Structures (VI) and (X) are considered to be especially stable because each of the atoms has a complete octet. For meta attack, any corresponding structure would require a long bond, as in (XVI), and would be expected to be less stable than the structures in which the lone pair on the nitrogen was unshared with the ring. Since most donor groups capable of forming coordinate bonds are also groups that activate an aromatic system for electrophilic substitution, presumably in a way similar to that proposed for the amino group, one would expect coordination to have a rather *drastic* effect on the reactivity of such ligands. The experimental results are found to be in direct opposition to such expectations.

The first really satisfactory test of these ideas is to be found in studies on palladium(II) complexes with aromatic amines.[100] The stability of these

100. R. L. Jetton and M. M. Jones, *Inorg. Chem.* **1**, 309 (1962).

complexes is sufficient to allow them to be brominated without disruption, so the complexes containing the brominated ligand can be isolated and characterized. It was found that complexes of the type [$PdBr_2$(amine)$_2$], where the amine was aniline, or o, m, or p-toluidine, could be brominated with ease. In each case the position of attack was ortho or para to the amino group. The most striking result is thus that there is no change in the orientation of the entering group induced by coordination. In the case of aniline, some deactivation resulting from complexation was noted, since both 4-bromoaniline and 2,4-dibromoaniline could be prepared by the bromination of the complex. Under similar conditions, free aniline always gave 2,4,6-tribromoaniline. The brominated complexes were decomposed by treatment with aqueous hydrogen sulfide under conditions that unambiguously precluded any rearrangement of the substituents in the ligand. The slight differences observed in the degree of bromination of the complexes and the free ligands (under strictly comparable conditions) were no greater than the differences known to arise from changes in the solvent. The absence of such anticipated differences means that either the valence bond picture of the coordinate bond or the explanation of aromatic orientation (or both) are wrong. It seems most probable that the simple valence bond picture of the coordinate bond overestimates enormously the extent of sharing of the donor's electron pair with the metal. A more reasonable model of the coordinate bond is found in ligand field theory; this model provides adequate opportunity for the polarization of the ligand, without building up large formal charges on the donor atom. A change in the reactive positions of pyridine upon coordination, which was described in a preliminary report,[101] has since been shown[102] to be in error.

At this point it must be noted that the number of alternative explanations which can be used to describe these results is not small. An initial objection might be raised on the basis that the aniline is momentarily dissociated, undergoes reaction with bromine, and the product of this reaction is then recoordinated. The simple testing of this notion by examining the exchange of the aniline complex with the substituted ligand, shows that such exchange is orders of magnitude slower than the actual bromination reaction. The exchange actually cannot be observed in a short period of time under the conditions used for the reaction. To dispose of a second alternative reaction scheme is more difficult. This involves an initial ionization of a proton

(A)   (B)

101. H. C. Brown and B. Kanner, *J. Am. Chem. Soc.* **75**, 3865 (1953).
102. N. Muller and W. J. Wallace, *J. Org. Chem.* **24**, 1151 (1959).

The compound (B) then has a lone pair on the nitrogen which can participate in the delocalized electron system and give rise to the same pattern of orientation as that found in aniline itself. The data presently on hand cannot be used to rule out such a process, though other studies on systems in which such ionization processes are impossible (e.g., pyridine, 8-hydroxyquinoline-5-sulfonic acid) indicate that it is not probable. The ideal solution to this type of question would be provided by studies of stable complexes of N,N-dimethylaniline. Such compounds have yet to be characterized and examined; attempts to prepare them, using the method which is satisfactory for $[Pd(C_6H_5NH_2)_2Br_2]$, did not give analogous complexes.

The chlorination of the copper(II) chloride or sulfate adduct with m-toluidine gives the complex with 6-chloro-3-aminotoluene. In this case the reaction can proceed further by the oxidation of the product.[103]

There are, in fact, a large number of reactions of this type involving mostly labile complexes. Surveys of these[104, 105] reveal the fact that the coordination of aromatic ligands to a *metal* does not change the orientation pattern for electrophilic substitution significantly.

When a Lewis acid such as aluminum chloride is involved in these reactions it is important to establish whether the products obtained from a given reaction system are determined by kinetic or thermodynamic factors. This point has been discussed in detail by G. Baddeley.[106]

Much of the unambiguous data available on the problem of ligand reactivity has been obtained on *chelated* systems, where the enhanced stability of the complexes has allowed the use of reactive media which would disrupt most complexes containing only unidentate ligands. This is to be contrasted with the most widely useful complexes in organic chemistry—these are almost invariably *labile* complexes of Lewis acids such as $AlCl_3$, $FeCl_3$, $SnCl_4$, $ZnCl_2$, or $SbCl_5$. As a result of this dichotomy, the information available in the literature falls into two broad classes:

(1) Information on the reactivity patterns of organic systems containing labile complexes. In these the participation of the complex in the reaction is often highly probable but genuinely unambiguous proof of such participation is usually lacking. Most of these reactions consist of systems for which it is difficult to prove that the complex itself, and not its dissociation products, is the literal substrate. The amount of information available on such systems is enormous.

103. M. Gentschev, I. Pojarliev, and D. Kolev, *Compt. Rend. Acad. Bulgare Sci.* **12**, 305 (1959).
104. M. M. Jones, *Advan. Chem. Ser.* **37**, 116 (1963).
105. M. M. Jones, *J. Tenn. Acad. Sci.* **38**, 87 (1963).
106. G. Baddeley, *Quart. Rev.* (*London*) **8**, 364 (1954). See also G. Olah, ed., "Friedel-Crafts and Related Reactions," Vol. I, Chapts. 4, 8, 11, 12. Wiley (Interscience), New York, 1963.

(2) Studies of the reactions of complexes in which the intermediate complexes, containing the altered ligands, have been isolated and characterized. These studies are almost invariably carried out on complexes inert to ligand exchange under the conditions of reaction used and the information on ligand reactivity obtained from such studies is indisputable. Many of the reactions of this sort are of no synthetic utility, although they can provide a much deeper understanding of the reactions of labile complexes, which are of much greater synthetic use.

Any discussion of ligand reactivity must *begin* with reactions of this second class. For aromatic ligands, these studies show that while the *rates* of typical electrophilic reactions *are* affected by coordination of the substrate, the *qualitative* patterns of ligand reactivity are the same in the complex as in the free ligand.

One of the earliest systematic studies can be found in the work of V. I. Kuznetsov and his co-workers on the diazo-coupling reactions of various phenols, which produce useful dyes. Kuznetsov established that the use of complexes, rather than the free phenols, reduced the extent of the side reactions in the oxidizing conditions of the diazo-coupling media and thus allowed the production of dyes with purer colors. In many cases the over-all yields can also be increased appreciably by reaction via the complex rather than the free ligand. An example is shown in the following scheme:

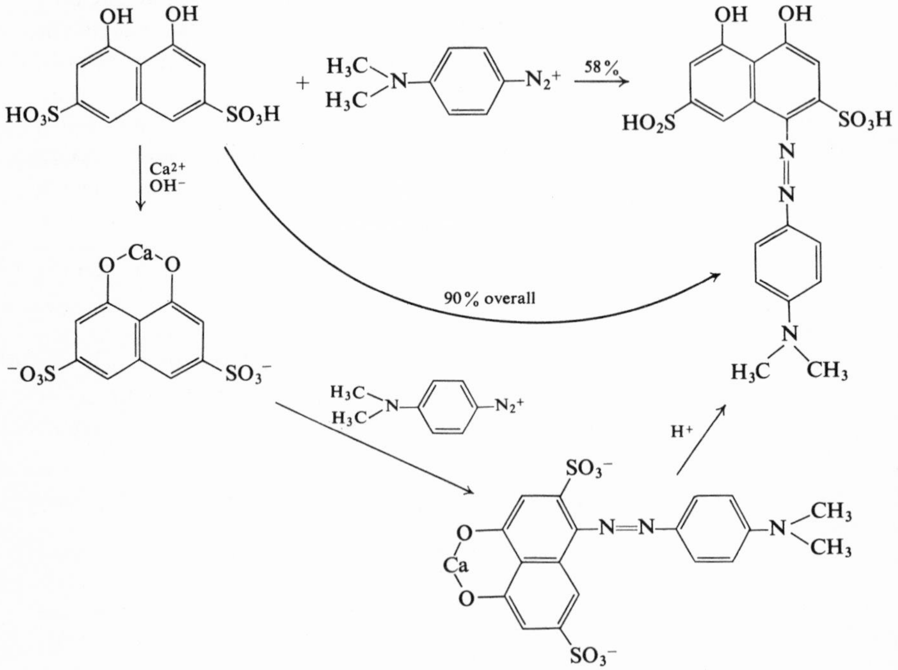

In this case the intermediate calcium complex can be isolated. Related reactions have also been examined by these workers.[107] The same principle was used much earlier in an empirical fashion to improve the quality of diazo dyes.[108]

Subsequent studies of the halogenation of stable complexes of 8-hydroxy-quinoline (actually present in the complex as the corresponding phenolate anion) established that the orientation of the entering groups was the same for these complexes as for the free ligand, although the complexes are slightly more reactive than the parent (phenolic) ligand in both chlorination and bromination. The proton on the oxygen draws the ligand electrons to it more strongly than does the metal ion that replaces it in the complex. In the cases of the iron(III), cobalt(III), and chromium(III) complexes with 8-hydroxy-quinoline the great stability is found to interfere with the characterization of the products. The complexes, after reaction, are found to be difficult or impossible to dissociate.[109] In such cases the occurrence of ligand reactions with rates enormously in excess of the rate of dissociation of the complex must occur. Furthermore, there is every evidence that these occur on the coordinated ligand and not on some of the momentarily dissociated ligands. Another route by which one can establish that reaction occurs with the coordinated ligand and not any dissociated species is by the use of optically active complexes. If the dextro or levo forms of the complex of catechol and arsenic acid are subject to either bromination or diazo coupling (in a basic solution), products are obtained which are also optically active and which contain substituted ligands. This type of experiment furnishes direct evidence for the reaction of the complex per se, as the dissociation of the ligand prior to such a process would lead to a racemic product.[110]

Before proceeding to a consideration of kinetic studies, it is helpful to review some of the results obtained by synthetic organic chemists working with labile complexes. In two cases, the Friedel-Crafts reaction with aliphatic dibasic acids and the Fries reaction, comprehensive surveys have been published. For the first of these reactions,[111] it was concluded that the groups already present on the aromatic ring, regardless of their involvement in a complex with aluminum chloride, determine the orientation of the entering groups and that they do so by "the usual rules governing aromatic substitution." A total of 73 such reactions were cited that involve an aromatic system

107. V. I. Kuznetsov, *Zh. Obshch. Khim.* **20**, 807 (1950); V. I. Kuznetsov and A. A. Nemodruk, *Zh. Obshch. Khim.* **25**, 117 (1955); **26**, 3657 (1956); **29**, 988 (1959); V. I. Kuznetsov and A. A. Nemodruk, *Sb. Statei Obshch. Khim.* **2**, 1373 (1953); A. A. Nemodruk, *J. Gen, Chem. USSR (English Transl.)* **28**, 1051 (1958) (Consultants Bureau transl.).
108. Farbwerke, vorm. Meister, Lucius, and Bruning, German Patents 174,905, 175,827, 177,624, 178,304, 188,189 (1904). These are also cited in P. W. Friedländer, *Fortschritte der Teerfarbenfabriken und verwandte Industriezweige* Vol. III, pp. 612, 616, 619, 620 (1904).
109. K. D. Maguire and M. M. Jones, *J. Am. Chem. Soc.* **84**, 2316 (1962).
110. T. H. Larkins, Jr. and M. M. Jones, *J. Inorg. Nucl. Chem.* **25**, 1487 (1963).
111. E. Berliner, *Org. Reactions* **5**, 229 (1949).

with substituents capable of acting as donor groups toward aluminum chloride. All of these reactions show the orientation expected for the parent aromatic compound. In the case of the Fries reaction there is an extensive review of the literature up to 1940.[112] In this reaction, a phenolic ester is converted to the corresponding o- or p-hydroxyketone.

Although the relative amounts of ortho and para products may vary, meta orientation is not observed. Of the 109 reactions cited by Blatt, all give products in which the orientation is ortho or para to a phenolic oxygen. Since more than one mole of aluminum chloride is required per mole of phenol ester, the reaction is one involving the aluminum chloride complex of the phenol ester plus some additional aluminum chloride which functions in a catalytic fashion.

At this point it should be recalled that the typical explanation of ortho and para orientation in both amines and phenols is somewhat unusual. Both oxygen and nitrogen are more electronegative than carbon and would be expected to withdraw electrons from any aromatic system to which they were attached and hence deactivate it toward electrophilic reagents. Experimentally it is found that phenols and amines are *extremely* reactive toward electrophilic reagents, so some counterbalancing shift of electron density must occur. The presence of π-bonding between the lone pair of the oxygen or nitrogen and the aromatic system has been invoked to explain the great reactivity. The coordination of a metal ion through this lone pair *should* have a considerable effect on the qualitative reactivity pattern of such a ligand—but doesn't. This may very well result from the fact that such a picture of the coordinate bond is a gross and unrealistic oversimplification. There is evidence from studies on pyridine that coordination can have an effect that is strongly dependent on the electronegativity of the coordination center. This dependence, which will be considered in detail below, indicates that the immobilization of the electron pair in the coordinate bond is always much *less* than would be expected on the basis of the valence bond theory picture of such a bond.

3.2.2. STUDIES ON PYRIDINE COMPLEXES

In the case of pyridine, evidence is available on a variety of species in which the lone pair on the nitrogen is involved in a bond of some sort. These contain

112. A. H. Blatt, *Org. Reactions* 1, 342 (1942).

bonds to a proton, oxygen, aluminum, chromium, ruthenium, copper, and mercury. Because of the basicity of pyridine, it is sometimes difficult to obtain information on those electrophilic reactions customarily run in an acidic solution, such as nitration or sulfonation. The usual point of attack of electrophilic reagents is the 3-position.

The *relative order* of the electronic charge densities at the 2-, 3-, and 4-positions is not changed by protonation.[113-115] The electrophilic substitution reactions of pyridine complexes with *metals* give the same orientation as is found with pyridine itself. When pyridine is coordinated to ruthenium in the neutral complexes [$RuCl_2$(Pyridine)$_4$] and [$RuCl_3$(Pyridine)$_3$], the product of nitration is the corresponding ruthenium complex containing 3-nitropyridine as a ligand; furthermore, the reaction proceeds more readily than with the pyridinium ion.[116] From the behavior of pyridine in mercuration reactions, where 3-pyridyl mercuric acetate is the principal product, it can be seen that coordination to a metal of low electronegativity does not markedly deter the reaction.[117] This reaction goes more readily than most electrophilic reactions of pyridine; it may be considered to involve the attack of HgOAc$^+$ species on a pyridine nucleus that is coordinated to mercuric acetate.

The mercuration of α-aminopyridine or α-picoline gives products in which mercuration has occurred in the 5-position. This is the same position that is attacked by electrophilic reagents in the free ligand. The halogenation of pyridine or picoline in the presence of a large excess of aluminum chloride also gives products in which the substituent is at the 3-position.[118]

113. D. W. Davies, *Trans. Faraday Soc.* **51**, 449 (1955).
114. D. W. Davies, *J. Chem. Soc.* p. 2412 (1955).
115. R. D. Brown and M. L. Hefferman, *Australian J. Chem.* **9**, 83 (1956).
116. J. Soucek, *Collection Czech. Chem. Commun.* **27**, 1645 (1962).
117. M. A. Swaney, M. J. Skeeters, and R. N. Shreve, *Ind. Eng. Chem.* **32**, 360 (1940).
118. D. E. Pearson, W. W. Hargrove, J. K. T. Chow, and B. R. Suthers, *J. Org. Chem.* **26**, 789 (1961).

The case of pyridine-N-oxide is of special interest, as it shows how an extreme type of coordinate bond can affect the qualitative patterns of reactivity of the ligand.[119] Ochiai used earlier dipole moment studies on this kind of compound[120] as a basis for estimating the relative importance of the various possible canonical forms. These indicated a moment of 4.24 D for pyridine-N-oxide, a value lower by a considerable amount from the 6.6 D predicted from the group moments of pyridine and the N-oxide linkage. Linton explained this on the basis that structures (B) to (D) were important for this molecule, in addition to the usual structure (A). These additional resonance structures

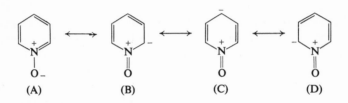

correspond to a back-donation from the oxygen which should increase the reactivity of the 2- and the 4-positions toward electrophilic reagents. If a transition state formulation is adopted, these would correspond to the extra resonance structures

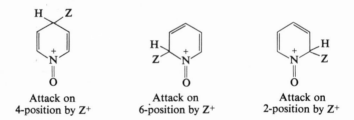

| Attack on
4-position by Z^+ | Attack on
6-position by Z^+ | Attack on
2-position by Z^+ |

No such additional structures can be written for the transition state for substitution at the 3-position. A molecular orbital treatment of this system has also been developed.[121, 122]

Ochiai found that pyridine-N-oxide was more reactive in nitration than pyridine, and he was able to prepare 4-nitropyridine-N-oxide in good yield by the direct nitration of this compound. A small amount of 2-nitropyridine-N-oxide is formed concurrently. The mercuration of pyridine-N-oxide also gives

119. E. Ochiai, *J. Org. Chem.* **18**, 534 (1953).
120. E. P. Linton, *J. Am. Chem. Soc.* **62**, 1945 (1940).
121. S. Basu and K. L. Saha, *Naturwissenschaften* **44**, 633 (1957).
122. G. Tsoucaris, *J. Chim. Phys.* **58**, 613 (1961).

the 4-substituted product.[123] The sulfonation of pyridine-N-oxide is not readily effected and the orientation is predominantly to the 3-position with small amounts of the 2- and 4-substituted compounds produced. Vigorous conditions are required.[124]

The orientation for bromination of this compound appears to depend upon the conditions of the reaction. At 200°C, in sulfuric acid that contains silver sulfate as a catalyst, 4-bromopyridine-N-oxide and 2-bromopyridine-N-oxide are produced in poor yields.[125] In a mixture of acetic acid, sodium acetate, and bromine in chloroform, however, the product is 3,5-dibromopyridine-N-oxide.[126] The bromination of pyridine-N-oxide in *fuming* sulfuric acid actually involves the sulfur trioxide adduct as the substrate and gives 3-bromopyridine-N-oxide as the chief product.[127] The multiply substituted products resulting from further bromination were the 2,5-, the 2,3-, and the 3,4-dibromopyridine-N-oxides. These indicate that the bromine atoms introduced into the ring subsequent to the first, take positions ortho or para to it, so that the first bromo substituent and not the N-oxide function determines the orientation of further entering groups.

All in all, the case of pyridine-N-oxide is of considerable interest, but somewhat anomalous. It appears to indicate that when coordination disturbs the delicately balanced electronic factors responsible for aromatic orientation, the disturbance may change the orientation for some substitution reactions but not for others. In such cases the attacking reagent's characteristics will be important in determining what products will predominate.

3.2.3. THE SWAMPING CATALYST EFFECT

When aromatic systems bear deactivating groups which are also donor groups, nuclear halogenation is considerably facilitated by the presence of an excess of aluminum chloride or bromide. This procedure, called the Swamping Catalyst Effect, was discovered by Pearson and his co-workers.[128]

The reaction of the aluminum chloride complex of acetophenone with bromine, carried out in the presence of a large excess of aluminum chloride, results in *m*-bromoacetophenone.[128] Here the coordination of the carbonyl oxygen prevents the normal course of the reaction (which is the bromination

123. T. Ukai, Y. Yamamoto, and S. Hirano, *Yakugaku Zasshi* **73**, 823 (1953); *Chem. Abstr.* **48**, 9946.
124. M. van Ammers and H. J. den Hartog, *Rec. Trav. Chim.* **78**, 586 (1959).
125. H. C. van der Plas, H. J. den Hartog, M. van Ammers, and B. Haase, *Tetrahedron Letters* p. 32 (1961).
126. M. Hamana and M. Yamazaki, *Chem. Pharm. Bull.* (*Tokyo*) **9**, 414 (1961); *Chem. Abstr.* **55**, 24749.
127. M. van Ammers, H. J. den Hartog, and B. Haase, *Tetrahedron Letters* **18**, 227 (1962).
128. D. E. Pearson and H. W. Pope, *J. Org. Chem.* **21**, 381 (1956); D. E. Pearson, H. W. Pope, and W. W. Hargrove, *Org. Syn.* **40**, 7 (1960).

of the terminal methyl group) and allows the substitution to be effected on the aromatic ring. The two reactions are

The usual site for electrophilic attack on uncomplexed acetophenone is the meta position. This same "swamping catalyst" procedure can be used with acetophenones containing alkyl substituents in the 4-position, analogous benzaldehydes, and propiophenones.[129] In all of these cases the reaction yields products in which substitution has occurred meta to the aromatic carbonyl group. Neither boron trihalides nor stannic chloride are reported to be able to replace the aluminum chloride in these reactions.

In one case, a change in the relative isomeric distribution of the products of electrophilic substitution has been claimed to result from the coordination of aniline to aluminum chloride.[130] In this case, however, the reaction mixtures contained appreciable amounts of hydrogen halides, either from the deliberate addition of it to the aniline–aluminum chloride complex prior to the addition of bromine (this complex readily absorbs one mole of hydrogen halide per mole), or by the absorption of the acid generated during the halogenation reaction itself. However, the percentage of meta orientation changes from 50 to 60 % observed when the aniline–aluminum chloride–hydrogen chloride is used as the starting material, to about 25 % when no hydrogen chloride is added initially. An excess of aluminum chloride was always present so that some remained free after the 1:1 complex with aniline was formed. These reactions appear to result in large measure from the anilinium ion with a smaller contribution from the complexes, as the normal course of the halogenation of an aromatic amine that is merely coordinated is to the positions ortho and para to the amino group.[100] As the reaction in an aniline–aluminum chloride mixture proceeds, one would expect all of the unreacted aniline–aluminum chloride complex to be converted to $[C_6H_5NH_3^+][AlCl_4^-]$ after half of the aniline was halogenated. Subsequently, the course of the reaction should be similar to that of a mixture in which this complex was prepared prior to the addition of the halogen. The yields of the meta-substituted product support such a contention. The activation of the halogen by the excess of the

129. D. E. Pearson, H. W. Pope, W. W. Hargrove, and W. E. Stamper, *J. Org. Chem.* **23**, 1412 (1958).
130. B. R. Suthers, P. H. Riggins, and D. E. Pearson, *J. Org. Chem.* **27**, 447 (1962).

aluminum halide in these systems, and the elevated temperatures employed ($\approx 70°–80°C$), must also be considered in any detailed explanation of the yields obtained.

The attempts to use the swamping catalyst procedure to acetylate acetophenone all failed,[131] presumably because the aromatic ring is too thoroughly deactivated. It is possible to acetylate acetophenones containing an alkyl group ortho to the acetyl grouping, and the acetylation of β-acetonaphthalene can be carried out to give 1,6-diacetonaphthalene.[131]

The swamping catalyst procedure has been used to obtain 3-bromopyridine by the bromination of pyridine,[132] polybrominated quinolines and isoquinolines,[133] and in the halogenation of a large number of derivatives of aromatic acids.[134] The conditions under which this reaction is carried out include the continuous generation of a hydrogen halide. This and the aluminum chloride or bromide originally present generate a medium in which rearrangements can occur. In the case of p-cresol and p-bromophenol, rearrangements were found in which the thermodynamically favored meta compounds were generated. This explains, in part, the apparent changes in orientation that were reported earlier. As an example, it was found that p-bromophenol rearranged to give 54% of the meta isomer and that the initial bromination of phenol using the swamping catalyst procedure gives para substitution; the product then undergoes rearrangement.[135]

3.2.4. KINETIC STUDIES ON AROMATIC SYSTEMS

The first comprehensive experimental study where the rates of a substitution reaction were determined for the coordinated *and* the free ligand may be seen in work done on the diazo coupling of 8-hydroxyquinoline-5-sulfonic acid and its zinc complex.[136] The attacking species was the diazotized sulfanilic acid zwitterion, p-diazobenzenesulfonate. The overall reaction is

7-(4-Sulfobenzeneazo)-5-sulfo-
8-hydroxyquinoline (a red dye)

131. D. E. Pearson and C. R. McIntosh, *J. Chem. Eng. Data* **9**, 245 (1964).
132. D. E. Pearson, W. W. Hargrove, J. K. T. Chow, and B. R. Suthers, *J. Org. Chem.* **26**, 789 (1963).
133. M. Gordon and D. E. Pearson, *J. Org. Chem.* **29**, 329 (1964).
134. D. E. Pearson, W. E. Stamper, and B. R. Suthers, *J. Org. Chem.* **28**, 3147 (1963).
135. L. A. Fury, Jr. and D. E. Pearson, *J. Org. Chem.* **30**, 2301 (1965).
136. K. D. Maguire and M. M. Jones, *J. Am. Chem. Soc.* **85**, 154 (1963).

The diazo-coupling reaction is especially suitable for sorting out the effects of coordination on electrophilic substitution patterns as it is a reaction of great selectivity. It proceeds readily with phenols *only* when they are present in the form of phenolate anions.[137] In the present case the rate of the coupling reaction could be determined by following the increase in the concentration of the product (a red dye) spectrophotometrically. The solutions must be buffered in order to regulate the various protonic equilibria in the system. When the reaction is carried out in an acetate buffer at pH 5.00, the addition of zinc acetate is found to reduce the measured pseudo first-order rate constant, but only to a certain point as the following data show (at pH = 5.00 and 15°C):

Zinc/ligand ratio	0.5	1.0	5.0	10.0	50.0	100
$k_1' \times 10^3$ (min^{-1})	33	26	13	10	7.9	7.9

The limiting value obtained here shows that the 1:1 complex, which is the form in which practically all of the ligand would be present with such an excess of zinc, is undergoing the diazo coupling reaction, though at a slower rate than the phenolate ion itself. If the free phenolate ion were the only reactive species in this system the rate of the reaction should be proportional to its concentration, [RO$^-$]. In such a system this is given by the expression

$$[RO^-] = \left\{ \frac{[ROH]_t}{K_b[Zn^{2+}] + ([H^+]/K_a) + 1} \right\}$$

where [ROH]$_t$ is the total concentration of the phenol in all its forms, K_b is the formation constant for the 1:1 zinc phenolate complex, and K_a is the ionization constant of the phenol. Under the conditions of pH employed, this expression would predict an approximately linear initial decrease in the rate with concentration of added zinc ion, *if* the phenolate anion were the only species capable of undergoing the diazo-coupling reaction. This is clearly *not* the case, thus the limiting rate observed is characteristic of the zinc complex present at high metal-to-ligand ratios.

The data obtained indicate that the order of reactivity towards diazo coupling is

Phenolate > Zinc complex ≫ Phenol

It can be estimated that the phenolate reacts approximately 10^4 times faster than the zinc complex. From previous work[138] it can also be estimated that

137. R. Wistar and P. D. Bartlett, *J. Am. Chem. Soc.* **63**, 413 (1941).
138. H. Zollinger, "Diazo and Azo Chemistry, Aliphatic and Aromatic Compounds," Chapt. X. Wiley (Interscience), New York, 1961.

the phenol reacts roughly 10^{-10} times as rapidly as the phenolate, so the rate of reaction of the zinc complex is approximately 10^6 times that of the free phenol. This result suggests the reactivity series for phenols

$$RO^- > ROM > ROH$$

and an analogous one

$$RNH_2 > RNH_2 : M^{x+} > RNH_3^+$$

for electrophilic attack of aromatic amines.

A more detailed analysis of the kinetic data shows that the principle source of difference in reactivity between the phenolate ion and the zinc complex is the much lower frequency factor for the zinc complex. This is shown in the following tabulation of data on activation parameters:

Substrate	E_a (kcal/mole)	A (sec^{-1})	ΔS^* (eu)
8-Hydroxyquinoline-5-sulfonic acid	19.3	9.7×10^{17}	23.8
1:1 Zinc complex of same	13.4	9.2×10^{12}	-17.7

These studies were extended to metal complexes of 8-hydroxyquinoline-5-sulfonic acid with numerous other metal ions[139]; the results obtained were similar to those found for the zinc complex and the activation parameters are shown in Table II. In the presence of the acetate buffer, the course of the

TABLE II

DERIVED KINETIC PARAMETERS

Metal	E_a (kcal/mole)	A (sec^{-1})	ΔS^* (eu)	ΔF^* (kcal/mole)
Lithium(I)	17.3	1.26×10^{12}	-3.0	18.1
Sodium(I)	16.7	4.21×10^{11}	-5.2	18.1
Potassium(I)	17.0	4.81×10^{11}	-5.0	18.4
Magnesium(II)	17.2	1.00×10^{12}	-3.5	18.2
Calcium(II)	15.0	2.15×10^{10}	-11.2	18.4
Strontium(II)	17.1	1.03×10^{12}	-3.4	18.1
Cadmium(II)	14.3	1.81×10^{10}	-11.5	17.5
Barium(II)	16.9	6.91×10^{11}	-8.8	19.3
Aluminum(III)	17.7	1.16×10^{11}	-7.8	19.9
Zinc(II)	13.4	7.7×10^8	-17.7	18.5
None (phenolate)	19.3	9.7×10^{17}	23.8	12.5

139.   J. B. Breinig and M. M. Jones, *J. Org. Chem.* **28**, 852 (1963).

reaction for the 1:1 complex is described by the equation

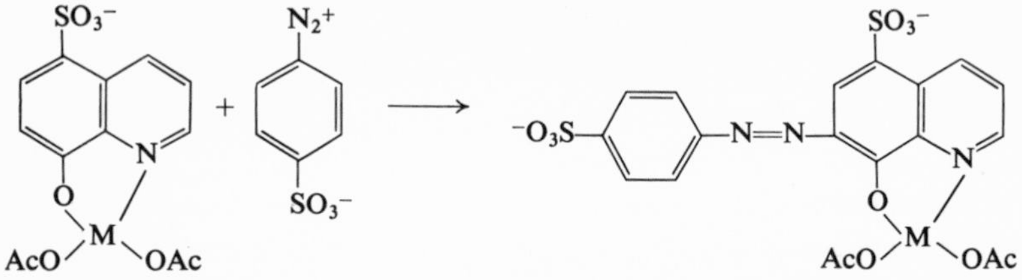

In the case of cadmium it was found that the gross rate of formation of the dye was greater when cadmium was present than for the pure ligand. This means simply that the relative importance of the terms in the rate expression

$$\text{Rate} = [\text{RN}_2^+]\{k_1[\text{RO}^-] + k_2[\text{CdOR}]\}$$

where k_1 is the rate constant for the reaction in which the diazonium ion attacks the phenolate anion and k_2 is the rate constant for the attack on the 1:1 cadmium complex, is such that $k_2[\text{CdOR}] > k_1[\text{RO}^-]$. It does not mean that $k_2 > k_1$.

The results obtained in these kinetic studies, as well as previous studies on the orientation in the products of such reactions, can be incorporated into the usual valence bond theory of organic chemistry in two ways. The first, and perhaps the most satisfactory, is to consider that no-bond resonance forms for the metal–ligand bond are important contributing structures, and that structures with typical electron pair coordinate bonds are much less important. The relative importance of canonical forms with electron pair coordinate bonds may be expected to increase as the electronegativity of the acceptor center increases. This explanation would account for both the deactivation that results from coordination and the lack of a change in orientation. An alternative explanation can be developed that is based upon the canonical forms given for the transition states (V) through (XVI) (p. 63). The canonical forms used to explain the ortho–para orientation in aniline or phenol are assigned a different relative importance than is customary. Those forms that have a positive charge on the nitrogen or oxygen are to be considered as much less important than those that do not. This means that structures (VI), (X), and (XVI) can be largely ignored. The remaining structures are to be weighted on the basis of the separation distance between the positive charges on the ring and the positive charge on the coordination center. On this basis, the structures for meta attack include two that place this positive carbon close [(XIV) and (XV)] and one that places it far (XIII) from the metal. For ortho or para attack there are two each [(IX), (XII), (VII), and (VIII)] that place this at some distance and two [(V) and (XI)] that place it very close. Although one could not predict the relative importance of these on an *a priori* basis, one can use the results to order these in importance as (VII) + (VIII) ≫ (XIII) and (IX) + (XII) ≫ (XIII). This second explanation is somewhat less flexible than the first, but both are capable of rationalizing the *absence* of a change in orientation for electrophilic attack when compounds such as aniline or phenol are coordinated to a metal ion.

Orthophenanthroline (ophen), though formally similar to pyridine, is significantly different in its reactions with electrophilic reagents. The most reactive positions are outside the heterocyclic systems proper, i.e., the 5- and 6-positions.

The effect of coordination on the rates of nitration of the diprotonated and the chelated forms of this ligand have been determined.[140] The replacement of the two protons by a metal ion such as Co(III) or Fe(III) (in the tris chelates) increases the rate of nitration by a factor greater than 10^2. The approximate second-order rate constants for the nitration in 98.07% sulfuric acid are

$[H_2ophen]^{2+}$	$k_2 = 3.4 \times 10^{-3}$ liter mole^{-1} min^{-1} at 100.7°C
$[Co(ophen)_3]^{3+}$	$k_2 = 1.6 \times 10^{-1}$ liter mole^{-1} min^{-1} at 80°C
$[Fe(ophen)_3]^{3+}$	$k_2 = 2.5 \times 10^{-1}$ liter mole^{-1} min^{-1} at 80°C

The product obtained in all cases is 5-nitroorthophenanthroline. The reactivity of the unprotonated free ligand was not determined but would probably be significantly greater than that of either the complexed or the protonated forms.

The rate of iodination of 8-hydroxyquinoline-5-sulfonic acid is affected in a similar manner.[141] Here the rate is extremely rapid. The kinetic data were obtained by recording the diffusion current for the iodine–iodide system as a

140. A. F. Richards, J. H. Ridd, and M. L. Tobe, *Chem. Ind.* (*London*) p. 1727 (1963).
141. C. Bostic, Q. Fernando, and H. Freiser, *Inorg. Chem.* **2**, 232 (1963).

function of time[142, 143] in a system in which the halogen was being electro-chemically generated. The rate was determined only in solutions with a metal-to-ligand ratio of 1:2, so the effects observed result in large measure from the relative stabilities of the complexes formed. The rate of the normal ligand reaction at 20°C and pH 7 with $[I^-] = 0.10$ M is 1.08×10^5 liter mole^{-1} min^{-1}. When the metal ion concentration is increased to give the gross composition of the 1:2 chelate complex (ignoring dissociation), the rates of iodination under comparable conditions are as follows:

Metal ion	Mn^{2+}	Zn^{2+}	Fe^{2+}	Co^{2+}	Ni^{2+}	Cu^{2+}
k_2 (liter mole^{-1} min^{-1} $\times$ 10^5)	1.86	0.506	0.482	0.375	0.15	No reaction

Because of the lack of information on the distribution of the ligand among its various free and complexed forms, it is not possible to decide how these data are to be interpreted in terms of the relative reactivities of such species. This experimental method should prove to be very useful in the study of other aromatic chelate systems. Because such aromatic chelating agents usually possess donor groups that are also powerful activators for aromatic systems in so far as electrophilic substitution is concerned, the rates of reactions of such systems are usually too fast to be measured by the usual sampling techniques.

A direct comparison of the rate of bromination of aniline, $[Co(en)_2$-$(NH_2C_6H_5)(H_2O)]^{3+}$, and the anilinium ion has been carried out using an amperometric technique.[144] The rate of bromination of aniline in 0.05 M KCl was estimated to be 3×10^{10} liter mole^{-1} sec^{-1}; under similar conditions, the rate for the complexed aniline in $[Co(en)_2(NH_2C_6H_5)(H_2O)]^{3+}$ was 1.44×10^{-1} liter mole^{-1} sec^{-1}. From other data it could be estimated that the maximum rate of bromination of the anilinium ion was 3×10^{-7} liter mole^{-1} sec^{-1}. These results are of interest in being the only information of this sort available on the electrophilic substitution reactions of monodentate aromatic ligands.

In addition to the literal rate studies mentioned above, there are also some related studies that furnish qualitative information on the relative rates of reaction of ligands and their metal complexes. The first of these is a study of the competition between 8-hydroxyquinoline and several of its metal chelates for bromine. In all cases the chelates took up the preponderant amount of bromine.[145] The relative rates, as estimated from the product ratios for the chelates of iron(III), cobalt(III), and chromium(III) gave a metal chelate-to-

142. G. S. Kozak and Q. Fernando, *Anal. Chim. Acta* **26**, 541 (1962).
143. G. S. Kozak and Q. Fernando, *J. Phys. Chem.* **67**, 811 (1963).
144. N. K. Chawla, D. G. Lambert, and M. M. Jones, *J. Am. Chem. Soc.* **89**, 557 (1967).
145. J. E. Hix, Jr. and M. M. Jones, *J. Inorg. Nucl. Chem.* **26**, 781 (1964).

ligand ratio of 35 : 1. In this same study, it was established that the heats of bromination of the ligand and the metal chelates were approximately the same. Rather similar results were obtained in later studies[146] in which the considerable difference in the rates of halogenation for the introduction of the first and the second halogen in the chelates was made the basis of a synthetic method for the preparation of monohalogenated 8-hydroxyquinolines.

3.2.5. REACTIONS OF COORDINATED ISONITRILES (ISOCYANIDES)

The reactions of aromatic isonitrile complexes have been examined in considerable detail by W. Z. Heldt.[147(a–h)] One of the most unusual features of the behavior of complexes of the type $[M(C\!\!=\!\!N\!\!-\!\!R)_x Y_z]$, in which M is Fe(II) or some other species that gives inert complexes, is the extreme resistance of these materials towards attack by reagents which normally attack the $:C\!\!=\!\!N\!\!-$ linkage in free isonitriles. As a result, it is possible to study the reactions of $[M(CNR)_x Y_z]$ toward typical electrophilic or nucleophilic reagents when R contains an aromatic system (e.g., when R is a benzyl group). In an extensive study of the reactions of cyanopentakis(benzylisonitrile)-iron(II), the aromatic system reacted rapidly in nitration, sulfonation, bromination, and hydroxymethylation [with $(CH_2O)_3$ and H_2SO_4] reactions to give products in which the substitution was predominantly in the position para to the methylene isonitrile group. For example, this is observed in the reaction

$$[Fe(CN)(CN\!\!-\!\!CH_2C_6H_5)_5] \xrightarrow[\text{H}_2\text{SO}_4]{\text{(CH}_2\text{O)}_3} [Fe(CN)(p\text{-CNCH}_2C_6H_4CH_2OH)_5]HSO_4$$

Although Heldt originally proposed an explanation to account for the observed orientation which started with the assumption that the *normal* orientation in benzyl isonitrile would be to the meta positions, it seems more reasonable to accept the para substitution as the normal mode. This para substitution is obscured customarily by the reaction of the $:C\!\!=\!\!N\!\!-$ group with electrophiles at a rate much greater than nuclear substitution. Such an explanation also relieves one of the burdens of explaining how coordination can both cause a deactivation *and* a shift from meta to para orientation, a change not observed in any strictly organic system.

Treatment of benzyl isonitrile complexes with nucleophilic reagents results, for the most part, in the polymerization of the complexes or their disruption. With cyanide ion, benzyl isonitrile is liberated, but the reaction is not a simple displacement process since when the cyanide is labeled with carbon-14, most

146. R. Prasad, H. L. D. Coffer, Q. Fernando, and H. Freiser, *J. Org. Chem.* **30**, 1251 (1965).
147. W. Z. Heldt (a) *J. Org. Chem.* **26**, 3226 (1961); (b) *J. Inorg. Nucl. Chem.* **23**, 305 (1961); (c) *J. Inorg. Nucl. Chem.* **24**, 73 (1962); (d) *J. Inorg. Nucl. Chem.* **24**, 265 (1963); (e) *J. Org. Chem.* **27**, 2604 (1962); (f) *J. Org. Chem.* **27**, 2608 (1962); (g) W. Z. Heldt and C. D. Weiss, *Inorg. Chem.* **2**, 1392 (1963); (h) W. Z. Heldt, *Advan. Chem. Ser.* **37**, 99 (1963).

of the activity is found in the *organic* reaction products. Heldt studied both the formation and the reactions of this class of complex and much of the previous literature is referred to in his papers. The mechanisms of many of the reactions described are quite complicated.

3.2.6. FRIEDEL-CRAFTS AND RELATED REACTIONS

The enormous number of studies that have been carried out on the Friedel-Crafts reaction have produced a great deal of information[148] but have not yet succeeded in establishing the detailed mechanisms of these reactions with any certainty. Because of its greater relevancy to the reactions described above, only the Friedel-Crafts acylation reaction will be considered here. At this point we must specify that our goal is an understanding of the mechanism of this reaction with a given catalyst, substrate, solvent, and reaction conditions. We should recognize that the mechanism *may* change as these are varied and that a multiplicity of mechanisms may be possible for such a reaction. Under a given set of conditions, the rate of the reaction along the different paths will be different and it may be that only one or two of these paths are responsible for the formation of most of the product.

A detailed kinetic study of the acylation of aromatic systems with benzoyl chloride revealed a variety of rate laws for the metal halide catalysts used.[149] When benzoyl chloride is used as a solvent, the rate laws observed experimentally are as follows (where the subscript zero refers to the initial concentration of the species within the brackets):

for $AlCl_3$

$$\text{Rate} = k_2[C_6H_5COCl \cdot AlCl_3][ArH]$$

for $GaCl_3$

$$\text{Rate} = \frac{k[C_6H_5COCl \cdot GaCl_3]^2[ArH]}{[GaCl_3]_0}$$

for $SbCl_5$

$$\text{Rate} = \frac{k[C_6H_5COCl \cdot SbCl_5][ArH]}{[SbCl_5]_0}$$

for $FeCl_3$

$$\text{Rate} = \frac{k[C_6H_5COCl \cdot FeCl_3]^2[ArH]}{[FeCl_3]_0}$$

148. G. Olah, ed., "Friedel-Crafts and Related Reactions." Wiley (Interscience), New York, 1963–1965. A comprehensive review in four volumes (bound as six).

149. F. R. Jensen, Ph.D. Thesis, Purdue Univ., Lafayette, Indiana, 1955; H. C. Brown and F. R. Jensen, *J. Am. Chem. Soc.* **80**, 3039 (1955).

for $SnCl_4$

$$Rate = k_4[C_6H_5COCl]^2[SnCl_4][ArH]$$

and for BCl_3

$$Rate = k_1[ArH] = k_2[BCl_3][ArH] = k_3[C_6H_5COCl][BCl_3][ArH]$$

The relative rates of benzoylation for these catalysts vary widely and are approximately as follows:

$SbCl_5 = 1500$	$GaCl_3 = 500$	$SnCl_4 = 1/350$
$FeCl_3 = 570$	$AlCl_3 = 1$	$BCl_3 = 1/1600$

A more detailed examination of the rate of the reaction using aluminum bromide as a catalyst in some solvents of low polarity (such as 1,2,4-trichloro-benzene) showed that an excess of aluminum bromide had a marked catalytic action. In such reactions, the overall rate expression proposed for the benzoylation of toluene was

$$Rate = k_0[C_6H_5COX\cdot AlX_3][C_6H_5CH_3] + k_1[C_6H_5COX\cdot AlX_3]^2[C_6H_5CH_3]$$

$$+ k_2[C_6H_5COX\cdot AlX_3][C_6H_5COC_6H_4CH_3\cdot AlX_3][C_6H_5CH_3]$$

$$+ k_3[C_6H_5COX\cdot AlX_3][AlX_3][C_6H_5CH_3]$$

Here the last term describes the role of the excess aluminum halide in the rate expression.

The mechanisms possible for these reactions are summarized by Jensen[149] as follows:

Mechanism 1

R—C=O:$AlCl_3$ ⇌ R—C=O
   | |
   Cl   Cl:$AlCl_3$
   (A)   (B)

$$(B) \rightleftarrows RCO^+ + AlCl_4^-$$
$$RCO^+ + ArH \rightleftarrows RCOArH^+$$
$$RCOArH^+ + AlCl_4^- \rightleftarrows RCOAr\cdot AlCl_3 + HCl$$

This is the mechanism favored in older interpretations and is based upon a variety of data supporting the existence of RCO^+ species in certain media. As written it requires the generation of free acylium ions, RCO^+, and would be expected to require a polar medium. The existence of two forms of complex, (A) and (B), in which the aluminum halide is bonded to the carbonyl oxygen and the halide, respectively, is supported by infrared evidence.[150] In solvents of low dielectric constant form (A) is predominant (as in chloroform), but in

150. D. Cook, *Can. J. Chem.* **37**, 48 (1959).

a solvent of high dielectric constant (such as nitrobenzene) form (B) is present in ionized form as RCO^+, AlX_4^-. The solvation of the complex by the nitrobenzene is probably as important here as the microscopic dielectric constant.

Mechanism 2

$$(B) \rightleftarrows RCO^+, AlCl_4^-$$
$$RCO^+, AlCl_4^- + ArH \rightleftarrows RCOArH^+, AlCl_4^-$$
$$RCOArH^+, AlCl_4^- \rightarrow RCOAr \cdot AlCl_3 + HCl$$

In this mechanism the ion pair, $RCO^+, AlCl_4^-$ is generated and attacks the aromatic substrate, so no prior ionization into its constituent ions is required. This again will be a mechanism which is assisted by a polar medium, but its demands in this respect will be much less severe than those of Mechanism 1.

Mechanism 3

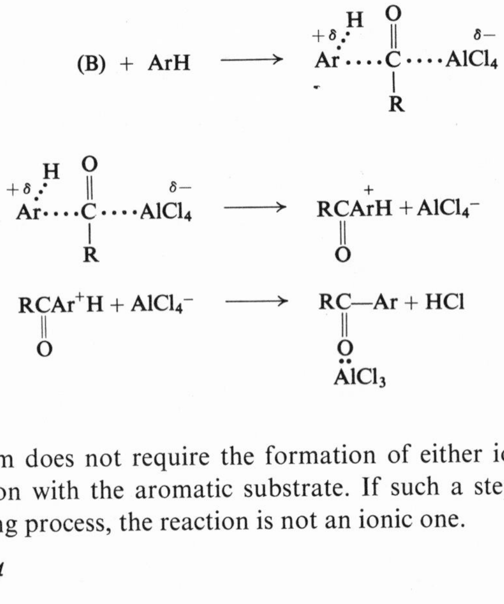

This mechanism does not require the formation of either ions or ion pairs prior to reaction with the aromatic substrate. If such a step represents the rate-determining process, the reaction is not an ionic one.

Mechanism 4

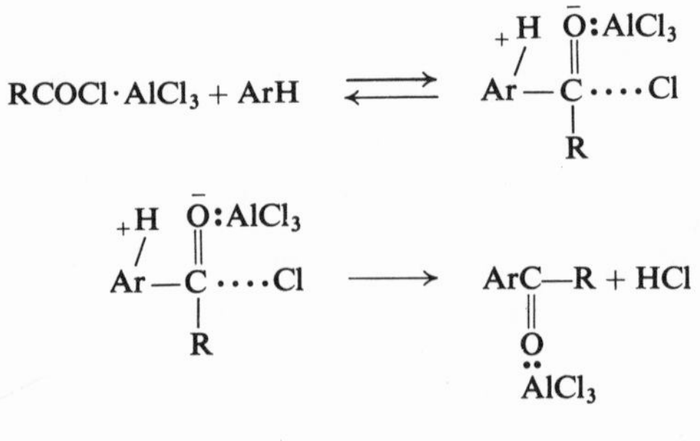

This mechanism does not require the formation of ions at any stage and is thus much more reasonable for nonpolar solvents than any of the previous mechanisms. The general nature of the results obtained for the benzoylation reaction in nonpolar solvents supports Mechanism 4 as the most probable one *under these conditions*. It is quite possible that a mechanism involving ions or ion pairs may become important in a more polar solvent or when the solvation properties of the solvent are more pronounced.

The effect of adding an excess of aluminum chloride is explained by Jensen in terms of further complexes such as

$$\mathrm{R-C}\!\!\begin{array}{c}\nearrow \mathrm{O:Al_2Cl_6}\\ \searrow \mathrm{Cl}\end{array} ,\quad \mathrm{R-C}\!\!\begin{array}{c}\nearrow \mathrm{O:Al_xCl_{3x}}\\ \searrow \mathrm{Cl:AlCl_3}\end{array} ,\quad \text{and}\quad \mathrm{R-C}\!\!\begin{array}{c}\nearrow \mathrm{O:Al_xCl_{3x}}\\ \searrow \mathrm{Cl:Al_xCl_{3x}}\end{array}$$

Unfortunately, the molecular weights of the complexes present in such mixtures have not been unequivocally established and the role of polymeric complexes has been neither proven nor disproven. It should also be noted that most of the solvents in which this reaction has been studied yield fairly stable complexes with the Lewis acids used as catalysts. For example, nitrobenzene forms the complex $C_6H_5NO_2 \cdot AlCl_3$. For some complexes the kinetic order of the acylation reactions does not appear to be sharply defined. This may be the result of two kinetic paths, peculiar solvent effects, competitive complexation with the solvents, or other reasons. The study of the Friedel-Crafts sulfonylation reaction[151] presents kinetic problems of the sort found with the acylation reaction. Brown and Jensen suggest a displacement mechanism as the basic one for sulfonylation.

$$\mathrm{R-\overset{\overset{\textstyle O:AlCl_3}{\|}}{\underset{\underset{\textstyle O}{\|}}{S}}-Cl} \;\;\rightleftharpoons\;\; \mathrm{R-\overset{\overset{\textstyle O}{\|}}{\underset{\underset{\textstyle O}{\|}}{S}}-Cl\cdot AlCl_3}$$

$$\mathrm{R-\overset{\overset{\textstyle O}{\|}}{\underset{\underset{\textstyle O}{\|}}{S}}-Cl\cdot AlCl_3 + ArH} \;\longrightarrow\; \mathrm{\overset{+\delta\;\;H\;\;O}{Ar}-\overset{\overset{\textstyle O}{\|/}}{\underset{\underset{\textstyle R}{\,}}{S}}-Cl\cdot AlCl_3^{\;\;\delta-}} \;\longrightarrow\;$$

$$\mathrm{RSO_2ArH^+ + AlCl_4^-} \;\longrightarrow\; \mathrm{RSO_2Ar\cdot AlCl_3 + HCl}$$

Attack by the RSO_2^+ ion may occur under some circumstances.

151. H. C. Brown and F. R. Jensen, *J. Am. Chem. Soc.* **80**, 4038 (1958).

3.3. Nucleophilic Reagents

3.3.1. GENERAL ASPECTS

Just as coordination is expected to *retard* the course of a reaction that consists of an attack on a ligand by an electrophilic species, so it would be expected to *assist* a reaction in which a nucleophilic reagent attacks a ligand. The amount of evidence on this point is large and covers a considerable number of reactions, and it is almost all in accord with the assumption that coordination does facilitate nucleophilic attack on a ligand. Much of this was cited earlier in the discussion of the ligand polarization which accompanies coordination. The electrostatic basis of this interaction can be altered if the ionization of the ligand occurs in several steps to give a series of complexes bearing different charges. The usual effect of this is seen as the pH is raised and successively more protons are removed from a complex to give species that are successively more resistant to attack by hydroxide or other nucleophiles.

The metal ion catalysis of nucleophilic organic reactions in solutions has been reviewed by Bender.[152] In addition to the types of reactions already considered, Bender lists hydrogenation and hydrations of unsaturated systems, olefin-forming elimination reactions, transaminations, aldol condensations, and nucleophilic displacement reactions.

An important example of this is seen in the Pt(II)-catalyzed hydrolysis of C_2H_4. It has long been known that the platinum metal salts and those of other elements that form complexes with unsaturated systems catalyze the hydrogenation of such unsaturated systems. The catalytic *hydrolysis* is now well characterized in the Smidt process, which is also a redox reaction.[153]

$$C_2H_4 + PdCl_2 + H_2O \rightarrow CH_3CHO + Pd + 2HCl$$

$$Pd + 2CuCl_2 \rightarrow PdCl_2 + Cu_2Cl_2$$

$$2CuCl + \tfrac{1}{2}O_2 + 2HCl \rightarrow 2CuCl_2 + H_2O$$

The coordination of olefins to palladium(II) chloride makes the olefins much more susceptible to attack by nucleophiles.[154, 155] Such reactions are carried out in nonaqueous solvents (all in the presence of Na_2HPO_4) and

152. M. L. Bender, *Advan. Chem. Ser.* **37**, 19 (1963).
153. J. Smidt, W. Hafner, R. Jira, R. Sieber, J. Sedlemeyer, and A. Sabel, *Angew. Chem. Intern. Ed. English* **1**, 80 (1960).
154. E. W. Stern and M. L. Spector, *Proc. Chem. Soc.* p. 370 (1961).
155. E. W. Stern, *Proc. Chem. Soc.* p. 111 (1963).

include the following:

$$(C_2H_4PdCl_2)_2 + CH_3COOH \xrightarrow{\text{Isooctane}} CH_2{=}CH{-}OOCCH_3$$

$$(C_2H_4PdCl_2)_2 + (CH_3)_2CHOH \longrightarrow$$
$$CH_2{=}CH{-}OCH(CH_3)_2 + CH_3{-}CH[OCH(CH_3)_2]_2$$

$$CH_2{=}CH{-}CH_3 + n\text{-}C_4H_9NH_2 \xrightarrow[\text{THF}]{\text{PdCl}_2} n\text{-}C_4H_9NH{-}CH(CH_3)_2$$

The mechanisms presented for such reactions are (a) a 1,2-shift of hydride from the carbon attacked followed by a proton loss from an adjacent carbon atom and (b) transfer involving an intermediate hydridopalladium complex.

The transamination reactions which illustrate metal ion catalysis include those of the general type

$$\underset{}{>}C{=}N{<}^R_M + R'NH_2 \rightleftharpoons {>}C{=}N{<}^{R'}_M + RNH_2$$

where the metal ion is coordinated to another donor atom which is part of the same Schiff base.[156–159] The aldol condensations are exemplified in the Knoevenagel reaction of the copper complex of glycine.

$$\begin{array}{c}
CH_2{-}NH_2 \diagdown \quad \diagup NH_2{-}CH_2 \\
\quad | \qquad Cu \qquad | \\
C{-}{-}{-}O \diagup \diagdown O{-}{-}C \\
\| \qquad\qquad\qquad \| \\
O \qquad\qquad\qquad O
\end{array} \xrightarrow[CH_3CHO]{Base} \begin{array}{c}
\quad\;\; H \qquad\qquad\qquad H\;\; H \\
CH_3{-}C{-}CH{-}NH_2 \diagdown\;\; NH_2{-}C{-}C{-}CH_3 \\
\quad | \qquad\qquad\qquad Cu \qquad | \;\; | \\
HO\;\; C{-}{-}{-}O \diagup \diagdown O{-}{-}C \;\; OH \\
\qquad \| \qquad\qquad\qquad \| \\
\qquad O \qquad\qquad\qquad O
\end{array}$$

This reaction was reported by Sato and his co-workers[160] and seems to represent a reaction of some generality for the copper complexes of glycine.

The hydration of acetylenic compounds has long been recognized as subject to catalysis by mercuric salts. A mechanism for this reaction with the bis-(acetylene)mercury complex as an intermediate has been presented on the basis of kinetic studies.[161] Here the incorporation of the neutral acetylene molecule into the positively charged complex makes it much more susceptible

156. P. Pfeiffer, W. Offermann, and H. Werner, *J. Prakt. Chem.* **159**, 313 (1941).
157. T. Muto, *Nippon Kagaku Zasshi* **76**, 252 (1955).
158. H. S. Verter and A. E. Frost, *J. Am. Chem. Soc.* **82**, 85 (1960).
159. D. F. Martin, *Advan. Chem. Ser* **37**, 192 (1963).
160. M. Sato, K. Okawa, and S. Akabori, *Bull. Chem. Soc. Japan* **30**, 937 (1957).
161. W. L. Budde and R. E. Dessy, *J. Am. Chem. Soc.* **85**, 3964 (1963).

to nucleophilic attack by the water in the system. A related reaction is the cuprous-chloride-catalyzed hydrochlorination of acetylene.

$$HC\!\!\equiv\!\!CH + HCl \xrightarrow[\text{in HCl}]{CuCl_x} CH_2\!\!=\!\!CHCl$$

A very thorough kinetic study of this system[162] led to the suggestion that *two* copper atoms are involved in the rate-determining step, but the complexity of the rate behavior precluded the formulation of a detailed mechanism.

The general factors governing the interactions in nucleophilic reactions have been reevaluated on the basis of the way they affect the rates of such reactions[163] and the equilibria.[164] These general factors governing the rates of nucleophilic reactions are the ones governing the effectiveness of the nucleophilic reagent: basicity, polarizability, and the presence of unshared electron pairs on the atom adjacent to the nucleophilic atom. The results attributable to this latter effect are called the *alpha* effect.* In many cases either the basicity (as measured by pK value) or the polarizability is the predominating factor, with the alpha effect superposed on these. The reactivities of substrates with a high positive charge and relatively few electrons in the outer orbitals of the central atom are dependent mostly on basicity. Coordination would tend to move a substrate into this category. For a substrate with a low positive charge and many electrons in the outer orbitals of the central atom, the reactivity is determined primarily by the polarizability. One would anticipate that the alpha effect would be subject to very large variations arising from a coordination process involving the alpha atom which would be based in part on steric factors. For the treatment of equilibria, acids and bases can be placed in either of two categories (1) slightly polarizable or "hard" and (2) very polarizable or "soft." Hard acids are bonded more firmly to hard bases and soft acids are bonded more firmly to soft bases. Although this is formally quite similar to the schemes proposed earlier by Ahrland *et al.*[165] and by Schwarzenbach,[166] it presents the reciprocal nature of acid–base interactions in a clearer perspective.

* The alpha effect is exemplified in reactions of nucleophiles such as NH_2OH, N_2H_4, H_2O_2 and related compounds in which they react more rapidly with *substrates* than can be explained by the *basicity*. Thus the reaction of benzonitrile with HO_2^- is much faster than the corresponding reaction of benzonitrile with OH^- [K. Wiberg, *J. Am. Chem. Soc.* **77**, 2519 (1955).] The availability of an unshared pair on the atom alpha to the reactive atom is a characteristic feature of such behavior.

162. R. Vestin and L. Arro, *Acta Chem. Scand.* **17**, 1093, 1225 (1963).

163. J. O. Edwards and R. G. Pearson, *J. Am. Chem. Soc.* **84**, 16 (1962).

164. R. G. Pearson, *J. Am. Chem. Soc.* **85**, 3533 (1963).

165. S. Ahrland, J. Chatt, and N. R. Davies, *Quart. Rev. (London)* **12**, 265 (1958).

166. G. Schwarzenbach, *in* "Chemical Specificity in Biological Interactions" (F. R. N. Gurd, ed.), pp. 164–192. Academic Press, New York, 1954.

A demonstration of the accelerating action of coordination for nucleophilic attack on certain quinones, which also shows how this process may be used to effect certain syntheses, has been presented by Corey and Konig.[167] The basic structures involved are the following:

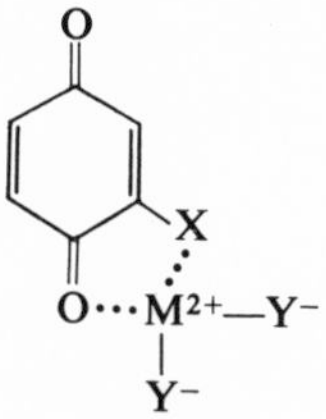

in the structure

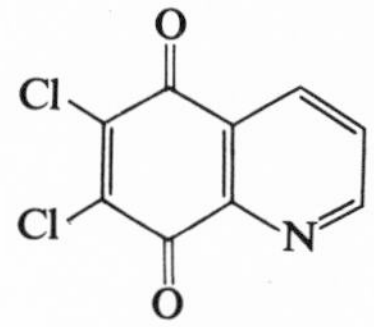

6,7-Dichloro-5,8-quinolinequinone
(DQQ)

where X is a donor group.

The coordination of this strongly oxidizing quinone to copper accelerates nucleophilic attack at the 6-position and facilitates the replacement of the chloro group. When the copper salt of a carboxylic acid is used, a reactive intermediate is formed that is capable of acylating suitable substrates.

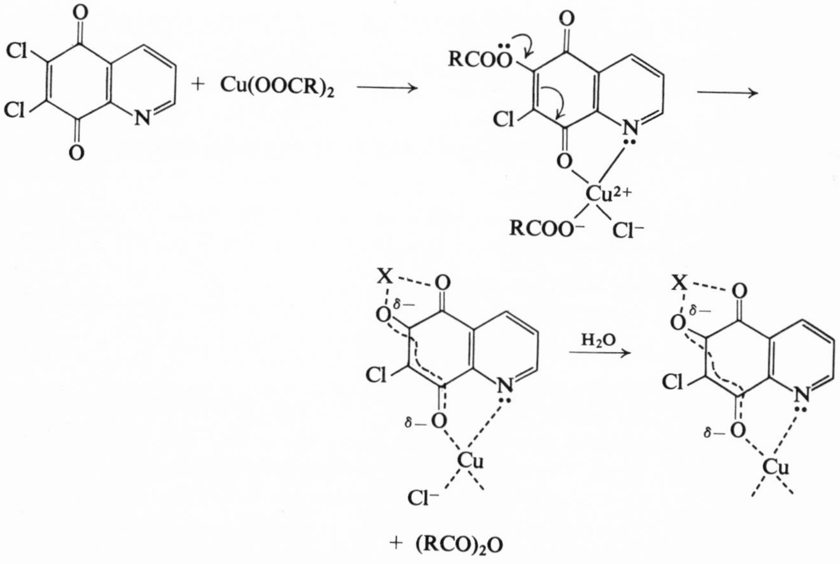

$+ Cu(OOCR)_2 \longrightarrow$

$\longrightarrow$

$\xrightarrow{H_2O}$

$+ (RCO)_2O$

The anhydride is formed here in a reaction in which the oxidation potential of the DQQ is used to effect an acylation by the transfer of an electron deficiency

167. E. J. Corey and H. Konig, J. Am. Chem. Soc. 84, 4904 (1962).

to an otherwise unreactive ionic group. This work was extended to show that under corresponding conditions with a phosphate anion, this same system can effect phosphorylation. Thus the reaction of DQQ and cupric trimethylene phosphate (at reflux for 110 hours in alcohol free chloroform) led to the formation of bis(trimethylene) pyrophosphate.

$$DQQ + \left(CH_2 \begin{array}{c} CH_2-O \\ CH_2-O \end{array} P \begin{array}{c} O \\ O \end{array} \right)_2 Cu \longrightarrow$$

$$CH_2 \begin{array}{c} CH_2-O \\ CH_2-O \end{array} \overset{O}{\underset{\|}{P}}-O-\overset{O}{\underset{\|}{P}} \begin{array}{c} O-CH_2 \\ O-CH_2 \end{array} CH_2$$

+ oxidation product of DQQ

3.4. Redox Reactions

3.4.1. GENERAL REMARKS

As the last example in the previous section illustrates, one type of reaction verges on the next and it is not possible to have a rigid classification scheme for ligand reactions. One would expect that the redox reactions of ligands would be affected in the same manner by coordination as other kinds of reactions. Coordination should make the ligand more eager to pick up electrons and less willing to give them up. Unfortunately the central metal ions of the complexes are themselves often capable of participating in such redox processes. As a result, one finds that the most thoroughly studied aspect of the redox reactions of complexes is that concerning the participation of the central metal ion in redox processes. It is now apparent that the ligand polarization that invariably accompanies coordination can function in two ways. In the first, we find the coordination center pulling on the electrons of the ligand until it removes one or more and undergoes reduction. Such a process can result in a catalytic oxidation of the ligand if oxygen is present to reoxidize the metal ion. Copper(II) is found to be a very effective catalyst for many of these reactions because of its ease of reduction and subsequent oxidation.

A very different situation is found with a large number of iron(II) complexes. In these, coordination with molecular oxygen occurs primarily by π-bonding in which electrons of the central metal are shared with the oxygen. These complexes undergo redox reactions, at varying rates, in which the iron(II) is oxidized to a higher oxidation state, iron(III) or iron(IV), and can, in turn, oxidize other species. Here we might say that the coordination of molecular oxygen facilitates *its* reduction. There are a reasonable number of complexes which can activate molecular oxygen in this manner, and in doing so, effect oxidations at room temperature which would otherwise be extremely slow if only molecular oxygen were available. Respiration depends upon such processes. The fixation of atmospheric nitrogen, which also requires metals, presumably in complexes, may well involve analogous steps in the reduction of N_2.

In an enormous number of oxidation reactions the role of metal ions is more direct. They are themselves oxidized by molecular oxygen and then oxidize some organic substrate, usually with the production of very reactive intermediate free radicals. An example is found in the catalysis of the oxidation of benzaldehyde by cobalt(II) salts.[168] Here the catalytic path for the reaction involves the generation of Co^{3+} from Co^{2+}, followed by the reactions

$$Co^{3+} + C_6H_5CHO \longrightarrow Co^{2+} + C_6H_5CO\cdot + H^+ \text{ (limiting step)}$$

$$C_6H_5CO\cdot + O_2 \longrightarrow C_6H_5COOO$$

$$C_6H_5COOO + C_6H_5CHO \longrightarrow C_6H_5COOOH + C_6H_5CO\cdot$$

$$Co^{2+} + C_6H_5COOOH \xrightarrow{\text{Fast}} Co^{3+} + OH^- + C_6H_5COO\cdot$$

$$Co^{3+} + C_6H_5COOOH \xrightarrow{\text{Very slow}} Co^{2+} + C_6H_5COOO\cdot + H^+$$

$$2C_6H_5COOO\cdot \longrightarrow \text{Molecular products}$$

This kind of reaction is to be differentiated clearly from oxidation reactions involving periodate, osmic acid, vanadate, and the like, which generally proceed through intermediate complexes and result in the destruction or drastic transformation of the coordination center. In many of the reactions of this latter class there is a very considerable degree of both chemical and steric specificity for the substrates attacked. These reactions are generally carried out in an acidic medium that is unfavorable for the reoxidation of the oxidant by elementary oxygen of the atmosphere.

In many cases the oxidation of more complicated organic molecules that possess a multiplicity of donor sites and several sites for the attack of an oxidizing agent, proceed *more* rapidly when only a fraction of the donor sites are coordinated. Kuznetsov[169] reported that the oxidation of tartrate by permanganate is notably accelerated by the addition of calcium ion to the reaction medium. However, the permanganate oxidation of EDTA (ethylenediaminetetraacetic acid) is much slower for the chromium(III) and bismuth(III) complexes than for the free ligand.[170] Such reactions seem to possess a variability that is both difficult to explain and embarrassing to organize. The reactions of Nitroso-R-salt (as the free ligand and its complexes) with hydrazine provide a good illustration of this.[171] It was found that the ferrous complex

168. C. E. H. Bawn and J. Jolley, *Proc. Roy. Soc.* (*London*) **A237**, 297 (1956).
169. V. I. Kuznetsov, *Zh. Obshch. Khim.* **20**, 807 (1950).
170. M. T. Beck and O. Kling, *Acta Chem. Scand.* **15**, 453 (1961).
171. J. A. Dean and J. H. Lady, *Anal. Chem.* **25**, 947 (1953).

of Nitroso-R-salt (1-nitroso-2-naphthol-3,6-disulfonic acid) possessed a considerably greater degree of stability toward reduction with hydrazine than either the free ligand *or* its complexes with copper(II), nickel, aluminum, or other ions. Treatment of a mixture of these metal ions, followed by an adjustment of the pH to the range 5–7 forms all the complexes; subsequent heating of such a mixture with hydrazine at 80°C destroys all the excess ligand and *all* complexes other than the ferrous one. As a result, the color of the solution after such a treatment results solely from the ferrous complex and the absorption of light at 690 mμ can be used for the quantitative estimation of iron(II). Most ligand reactions of complexes do *not* show such a dramatic specificity with respect to the central metal ion.

3.4.2. OXIDATION OF ORGANIC SUBSTRATES

The oxidation of organic compounds by chromate, vanadate, permanganate, and other oxidants has been the subject of kinetic investigations by many groups.[172–182] Of these systems, one of the most interesting is the chromate oxidation of alcohols, which has been extensively studied. In an important review,[173] Westheimer proposed that the mechanism of the chromic acid oxidation of alcohols involved, as a first step, the rapid reversible acid-catalyzed esterification of the alcohol.

$$HCrO_4^- + 2H^+ + HOCR_2H \rightleftarrows HCR_2—O—CrO_2—OH_2^+ + H_2O$$

This is followed by a second, slower step which involves oxidation.

$$H_2O + H—CR_2—O—CrO_2—OH_2^+ \xrightarrow{\text{Slow}} H_3O^+ + R_2C{=}O + H_2CrO_3$$

Since chromate esters are well known, the first step is quite reasonable. Because of the structural similarities among many of the common oxidizing agents, this type of initial step is thought to occur in a large number of their reactions. With oxidation states such as Mn^{3+}, which must be stabilized by

172. W. A. Waters, *Quart. Rev. (London)* **12**, 277 (1958).
173. F. H. Westheimer, *Chem. Rev.* **45**, 419 (1949).
174. J. W. Ladbury and C. F. Cullis, *Chem. Rev.* **58**, 403 (1958).
175. R. Criegee, *Ann. Chem. Liebigs* **522**, 75 (1936).
176. J. M. Babbitt, *Advan. Carbohydrate Chem.* **11**, 1 (1956).
177. R. D. Guthrie, *Advan. Carbohydrate Chem.* **16**, 105 (1961).
178. W. A. Waters, "Mechanisms of Oxidation of Organic Compounds." Methuen, London, 1964.
179. R. Stewart, "Oxidation Mechanisms." Benjamin, New York, 1964.
180. T. A. Turney, "Oxidation Mechanisms." Butterworth, London and Washington, D.C., 1965.
181. K. B. Wiberg, ed., "Oxidation in Organic Chemistry." Academic Press, New York, 1965; K. B. Wiberg, *Surv. Progr. Chem.* **1**, 211 (1963).
182. J. K. Kochi, *Science* **155**, 415 (1967).

complexation in aqueous media, oxidation of 1,2-diols,[183] α-hydroxy acids,[184] and malonic acid,[185] occurs via a chelated complex. For malonic acid, the first step in its oxidation by manganic pyrophosphate would be the rapid reaction

$$CH_2(CO_2H)_2 + [Mn(H_2P_2O_7)_3]^{3-} \rightleftharpoons H_2P_2O_7^{2-} + Mn[CH_2(COOH)_2](H_2P_2O_7)_2^{-}$$

It must be recognized that many oxidation reactions proceed via free radical mechanisms that do not involve chelation. Furthermore, in cases in which chelates *can* be involved as intermediates, it is often possible to develop very satisfactory mechanisms in which such chelation does not play any role. A case of this sort may be seen in an alternate mechanism proposed for chromic acid oxidations.[186] Direct transfer of hydrogen, as hydride anion, from carbon to the oxidizing agent is proposed. Here the oxidant, in an acidic medium, would be present as $H_3CrO_4^{+}$ or $HCrO_3^{+}$ and the reaction with isopropyl alcohol is envisaged as proceeding through a step such as

The critical step in determining the rate is the breaking of the C—H bond.

In at least some cases coordination seems to suppress completely a normal oxidation reaction of a ligand. The rate of oxidation of the oxalato complexes of Al(III), Fe(III), Cr(III), and Co(III) by bromine has been shown to be inversely related to the stability constants of the complexes.[187] In the presence of an excess of the complex one obtains a pseudo first-order reaction in bromine. These pseudo first-order rate constants fall in the order

$$k_{Al(ox)_3} \qquad > k_{Fe(ox)_3} \qquad \gg k_{Cr(ox)_3} \qquad > k_{Co(ox)_3}$$

$$6.0 \times 10^{-3}\,sec^{-1} > 4.9 \times 10^{-3}\,sec^{-1} \gg 1.9 \times 10^{-5}\,sec^{-1} > 8.0 \times 10^{-6}\,sec^{-1}$$

183. A. Y. Drummond and W. A. Waters, *J. Chem. Soc.* p. 440 (1953).
184. P. Levesley and W. A. Waters, *J. Chem. Soc.* p. 217 (1955).
185. A. Y. Drummond and W. A. Waters, *J. Chem. Soc.* p. 2456 (1954).
186. J. Rocek and J. Krupicka, *Chem. Ind. (London)* p. 1668 (1957); J. Rocek and J. Krupicka, *Collection Czech. Chem. Commun.* **23**, 2068 (1958); J. Rocek and F. Mares, *ibid.* **24**, 2741 (1959); J. Rocek, *ibid.* **25**, 1052 (1960); F. Mares and J. Rocek, *ibid.*, **26**, 2370, 2389 (1961); F. Mares, J. Rocek, and J. Sicher, *ibid.* **26**, 2355 (1961). See, however, J. Rocek, F. H. Westheimer, A. Eschenmoser, L. Moldovanyi, and A. Schreiber, *Helv. Chim. Acta* **45**, 2554 (1962).
187. S. Zsindely and E. Pungor, *Mikrochim. Acta* **2**, 209 (1963).

From these rate constants it would appear that the oxalate dissociated from the complex is oxidized, while that coordinated is masked; at least to a very considerable extent, against the oxidative action of bromine.

An oxidation reaction that possesses both specificity and synthetic applicability is that in which copper(II) chelates with, and then oxidizes α-hydroxyketones. This requires a stoichiometric amount of the copper(II) when the reaction is run in a medium in which the copper(II) is not regenerated. The reaction is usually carried out in an aqueous pyridine solution, and the overall reaction requires *two* moles of copper(II) per mole of α-hydroxyketone.

$$
\begin{array}{c}
\text{H} \\
|
\end{array}
$$

$$
R\!-\!\underset{\underset{\text{H}}{\overset{|}{\underset{O}{\overset{|}{O}}}}}{\overset{|}{C}}\!-\!\underset{O}{\overset{\|}{C}}\!-\!R + 2Cu^{2+} \;\rightarrow\; R\!-\!\underset{O}{\overset{\|}{C}}\!-\!\underset{O}{\overset{\|}{C}}\!-\!R + 2Cu^{+} + 2H^{+}
$$

The copper is initially present as the complex with pyridine. Though very striking color changes are observed in such a solution as the reaction proceeds, few details are available on the kinetics of the reaction. This reaction can be used to prepare benzil from benzoin[188, 189] and furil from furoin.[190] The yield in this second case is 68 %. If air is used as the oxidant with benzoin the product is benzoic acid.[191] It has also been shown[191] that copper dissolves in many solutions containing pyridine and benzoin or aromatic aldehydes. From such solutions a deep blue crystalline material can be isolated that contains one mole of benzoin per copper atom and also some pyridine. The blue pyridine-containing compound can be changed to a deep green pyridine-free compound by heating at 140°C. Benzoin and related compounds also reduce Fehling's solution.

The study of this kind of oxidizing reaction using a cuprous chloride–pyridine catalyst has been carried out in some detail by Kinoshita.[192] He established a number of points of difference between the systems that use molecular oxygen and those that use the cupric ion as the oxidant; the most important of these is the greater oxidizing power of the O_2-based system, which frequently results in more extensive oxidation than is found with that using cupric ion.

A very extensive series of studies of the use of copper complexes as catalysts for oxidations has been carried out by W. Brackman and his co-workers. One of the most interesting of these has resulted in a new synthesis for nitriles.[193]

188. H. T. Clarke and E. E. Dreger, *Org. Syn.* Collected Vol. 1, p. 87 (1941).
189. E. Fischer, *Ann. Chem. Liebigs* **211**, 214 (1882).
190. W. W. Hartman and J. B. Dickey, *J. Am. Chem. Soc.* **55**, 1228 (1933).
191. H. Mohler, *Helv. Chim. Acta* **8**, 740 (1925).
192. K. Kinoshita, *Bull. Chem. Soc. Japan* **32**, 777, 780, 783 (1959).
193. W. Brackman and P. J. Smit, *Rec. Trav. Chim.* **82**, 757 (1963).

Here the overall process may start either from an alcohol or the aldehyde produced in the first step.

$$RCH_2OH \xrightarrow{\text{Cu complex}} RCHO + H_2O$$

$$RCHO + NH_3 \longrightarrow RCH{=\!=}NH + H_2O$$

$$RCH{=\!=}NH \xrightarrow{\text{Oxidation}} RC{\equiv}N$$

The use of aldehydes as starting materials is recommended because of the slowness of the first reaction. Benzonitrile can be prepared from benzaldehyde in yields of up to 79 % by this process. The reaction is run in methanol (water concentrations in excess of 5 % retard the reaction) and a typical solution will contain $CuCl_2 \cdot 2H_2O$ (4 mmole), NH_3 (400 mmole), $NaOCH_3$ (30 mmole), and benzaldehyde (50 mmole). The reaction is run at 30°C: oxygen is passed through the solution for 6 hours and it is then treated with water, acidified, and extracted with ether. The benzonitrile is obtained from the ether extract by allowing the ether to evaporate, removing the unreacted aldehyde with bisulfite, and then distilling off the benzonitrile. This oxidation can be effected by the use of the copper(II) complex by itself, without oxygen. In this case the copper(II) must be used in stoichiometric amounts; the use of oxygen allows the copper(II) to be introduced in only catalytic amounts. The copper(II) complex to which the catalytic activity is ascribed in this case is written as $[Cu(NH_3)_4OCH_3]^+$ by Brackman, and the deleterious action of water is ascribed to the formation of the catalytically inactive species $[Cu(NH_3)_4OH]^+$. The following mechanism was proposed:

$$RCHO + NH_3 \rightleftharpoons RCH{=\!=}NH + H_2O$$

$$RCH{=\!=}NH + Cu^{II}\text{ complex} \xrightarrow{\text{Slow}} \text{Imine radical} + H^+ + Cu^I \text{ complex}$$

$$\text{Imine radical} + O_2 \longrightarrow RC{\equiv}N + HO_2\cdot$$

$$HO_2\cdot + Cu^I \text{ complex} \longrightarrow HO_2^- + Cu^{II} \text{ complex}$$

$$HO_2^- + H^+ \longrightarrow H_2O_2$$

Overall

$$RCHO + NH_3 + O_2 \longrightarrow RCN + H_2O + H_2O_2$$

$$H_2O_2 + \text{Substrates} \xrightarrow{Cu^{II}} H_2O + \text{Products}$$

In the absence of oxygen, the nitriles are produced by the disproportionation of the imine radicals.

$$2R{-}\underset{H}{\overset{}{C}}{=\!=}N\cdot \;\rightarrow\; RCN + R\underset{H}{C}{=\!=}NH$$

The relation observed between the rates of the anaerobic and the aerobic rates is in accord with the slow step given, as it is

$$-\left(\frac{dCu^{II}}{dt}\right)_{anaerobic} = -\left(\frac{dO_2}{dt}\right)_{aerobic}$$

Other copper(II) complexes should be catalytically active in this reaction, though there is little information available on this point.

There are a very large number of related reactions in which a copper complex with an amine is used to effect the oxidation of an organic compound. Copper(II) acetate in a mixture of methanol and pyridine is an effective reagent for the oxidative coupling of acetylenes.[194] This same catalyst has been used to prepare macrocyclic rings,[195] and the related copper(I) complexes with tertiary amines catalyze the oxidative polymerization of some 2,6-disubstituted phenols with oxygen to give polyarylene ethers.[196] The oxidative coupling of acetylenes can be effected by the use of air and an ammoniacal solution of copper(I) chloride,[197] however, a pyridine solution of a copper(I) salt is an even more effective catalyst.[198] A comparative study of the use of pyridine and N,N,N',N'-tetramethylethylenediamine complexes for the oxidative coupling of acetylene showed that the latter amine was much more effective than pyridine.[199] These reactions are of the type

$$2RC{\equiv}CH + 2Cu(II) \rightarrow RC{\equiv}C{-}C{\equiv}CR + 2H^+ + 2Cu(I)$$
$$2Cu(I) + \tfrac{1}{2}O_2 + H_2O \rightarrow 2Cu(II) + 2OH^-$$

Copper(II) complexes with ammonia are capable of catalyzing the oxidation of hydrogen by oxygen; in this system there is a concurrent oxidation of the ammonia.[200]

The catalytic hydroxylation of allyl alcohol with hydrogen peroxide can be effected by a number of species, among which osmium tetroxide is a very

194. G. Eglinton and A. R. Galbraith, *J. Chem. Soc.* p. 889 (1959).

195. F. Sondheimer, R. Wolovsky, and Y. Gaoni, *J. Am. Chem. Soc.* **82**, 755 (1960).

196. A. S. Hay, H. S. Blanchard, G. F. Andres, and J. W. Eustace, *J. Am. Chem. Soc.* **81**, 6335 (1959); A. S. Hay, *J. Polymer Sci.* **58**, 581 (1962); G. F. Endres and J. Kwiatek, *J. Polymer Sci.* **58**, 593 (1962); G. F. Endres, A. S. Hay, and J. W. Eustace, *J. Org. Chem.* **28**, 1300 (1963); H. S. Blanchard, H. L. Finkbeiner, and G. A. Russell, *J. Polymer Sci.* **58**, 469 (1962).

197. R. A. Raphael, "Acetylene Compounds in Organic Synthesis," p. 127. Academic Press, New York, 1955.

198. A. S. Hay, *J. Org. Chem.* **25**, 1275 (1960).

199. A. S. Hay, *J. Org. Chem.* **27**, 3320 (1962).

200. T. V. Berlina and V. A. Tulupov, *Katalicheskie Reaktsii v Zhidkoi Faze, Akad. Nauk Kaz. SSSR, Kazakhsh. Gos. Univ. Kazakhsk. Resp. Pravlenie Mendeleevskogo Obshchestva, Tr. Vses. Konf. Alma-Ata, 1962* pp. 330–333 (1963); *Chem. Abstr.* **61**, 2520.

effective catalyst. This reaction results in the addition of two hydroxyl groups in cis positions. Pertungstic and pervanadic acids and selenium dioxide catalyze this addition also but give a product in which the two hydroxyl groups have been added in trans positions.[201]

The number of instances in which metal salts or complexes catalyze the oxidation of organic compounds is very large. Some of these are collected in Table III.

TABLE III

METAL-CATALYZED OXIDATIONS

Substrate	Catalyst	Products	Reference
Isobarbituric acid (and 5-aminouracil and hydantoin)	$Na_3[Fe(CN)_5(NH_3)]$	4,4′-Diisobarbituric acid identified	202
Mercaptans	Co(II) pyrophosphate and other transition metal complexes	Disulfides	203
Phenols	Cu(II) complexes with morpholine or collidine	Quinones	204, 205
Dihydroxyphenylamino acids and their derivatives 2,3-, 2,4-, and 2,5-Dihydroxyphenylalanine 3,4 Dihydroxyphenylalanine methyl esters and amides, DL-leucyl-DL-3,4-dihydroxyphenylalanine 3,4-Dihydroxyphenylacetic acid	Fe and Cu chelates	o-Diphenols formed which undergo ring closure to give indole derivatives	206

201. M. Mugdan and D. P. Young, J. Chem. Soc. p. 2888 (1949).
202. O. Baudisch and D. Davidson, J. Biol. Chem. **64**, 619 (1925); **71**, 501 (1927).
203. T. J. Wallace, A. Schreisheim, H. Hurwitz and M. B. Glaser, Ind. Eng. Chem. Process Design Develop. **3**, 237 (1964).
204. W. Brackman and E. Havinga, Rec. Trav. Chim. **74**, 937, 1021, 1070, 1100, 1107 (1955).
205. W. Brackman, in "International Conference on Coordination Chemistry," Spec. Publ. No. 13. Chem. Soc., London, 1959.
206. G. Lasse, A. Barth, and W. Langenbeck, Chem. Ber. **95**, 918 (1962).

TABLE III —*continued*

Substrate	Catalyst	Products	Reference
o-Phenylenediamine	Cu^{2+}	$\left(H_2N-\langle\rangle-\overset{H}{\underset{}{N}}- \right)_x$	207, 227
Formazyl compounds	Zn^{2+}	Tetrazolium salts	208
1-Hydrazinophthalazine	Fe^{2+}	Tetrazane (dimerization)	209
Pyrogallol and phloroglucinol	Copper complexes with amines such as isopropanolamine	Polymers derived from intermediate radicals	210
α-Ketoglutarate	Co^{2+} and Mn^{2+}	CO_2, succinate, malate, oxalate, and acetate	211
α-Acetolactic acid	Fe^{3+}, Cu^{2+}, Al^{3+}	Diacetyl and acetone	212
Hydroxylamine	Cu^{2+}	N_2O	213
Hydrazine	Fe^{2+}	—	214
Ascorbic acid	FeEDTA	—	215
Adrenaline, linoleic acid, and ascorbic acid	Fe(II)EDTA	—	216
Salicylate	Fe(III)EDTA	—	217
Aromatic amines	Cu^{2+} complexes	2-Amino-5-anilino-quinoneanil	218–221

207. S. Fallab, *J. Inorg. Nucl. Chem.* **8**, 631 (1958).
208. S. Fallab and H. Erlenmeyer, *Helv. Chim. Acta* **42**, 1152 (1959).
209. S. Fallab and D. Walz, *Helv. Chim. Acta* **43**, 540 (1960).
210. R. D. Korpusova, *Nauchn. Dokl. Vyyshei Shkoly, Khim. i Khim. Tekhnol.* **1**, 94 (1958); *Chem. Abstr.* **53**, 834f.
211. J. J. Rachis and G. Kalnitsky, *J. Biol. Chem.* **225**, 751 (1957).
212. J. C. de Man, *Rec. Trav. Chim.* **78**, 480 (1959).
213. P. C. Moews and L. F. Audrieth, *J. Inorg. Nucl. Chem.* **11**, 242 (1959); J. H. Anderson, *Analyst* **89**, 357 (1964).
214. W. C. Higginson and P. Wright, *J. Chem. Soc.* p. 1551 (1955).
215. R. Grinstead, *J. Am. Chem. Soc.* **82**, 3464 (1960).
216. C. Flesch, W. Schuler, and R. Meier, *Helv. Chim. Acta* **43**, 2014 (1960).
217. R. Grinstead, *J. Am. Chem. Soc.* **82**, 3472 (1960).
218. W. Brackman, Dutch Patent 94,613, 1960; cf. *Chem. Abstr.* **55**, 22345e.
219. W. Brackman, U.S. Patent 2,883,426, 1959.
220. W. Brackman, Dutch Patent 94,612, 1960; *Chem. Abstr.* **55**, 22343i.
221. G. Engelsma and E. Havinga, *Tetrahedron* **2**, 289 (1958).

TABLE III –*continued*

Substrate	Catalyst	Products	Reference
Primary and secondary alcohols	Cu^{2+} as primary or secondary amine complex	Aldehyde from primary alcohol; ketone from secondary alcohol	222
4-Hydroxybenzoxazole	Cu(II)	—	223
Thiols and mercapto-acetate	Fe(III)	Disulfides	224
Phenols	Cu(II) carboxylates	Ortho-coupled products	225
Aldehydes	Co(II)	Carboxylic acids	226
p-Xylene	Co(II) stearate	p-Toluic acid	228
Ethylene	$[PdCl_4]^{2-}$	CH_3CHO	229
Ascorbic acid	Cu^{2+}	(see structure)	230
Acetylenes	Cu^I	Diacetylenes	231
Benzaldehyde + NH_3	Cu^{II} + $NaOCH_3$	Benzonitrile	232
a3-Keto-Δ^5-steroid	Cu(II)·pyridine + triethylamine in methanol	3,6-Diketo-Δ^4-steroid	233

222. W. Brackman, Brit. Patent 868,460, 1961; *Chem. Abstr.* **56**, 1434c.
223. Q. Fernando, R. Resnik, and T. Cohen, *J. Am. Chem. Soc.* **83**, 3344 (1961).
224. D. L. Leussing and T. N. Tischer, *Advan. Chem. Ser.* **37**, 216 (1963).
225. W. W. Kaeding, *J. Org. Chem.* **28**, 1063 (1963).
226. H. Hock and H. Kropf, *J. Prakt. Chem.* (4) **14**, 71 (1961).
227. L. Michaelis, M. P. Schubert, and S. Granick, *J. Am. Chem. Soc.* **61**, 1981 (1939).
228. K. A. Chervinskii, A. M. Ivanov, and L. A. Nikitina, *Khim. Prom.* No. 10, 742 (1963); *Chem. Abstr.* **60**, 5362.
229. J. Smidt, *Chem. Ind.* (*London*) p. 54 (1962).
230. A. E. Martell, *in* "Kirk-Othmer Encyclopedia of Chemical Technology," (H. F. Mark, ed.) Vol. 6, p. 21. Wiley (Interscience), New York, 1965.
231. W. J. Gensler, *Chem. Rev.* **57**, 215 (1957).
232. E. Fischer, *J. Prakt. Chem.* (4) **29**, 199 (1965).
233. H. C. Volger and W. Brackman, *Rec. Trav. Chim.* **84**, 579 (1965).

Before passing on to other reactions, it is of interest to note some of the earlier work in this area that was carried out in Japan prior to World War II. This consisted mainly of a very extensive series of studies of the catalytic activity of metal complexes which was carried out by K. Shibata, Y. Shibata, and their co-workers.[234] These were concerned with the catalytic properties in redox reactions and in autoxidations, though a preliminary study of hydrogenation was also carried out. These studies are of special interest as they involve many complexes not normally considered to undergo redox reactions readily. Thus, $[Co(NH_3)_5Cl]Cl_2$ was the complex used in early studies to catalyze the oxidation of an oxyflavone. The substrate used for a few of these studies was 2-hydroxy-3-methoxytoluene, though myricetin,

was used for many more. The addition of 1 ml of a 0.001 M solution of various complexes to 5 ml of a 0.001 M solution of myricetin led to an instantaneous reaction and the formation of a violet precipitate for a large number of complexes including $[Co(NH_3)_3Cl_2(H_2O)]Cl$, $[Co(NH_3)_3(NO_2)_3]$, $[Ni(NH_3)_6]Cl_2$, $Cu(NH_3)_2Cl(C_2H_3O_2)$, and $[Zn(NH_3)_5]SO_4$. A number of other complexes exhibited a somewhat slower reaction and some complexes proved to be incapable of exerting any such catalytic activity. The complexes that had no action included those of chromium(III), and the cobalt(III) complexes $[Co(NH_3)_6]Cl_3$, $[Co(en)_3]Cl_3$, and $[Co(en)_2X_2]^{y+}$ where X is Cl^-, Br^-, or H_2O. It appears that the requirements for catalytic activity include (1) a multiplicity of available donor sites, or (2) oxidizing ligands. One of the very unusual features of some of these reactions is their extreme rapidity. It is possible that some of these reactions have rates that exceed those of the ligand substitution reactions for the complexes used as catalysts.

In a study of the catalysis of the oxidation of pyrogallol (with oxygen) by various complexes, an apparatus essentially equivalent to a Warburg apparatus was used.[234] The oxygen uptake, which is negligible over a 24-hour period in the absence of a catalyst, is accelerated by many cobalt complexes. The resulting rates are from 100 to 1000 times greater than those found for the uncatalyzed reaction. A group of complex cations which exhibited an especially pronounced catalytic activity consisted of cobalt(III) complexes that contained

234. K. Shibata and Y. Shibata, "Katalytische Wirkungen der Metallkomplexverbindungen," Publ. No. 2. Iwata Inst. of Plant Biochem., Tokyo, 1936.

five neutral ligands (ammonia or water) and one negative ligand (chloride or hydroxide). For these complexes the catalytic reaction was very rapid, there was no induction period, and the reaction was first order in oxygen. For some other complexes, such as $[Co(NH_3)_5SCN]Cl_2$, $[Co(NH_3)_5(H_2O)]_2(C_2O_4)_3 \cdot 4H_2O$, $[Co(NH_3)_5(H_2O)]Cl_3$, and $[Co(NH_3)_5(H_2O)]_2(SO_4)_3 \cdot 3H_2O$, the reaction begins only after an induction period during which the catalytically active species is generated. With complexes of both classes the addition of hydrochloric acid is found to decrease the reaction rate and lengthen the induction period for those compounds that normally have one or introduce an induction period for those complexes that previously did not show one. For catalysis by cobalt complexes, the addition of the chromium complex, $[Cr(NH_3)_5Cl]Cl_2$, is found to decrease the reaction rate, though such an addition has little effect on the rate of the reaction when it is catalyzed by $[Ni(NH_3)_6]Cl_2$.

In this same book [234] one may find a similar study of the catalytic properties of these complexes in the oxidation of iodide solutions. There is, strangely enough, no obvious correlation, though the single most effective catalyst in both cases was found to be $[Co(NH_3)_3(H_2O)Cl_2]Cl$. These reactions are quite unusual in many respects and do not merit the neglect they have been shown since the Shibatas completed their studies.

3.4.3. DECOMPOSITION OF HYDROGEN PEROXIDE

The decomposition of hydrogen peroxide, and many other peroxides, has long been recognized as a reaction susceptible to catalysis by a wide variety of both simple and complex species. Hydrogen peroxide is thermodynamically unstable with respect to its decomposition into water and oxygen.

$$2H_2O_2(g) \rightarrow 2H_2O(g) + O_2(g); \quad \Delta F° = -58.86 \text{ kcal}$$

Furthermore, hydrogen peroxide may function as an oxidizing agent

$$2H_2O \rightleftharpoons H_2O_2 + 2H^+ + 2e; \quad E° = -1.77 \text{ volts}$$

or as a reducing agent [235]

$$H_2O_2 \rightleftharpoons O_2 + 2H^+ + 2e; \quad E° = -0.682 \text{ volts}$$

As a result, the path of the catalytic decomposition with elements with variable oxidation states may involve the alternate oxidation and reduction of such elements. This mechanism in its simple form is usually described as one of "compensating reactions." If the oxidation potential of a transition element redox system falls between -0.682 and -1.77 volts, hydrogen peroxide can

235. W. M. Latimer, "The Oxidation States of the Elements and Their Potentials in Aqueous Solutions," 2nd Ed., pp. 43–45. Prentice-Hall, Englewood Cliffs, New Jersey, 1952.

both oxidize the reduced form and reduce the oxidized form. One such simple system is the Mn^{2+}–MnO_2 couple.[236]

$$Mn^{2+} + 2H_2O \rightarrow MnO_2 + 4H^+ + 2e; \quad E^\circ = -1.23 \text{ volts}$$

Iron salts are similarly effective catalysts.[237] An alternative theory of the catalysis of peroxide decomposition invokes the formation of intermediate peroxy complexes, such as are known to form with vanadate, chromate, tungstate, and similar species.[238,239] Most cases of catalysis of peroxide decomposition fall roughly into one of these two categories (i.e., intermediate complex or compensating reactions) though the detailed rate behavior is often more complex than either one alone would predict.[240]

The catalytic activity of complexes for the decomposition of hydrogen peroxide has been known for many years, and a surprising variety of these materials have been found to be effective. The complexes which are catalysts here include[241] $Na_3[Fe(CN)_5(OH_2)]$ and especially the hexammines and tetrammines of nickel(II) and copper(II) such as $[Ni(NH_3)_6]Cl_2$ and $[Cu(NH_3)_4]Cl_2 \cdot H_2O$. Some other complexes which have been found to catalyze the reaction are summarized in Table IV. A general review of this topic is also available.[240]

TABLE IV

COMPLEXES WHICH CATALYZE H_2O_2 DECOMPOSITION

Complex	Reference
$K_3[Fe(CN)_6]$	242. W. Kistiakowsky, Z. Physik. Chem. (Leipzig) 35, 431 (1900).
	243. B. S. Srikantan and A. R. Rao, J. Indian Chem. Soc. 10, 299 (1933).
$Fe^{2+,3+}$ complexes with dipyridyl or orthophenanthroline	244. R. Kuhn and A. Wassermann, Ann. Chem. Liebigs 503, 203 (1933).
	245. A. Simon and W. Haufe, Z. Anorg. Allgem. Chem. 230, 160 (1936).
$Co(NH_3)_x^{2+}$, cobalt(II) complex with citric acid	246. M. Bobtelsky and M. Rappoport, Compt. Rend. 205, 234 (1937).
Ammines of Cu^{2+}, Ni^{2+}, Co^{2+}, and Ag^+	247. L. A. Nikolaev, Zh. Fiz. Khim. 19, 323 (1945); Chem. Abstr. 40, 514.

236. E. S. Gould, "Inorganic Reactions and Structure," 2nd Ed., p. 78. Holt, New York, 1962.
237. J. von Bertalan, Z. Physik. Chem. (Leipzig) 95, 328 (1920).
238. E. Spitalsky, Z. Physik. Chem. (Leipzig) 122, 257 (1926).
239. E. Spitalsky and N. Koboseff, Z. Physik. Chem. (Leipzig) 127, 129 (1927).
240. J. H. Baxendale, Advan. Catalysis 4, 31 (1952).
241. O. Baudisch, Ber. Deut. Chem. Ges. 62, 2699 (1929).

TABLE IV—*continued*

Complex	Reference
Iron phthalocyanines	248. A. H. Cook, *J. Chem. Soc.* pp. 1761, 1768, 1774, 1845 (1938); (Also catalyze oxidations by O_2.)
Fe^{3+}–citrate complex	249. M. Bobtelsky and B. Kirson, *Compt. Rend.* **208**, 1577 (1939).
Chelates of Co^{2+}, Fe^{3+}, and Cu^{2+}	250. H. Mix, W. Tittleback-Helmrich, and W. Langenbeck, *Chem. Ber.* **89**, 69 (1956).
cis- and *trans*-$[Co(NH_3)_4(NO_2)_2]^+$	251. L. Nikolaev, *Zh. Fiz. Khim.* **27**, 1592 (1953); *Chem. Abstr.* **49**, 3714.
Ammines of Cu(II) and Ni(II)	252. H. Erkut, *Rev. Fac. Sci. Univ. Istanbul* **18A**, 153 (1953); *Chem. Abstr.* **48**, 31c.
Cu^{2+} piperidine complex	253. B. Kirson, *Bull. Soc. Chim. France* p. 157 (1954); *Chem. Abstr.* **48**, 6307.
Adsorbed ammines	254. H. W. Jacobsen and G. W. Smith, *J. Am. Chem. Soc.* **79**, 4494 (1954).
Cu^{2+}, various complexes	255. S. Petri, H. Sigel, and H. Erlenmeyer, *Helv. Chim. Acta* **49**, 1778 (1966).
Fe(II) halo and halo–anion complexes	255a. C. F. Wells and M. A. Salam, *Trans. Faraday Soc.* **63**, 620 (1967).

It is apparent that the change in redox behavior that accompanies the coordination of a central ion can be very important in determining the catalytic effectiveness of the complex produced.

The ability of certain coordination centers, such as Ta(V),[256] W(VI),[257,258] and Mo(VI)[258] to catalyze oxidations by hydrogen peroxide is well established. Since all of these species form peroxy complexes, it is very probable that the literal oxidant is the peroxy complex. These cases include the Ta(V) catalysis of the oxidation of $S_2O_3^{2-}$ to SO_4^{2-} and the W(VI) and Mo(VI) catalysis of the oxidation of I^- to I_2. In the latter system, it has been demonstrated that in the presence of oxalate [which chelates with W(VI)] a masking of the catalysis

256. K. B. Yatsimirsky, R. P. Morozova, T. A. Voronova, and R. M. Gershkovich, *Zh. Analit. Khim.* **19**, 704 (1964); *Chem. Abstr.* **61**, 7696.
257. (a) K. B. Yatsimirsky and V. F. Romanov, *Zh. Neorgan. Khim.* **9**, 1578 (1964); *Chem. Abstr.* **61**, 7762. (b) K. B. Yatsimirsky and K. E. Prik, *Zh. Neorgan. Khim.* **9**, 1838 (1964); *Chem. Abstr.* **61**, 12685. (c) K. B. Yatsimirsky and V. I. Rigin, *Zh. Analit. Khim.* **13**, 112 (1958); *Chem. Abstr.* **52**, 9862.
258. K. B. Yatsimirsky and R. P. Morozova, *Kinetika i Kataliz* **4**, 772 (1963); *Chem. Abstr.* **63**, 2536.

occurs as a result of the suppression of the formation of the necessary intermediate peroxy complex. This type of reaction, in which the catalytic effect of metal salts in promoting oxidations by hydrogen peroxide is quite pronounced, has been studied in detail by Yatsimirsky[259] and his collaborators. The catalysis of oxidations by these salts is also found in a number of cases where the oxidant is iodate, bromate, or chlorate, though the mechanisms of these other reactions is quite different.

Metal ions have also been found to exert rather pronounced influences over both the rates and the products of reactions involving organic peracids. An example may be seen in the oxidation of primary aromatic amines by peracetic acid.[260] In the oxidation of 3-nitroaniline, the product is found to be 3,3′-dinitroazoxybenzene, while in the presence of cupric chloride the primary product is 3,3′-dinitroazobenzene.

This reaction proceeds through the intermediates R—NHOH and R—NO. In the presence of vanadate, the product is the quite unexpected

This product arises because the vanadate–peracetic acid oxidizing mixture is itself capable of oxidizing acetic acid (used as a solvent for the peracetic acid) via the formation of an intermediate pervanadate [at least in solutions containing appreciable amounts of vanadium(V)]. The products of this reaction are first glycolic acid and then carbon dioxide and formaldehyde and this formaldehyde furnishes the extra carbon atom in these products. This last reaction is thus related to those examined by Yatsimirsky in that an intermediate peroxy complex is utilized to furnish an alternative and more rapid

259. K. B. Yatsimirsky, "Kinetic Methods of Analysis," transl. by P. J. J. Harvey. Macmillan (Pergamon), New York, 1966.
260. E. Pfeil and K. H. Schmidt, Ann. Chem. 675, 36 (1964).

path for the oxidation reaction. It must be noted that the oxidation of acetic acid under such mild conditions is quite unusual.

3.4.4. THE HYDROGENATION OF COMPLEXED SUBSTRATES

The role of metal ions as catalysts for hydrogenation has been recognized for many years. Since, in homogeneous systems, these exert their catalytic effect through the formation of unstable hydride complexes or by coordination of the substrate, the amount of information bearing on the hydrogenation of complexes is quite large, even if much of it is indirect. At this point, reactions involving the literal hydrogenation of complexed substrates will be examined and the topic of catalytic hydrogenation will be considered elsewhere.

The hydrogenation of $[PtCl_2(C_2H_4)]_2$ was first carried out by Anderson[261] and represents an early proof that coordination *"facilitates"* the hydrogenation of ethylene. The hydrogenation reaction, which proceeds readily at room temperature, is

$$[PtCl_2(C_2H_4)]_2 + 4H_2 \rightarrow 2Pt + 4HCl + 2C_2H_6$$

A subsequent study[262] showed that this reaction proceeds at an appreciable rate at $-40°C$ in the solvents chloroform, acetone, or toluene. The reaction is catalyzed by the elemental platinum which is formed as it proceeds. The activation energy for this reaction was estimated to be 2.5 kcal, a surprisingly low value. The metal ions which are capable of forming similar, if somewhat less stable, complexes with olefins, are generally capable of catalyzing their reduction also. These include specifically, Pd^{2+}, Ag^+, Rh(III), and Ir(III). Their use as catalysts, however, is often more directly related to their ability to form hydride complexes and activate molecular hydrogen, rather than their ability to form complexes with the olefins.

This ability of many complexes to add hydrogen in two radically different ways (i.e., as hydride or across the double bond of a ligand) has led to a renewed interest in the existence and properties of transiently formed metal hydrides.[263] The studies carried out have indicated that most of the examples of what have been considered to be hydrogenations of coordinated substrates actually proceed through *hydride* intermediates. As a result it is not possible to cite unequivocal evidence that indicates just how coordination, in the absence of concurrent or subsequent metal hydride formation, does affect the ease of reduction of typical unsaturated ligands. The great mass of evidence presently available favors the formulation of such metal-catalyzed hydrogenations in terms of the activation of hydrogen rather than the activation of

261. J. S. Anderson, *J. Chem. Soc.* p. 971 (1934).
262. J. H. Flynn and H. M. Hulburt, *J. Am. Chem. Soc.* **76**, 3393, 3396 (1954).
263. Much of the literature has been collected and critically evaluated by J. Halpern, *Ann. Rev. Phys. Chem.* **16**, 103 (1965); *J. Phys. Chem.* **63**, 398 (1959); *Advan. Catalysis* **9**, 302 (1957).

the substrate. The separation of these two effects is not easy as the ability to form complexes with olefins presently appears to be limited to those ions which can also activate molecular hydrogen by the formation of hydride complexes. What is needed is information on the relative change in the ease of reduction of ligands when they are coordinated to metal ions incapable of activating molecular hydrogen via metal hydride formation.

The hydrogenation of complexes per se has been studied intermittently for many years. One of the early reports is that of the hydrogenation of bis(salicyl-aldehydato)copper(II) and the corresponding nickel(II) complex.[264,265] This copper complex, which had been used as an hydrogenation catalyst earlier by Calvin,[266] was found not to exhibit a change in magnetic susceptibility on hydrogenation. The color, which was originally green, usually changed to a deep ruby red upon hydrogenation. For both the starting complex and the hydrogenated material a magnetic moment of 1.9 Bohr magnetons was found. This corresponds to a single unpaired electron. It was proposed by Tyson and Vivian that the hydrogenation reaction could be represented by the equation

The hydrogenated material is *very* susceptible to oxidation by air. The nickel(II) complex behaved in a similar manner. It changed from green to yellow upon hydrogenation, but still had a magnetic susceptibility correspond-ing to 3.0 Bohr magnetons or two unpaired electrons. Since both of these hydrogenations were carried out in pyridine, there is a strong suspicion that the literal reactants were the octahedral complexes in which two pyridines were coordinated axially. The results obtained here have been disputed by Wilmarth and his co-workers.[267]

The reduction of 3-nitroacetylacetone in complexes has been effected in the case of the chromium(III) complex, though most other complexes with this ligand are very resistant to reduction. When chromium(III) acetylacetonate is treated with $Cu(NO_3)_2 \cdot 3H_2O$ in acetic anhydride one of the rings is nitrated on the 3-position. The resulting complex can be reduced to the corresponding amino compound by hydrogenation in ethanol using $Pd(OH)_2$ as a catalyst.[268]

264. G. N. Tyson and R. E. Vivian, *J. Am. Chem. Soc.* **63**, 1403 (1941).
265. M. A. Forbes and G. N. Tyson, *J. Am. Chem. Soc.* **63**, 3530 (1941).
266. M. Calvin, *Trans. Faraday Soc.* **34**, 1181 (1938).
267. W. K. Wilmarth, M. K. Barsh, and S. S. Dharmatti, *J. Am. Chem. Soc.* **74**, 5035 (1952).
268. J. P. Collman and M. Yamada, *Chem. Ind. (London)* p. 692 (1963).

3.5. Ligand Polarography

The reduction of a species at the dropping mercury electrode can be classified as a reaction with a nucleophile, albeit an unusual one. It has been found[269] that the characteristic half-wave potentials at which typical organic groupings undergo reduction are reasonably constant and reproducible from compound to compound. These half-wave potentials are affected by the pH of the solution and by the exact nature of the molecule of which they form a portion. Since many molecules containing such reducible groups can also function as donor species, it is apparent that it should be possible to utilize the shifts in such potentials that result upon the formation of a coordinate bond to obtain information on the way in which coordination affects the electronic density pattern of the ligand.

There is relatively little information of this sort, but that available shows that coordination need not have a very large effect on the half-wave potentials for reductions. A fairly thorough study of the reduction of the nitro group of 5-nitrosalicylaldehyde showed that it was affected very slightly by the incorporation of the ligand in complexes.[270] In some cases, the involvement of a reducible group as a *donor* may result in its complete masking toward reduction at the dropping mercury electrode, or in a large shift in its half-wave potential for reduction.

Zuman and Kabat[271] reported that the polarographic behavior of the nitroprusside ion, $[Fe(CN)_5(NO)]^{2-}$, was similar to that of the free nitrosyl ion, NO^+, but reduction occurred much more readily than for the free NO^+. This fact could conceivably be used for differentiating between complexes containing NO and NO^+. The greater ease of reduction was considered to be a result of the polarization of the NO^+ after it had donated a share in a pair of electrons to the iron(II).

3.6. Free Radical Reactions

Coordination of a substrate or a reagent may have a profound influence on the course of a free radical reaction. The coordination process may be used to facilitate the generation of free radicals from species as diverse as oxygen and ascorbic acid. The coordination centers active in such reactions are almost invariably those which can undergo a change in oxidation number. The ligand species generated by such a process is frequently a very reactive free radical.

269. (a) I. M. Kolthoff and J. J. Lingane, "Polarography," Vol. 2, pp. 623–846. Wiley (Interscience), New York, 1952. (b) M. Brezina and P. Zuman, "Polarography in Medicine, Biochemistry and Pharmacy," p. 183 ff Wiley (Interscience), New York, 1958.
270. R. C. McNutt and M. M. Jones, *J. Inorg. Nucl. Chem.* **27**, 1071 (1965).
271. P. Zuman and M. Kabat, *Collection Czech. Chem. Commun.* **19**, 873 (1954).

One example of such behavior is Fenton's reagent, which consists of a ferrous salt and hydrogen peroxide. Here the reaction probably goes through the stages

$$Fe^{2+} + H\!-\!O\!-\!O\!-\!H \longrightarrow Fe^{2+}\!-\!O\!\!<^{H}_{OH} \longrightarrow FeOH^{2+} + \cdot OH$$

The hydroxyl radical generated here can initiate a wide variety of free radical reactions, such as the polymerization of acrylonitrile.

A reaction of this type that has been studied in detail is the cupric-ion-catalyzed autoxidation of ascorbic acid.[272,273] Here the mechanism involves, as a first step, the formation of a complex between the ascorbate ion HA⁻, and the cupric ion. The polarization of the ligand by the cupric ion occurs under conditions favorable to the complete transfer of the electron to the copper to produce copper(I) and HA. This is the rate-determining step. Both of these species are then oxidized by molecular oxygen. The effect of adding chelating agents indicates that at least two coordination sites must be available for the critical electron transfer step.[272] Thus EDTA can completely prevent the reaction from following its normal course by simply preventing the ascorbate ion from occupying two adjacent coordination sites. The chelates with dipyridyl and orthophenanthroline seem to exhibit some of the same peculiarities in this system that have been noted previously in simpler cases: electron transfer is apparently possible through the aromatic system of the chelate, so chelation does not result in a complete stoppage of the reaction. Some of the reactions of this class that have been reported include the decomposition of diazoketones,[274] a variety of organic oxidations,[275] oxidations with the ferric ion,[275,276] and the oxidation of phenols with copper(II).

The characteristic preconditions for such a free radical catalytic process are (1) a readily oxidizable substrate, (2) a simple or complex metal ion of suitable redox potential, and (3) oxygen. Whether such a reaction will occur at a measurable rate will be determined by the ease of electron transfer from the substrate to the metallic species.

The factors governing electron transfer in metal complexes have been reviewed by Fraser.[277] For suitably poised systems, it should also be possible

272. V. S. Butt and M. Hallaway, *Arch. Biochem. Biophys.* 92, 24 (1961).
273. A. E. Martell and M. S. Calvin, "Chemistry of the Metal Chelate Compounds." Prentice-Hall, Englewood Cliffs, New Jersey, 1952.
274. F. Haupter and A. Pucek, *Chem. Ber.* 93, 249 (1960).
275. R. G. R. Bacon, *Chem. Ind. (London)* p. 19 (1962).
276. F. S. Dainton, "Electron Transfer Reactions." Spec. Publ. No. 1, p. 47. Chem. Soc., London, 1954.
277. R. T. M. Fraser, *Rev. Pure Appl. Chem.* 11, 64 (1961).

to have an analogous free-radical catalytic reduction, occurring in an atmosphere of hydrogen or some suitable reducing agent. In many of the systems which might be suspected of being of this latter type, the hydrogen participates more directly as a hydrido source or by the attack of the substrate metal complex.

The ability of suitable systems to undergo an electron transfer process via remote attack on a normally unreactive ligand site has been established in extensive studies on systems of the sort

$$[(H_3N)_5CoL]^{2+} + Cr^{2+} + 5H^+ \rightarrow 5NH_4^+ + Co^{2+} + CrL^{2+}$$

where L is a group such as terephthalate, fumarate, or acetate.[278-280] Where L is a conjugated diacid, the reaction is often found to proceed more rapidly than it does when L is the corresponding nonconjugated ligand. In a sense these systems are rather closely related to metal-catalyzed redox reactions involving typical organic molecules. They reveal that the transfer of an electron may be facilitated by such conjugated groups and thereby obviate the necessity of the direct approach of the two reactants. A reasonably success-ful theoretical model of this reaction has been developed[280,281] by combining the concept of mobile bond orders (mbo) and the electrostatic effects. The mobile bond order is the parameter

$$P_{rs} = \sum_i N_i C_{ir} C_{is}$$

where N_i is the number of electrons in the ith (π) molecular orbital and C_{ir} and C_{is} are the coefficients of the rth and sth atoms in the LCAO approxima-tion to the molecular orbital of the ligand. The probability of electron transfer through the system is dependent upon P_{rs}. The electrostatic factor is calculated on the basis of a transition state

$$(H_3N)_5CoL^{2+} \cdots Cr^{2+}$$

with a 4+ overall charge. For reaction at zero ionic strength,

$$k_0 = k_{f0}P$$

where k_0 is the observed second-order rate constant for electron transfer, k_{f0} is the rate of formation of the activated complex, and P is the probability

278. D. K. Sebera and H. Taube, *J. Am. Chem. Soc.* **83**, 1785 (1961).
279. R. T. M. Fraser, *Inorg. Chem.* **3**, 255 (1964).
280. J. Halpern and L. E. Orgel, *Discussions Faraday Soc.* **29**, 32 (1960).
281. P. V. Manning, R. C. Jarnagin, and M. Silver, *J. Phys. Chem.* **68**, 265 (1964). See W. L. Reynolds and R. W. Lumry, "Mechanisms of Electron Transfer." The Ronald Press Co., New York (1966) for a more detailed treatment of cases of this sort as well as related ones.

of the decomposition of the activated complex to form the products. Halpern and Orgel[280] showed that

$$P \approx (C_1 P_{rs} \tau)^2$$

where τ is the mean lifetime of the activated complex, P_{rs} is the mobile bond order, and C_1 is a constant which can be taken to be independent of the nature of the ligand as a first approximation. If τ_0 is taken as the mean lifetime for uncharged reactants, τ for the charged reactants is

$$\tau \approx \tau_0 \exp(-Z_A Z_B \epsilon^2 / Dk Tr_{ab})$$

where Z_A and Z_B are the charges on the reactants; r_{ab}, their separation distance in the activated complex; ϵ is the electronic unit of charge; D, the dielectric constant (4 used); k, Boltzmann's constant; and T, the absolute temperature. Using these expressions one can show that

$$\ln k_0 = C_0 + \ln P_{rs}^2 - (3Z_A Z_B \epsilon^2 / Dk Tr_{ab})$$

The parameters of interest may be combined to give a single one, M, defined as

$$M = \log P_{rs}^2 - (3Z_A Z_B \epsilon^2 / 2.3 Dk Tr_{ab})$$

with large (more positive) values of M corresponding to a fast reaction. When this equation was tested on a series of reactions, it was found to give a generally satisfactory fit of the data. Complexes which could give atypical transition states (such as the ring-stabilized ones found with oxalate and maleate) had to be excluded. In spite of these minor shortcomings, the theoretical treatment is important in that it furnishes a reasonably exact model for a very important type of redox reaction.

A study of the reaction of some metal acetylacetonates with the *tert*-butoxy radical shows quite a variation in behavior as the *metal* is changed.[282] The possible reactions are (1) the abstraction of a hydrogen from the chelate to give *tert*-butyl alcohol or (2) the decomposition of the radical to give acetone and a methyl radical. Thus, the relative amounts of *tert*-alcohol and acetone should be a measure of the relative strengths of the carbon–hydrogen bonds being broken. The relative amount of *tert*-butyl alcohol was found to increase with the number of electrons in the $3d$ orbitals, as would be expected if back-donation were important. In the complexes the hydrogen is abstracted from a methyl group while in the free ligand it comes from the 3-position. These results indicate that the free radical reactions of coordinated ligands may show a greater variety than reactions with charged or polar species.

282. R. J. Gritter and E. L. Patmore, *Proc. Chem. Soc.* p. 328 (1962).

3.6.1. SYNTHETIC OXYGEN-CARRYING CHELATES

The literature on synthetic *reversible* oxygen-carrying chelates has been reviewed.[283-285] For many of these complexes further reactions are possible. Examples of such reversible oxygen carriers include the cobalt(II) complexes with Schiff bases, glycylglycine, and histidine, and the iron(II) complex with dimethylglyoxime.

The absorption of oxygen takes place both with the solid metal chelates and their solutions in various solvents. These complexes facilitate the reduction of oxygen as has been shown by polarographic studies, a reaction which may be assisted primarily by the stabilization of the products rather than by activation of the initial reactants. The formulation of the products is still under active investigation. The reaction of the cobalt(II) complex of glycylglycine with oxygen in an alkaline medium proceeds to give the product [Co(glycylglycine)$_2$]$_2$(O$_2$)(OH), presumably by the reaction

$$2\text{Co(GG)}_2 + \text{OH}^- + \text{O}_2 \;\rightleftharpoons\; \left[(\text{GG})_2\text{Co} \overset{\text{OH}}{\underset{\text{O}_2}{\diagup\hspace{-0.3em}\diagdown}} \text{Co(GG)}_2 \right]^{1-}$$

This is a reversible reaction, since the oxygen may be removed by bubbling nitrogen through the solution. The substitution of glycylproline for glycylglycine results in a complex that does not undergo this type of a reaction.[286] This indicates that an amide hydrogen must be present in a peptide if it is to form a cobalt(II) complex of this type which can undergo such a reversible oxygenation reaction. In the alkaline solutions used for this reaction, the coordination of an amide nitrogen will increase considerably the acidity of any hydrogen atom it bears. The consequent ionization of this hydrogen then appears to be a necessary prerequisite to the formation of such an oxygenated complex, which is made possible by virtue of the altered conformation of the coordinated peptide chain.

Irreversible carriers are often of more practical chemical interest and some of these do not involve chelates at all, but merely complexes with monodentate ligands. These generally involve free radical oxidations, though detailed information on the mechanisms of such reactions are missing in most cases. Many of the autoxidations listed in the section on Redox Reactions (Section

283. T. A. Geissman, *in* "Summary Technical Report of Division," Chapt. 11, pp. 242–267. National Defense Research Committee, Washington, D.C., 1946.
284. L. H. Vogt, Jr., H. M. Faigenbaum, and S. E. Wiberley, *Chem. Rev.* **63**, 269 (1963).
285. A. E. Martell and M. Calvin, "Chemistry of the Metal Chelate Compounds," pp. 337–358. Prentice-Hall, Englewood Cliffs, New Jersey, 1952.
286. P. Tang and N. C. Li, *J. Am. Chem. Soc.* **86**, 1293 (1964).

3.4) are of this type. An example is found in a solution of cuprous chloride in pyridine that absorbs oxygen to give an oxidizing agent that is very selective. The use of this reagent for the oxidation of amines has been studied by Terent'ev and his co-workers.[287-289] The oxidation of aniline to azobenzene proceeds quite smoothly with such a reagent and results in a yield of 88 %. It was found that other cuprous or cupric compounds were ineffective as catalysts, and that pyridine (which was used as a solvent) could not be replaced by alcohols, dioxane, dichloroethane, or quinoline. This reaction is one of considerable generality for oxidations of this type.

This reaction requires only a catalytic amount of cuprous chloride. A similar set of reactions was studied by Kinoshita,[192] who examined the use of such a catalytic system to oxidize benzoin to benzil and thence to benzoic acid.

When cupric chloride is used as a catalyst, the reaction stops at benzil with a nearly quantitative yield. For the oxidation of benzoin, the cuprous acetate–pyridine complex was found to be an effective catalyst.

Many other reactions of this sort are included in other sections of this book.

287. A. P. Terent'ev, *Bull. Soc. Chim. France* **35**, 1164 (1924).
288. A. P. Terent'ev and Y. D. Mogilianski, *Dokl. Akad. Nauk SSSR* **103**, 91 (1955).
289. A. P. Terent'ev and Y. D. Mogilianski, *J. Gen. Chem. USSR* (*English Transl.*) **28**, 2002 (1958); **31**, 298 (1961).

3.7. Internal Ligand Reactions (Intramolecular)

In some cases coordination creates conditions especially favorable for intramolecular reactions of a ligand. The factors that appear to favor such reactions include the polarization of the ligand and its retention of a specific conformation in the complex, because of the formation of chelate rings.

A good example of such a reaction is the rearrangement of o-amino diazo compounds to triazoles. This occurs quite readily with the copper complexes of o-amino diazo ligands.[290] These reactions are of the type

When X is a —$COOCH_3$ group, the ester is hydrolyzed in the formation of the intermediate complex. This process was patented in 1914 as a method for preparing triazoles from o-amino diazo compounds.[291]

Another example of this type of reaction is racemization of optically active amino acid esters when incorporated into metal complexes as their derivatives with Schiff bases. These reactions are similar to those of vitamin B_6. This was first examined by Pfeiffer and his collaborators.[292] This reaction can be summarized as

The formation of the Schiff base also facilitates the oxidative deamination of amino acid esters as well as their exchange with alcohols in a solution in which they are present. When simple amines are used to form Schiff base complexes,

290. V. I. Mur, *in* "Soviet Research on Complex and Coordination Compounds," Part II, p. 858. Consultants Bur., New York, 1961.

291. German Patent 273,443, (1914); P. W. Friedländer, *Fortschr. Teerfarbenfabriken Verwandte Industriezweigl,* **XII**, 424 (1914).

292. P. Pfeiffer, W. Offermann, and H. Werner, *J. Prakt. Chem.* **159**, 313 (1941).

these are found to be capable of interchanging the amine portion with amines in solution.

The transesterification reactions of such complexes have been examined in detail,[293] and are of the type

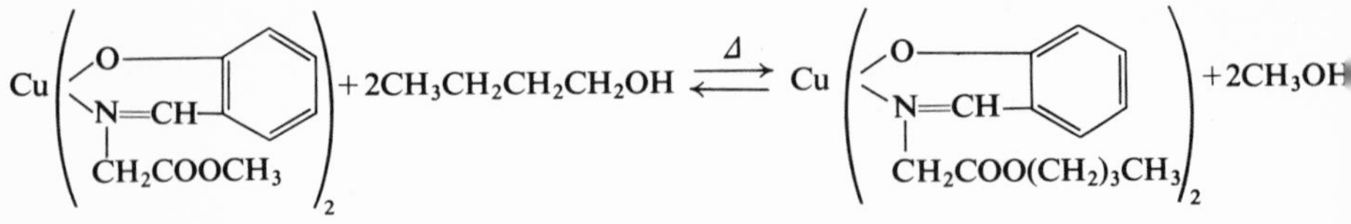

$$Cu\left(\begin{array}{c} O\!-\!\!\!\!\diagdown \\ N\!=\!CH\!-\!\!\diagup \\ CH_2COOCH_3 \end{array}\right)_2 + 2CH_3CH_2CH_2CH_2OH \overset{\varDelta}{\rightleftarrows} Cu\left(\begin{array}{c} O\!-\!\!\!\!\diagdown \\ N\!=\!CH\!-\!\!\diagup \\ CH_2COO(CH_2)_3CH_3 \end{array}\right)_2 + 2CH_3OH$$

The reactions of pyridoxal and its derivatives are of interest because of their possible involvement in biochemical mechanisms. Vitamin B_6 is 2-methyl-3-hydroxy-4,5-(dihydroxymethyl)pyridine.

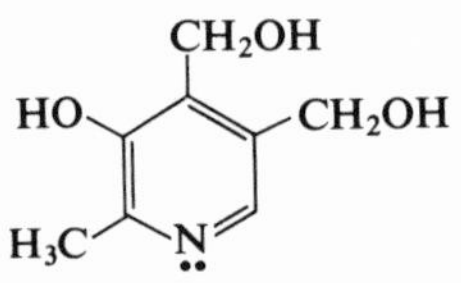

Vitamin B_6 (pyridoxine) 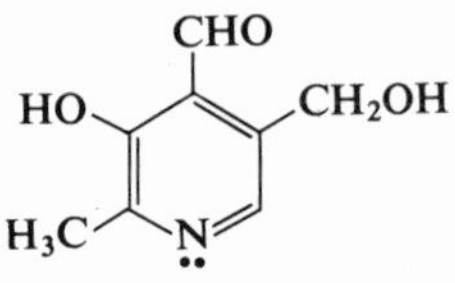   Pyridoxal

An example of a transamination reaction involving pyridoxal, an α-amino acid, and copper(II), is the following:

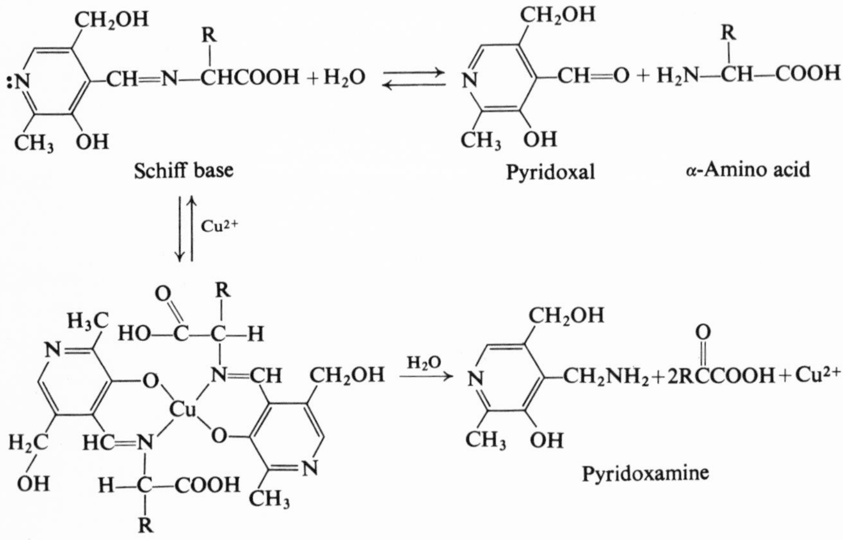

Schiff base   Pyridoxal α-Amino acid

Pyridoxamine

293. H. S. Verter and A. E. Frost, *J. Am. Chem. Soc.* **82**, 85 (1960).

Here the formation of the metal complex provides an especially favorable intermediate for the transamination reaction, though the process is not strictly an intramolecular one because of the intervention of a water molecule in the final step. Much of the literature on various aspects of the catalytic reactions involving pyridoxal may be found in the published papers of a symposium on this topic.[294]

Some, but not all, of the reactions in which the coordination sphere of a metal is used to create a reaction template fall into this class of intramolecular reactions. Because an external reagent is often important in these "template" reactions, they will be considered as a separate class.

The detailed study of the various complexes in a metal ion–glycine–pyruvic acid system has shed some light on the nature of the metal-catalyzed transamination reactions.[295] In such systems, the mixed complexes MPG and $MP_2G_2^{2-}$ are found to have high stability constants, in fact the prior coordination of one of the ligands enhances the tendency of the metal ion to coordinate to the other ligand relative to the tendency of the aquo metal ion to coordinate to the other ligand. For mixtures of pyruvic acid and glycine, such an enhanced stability of the mixed ligand complexes was found for the ions Mn(II), Zn(II), and Ni(II). Such a result is consistent with the formation of the Schiff base from the two ligands and its presence in the complex as a tridentate ligand. The complexes presumably involve the ligand

$$CH_3—\underset{\underset{H—\underset{\underset{H}{|}}{C}—\overset{\displaystyle O}{\overset{\|}{C}}—O^-}{\overset{\displaystyle N:}{\underset{|}{\|}}}}{C}—\overset{\displaystyle O}{\overset{\diagup}{C}}—O^-$$

The considerable stability of the complexes in this type of system provides assistance in the first part of the transamination process, the formation of the Schiff base. The subsequent steps involve the breakup of the ligand in a different manner from that in which it was formed. These are not stopped by coordination to a metal, and evidence available indicates that the formation of the metal complex makes the ligand more susceptible to hydrolysis.

The metal complexes of Schiff bases derived from pyridoxal furnish a suitable intermediate for several types of reaction, depending upon the point where they undergo disruption. Metzler et al.[296] proposed that the formation

294. E. E. Snell, P. M. Fasella, A. Braunstein, and A. Rossi Fanelli, eds., "Chemical and Biological Aspects of Pyridoxal Catalysis." Macmillan, New York, 1963.
295. D. L. Leussing and D. C. Schultz, J. Am. Chem. Soc. 86, 4846 (1964).
296. D. E. Metzler, M. Ikawa, and E. E. Snell, J. Am. Chem. Soc. 76, 648 (1954).

of the metal complex provided additional electron attraction to the metal ion and away from the α-carbon atom of the amino acid (in the form of its Schiff base). This can then facilitate the loss of a cationic group from this carbon atom. The possible courses of such a process are seen from the structure of the intermediate.

When cleavage occurs at *a*, it results in the loss of a proton. The intermediate formed is then a suitable one for the racemization of the amino acid. The addition of a proton to this intermediate, followed by the hydrolysis of the Schiff base, leads to a racemic amino acid. An alternative, and more probable course for the racemization reaction would involve loss of a proton at *a*, followed by proton attack at the formyl carbon of pyridoxal to give an intermediate

which then undergoes hydrolysis at *d*. The products of this reaction are an α-keto acid and pyridoxamine.

If the intermediate loses an R^+ group by cleavage at *b*, the resulting reaction is one in which glycine is made from another amino acid. Reactions of this sort are known, though they may proceed by a different mechanism.

Finally, if cleavage occurs at *c*, a decarboxylation reaction results. This again is a type of reaction found with the enzymes called amino acid decarboxylases. These enzymes generally require pyridoxal phosphate for their activity and pyridoxal and pyridoxal phosphate have also been reported to catalyze the nonenzymatic decarboxylation of histidine.[297]

The discussion of such mechanisms emphasizes a salient point: The course

297. E. Werle and W. Koch, *Biochem. Z.* **319**, 305 (1949).

of the reaction of metal complexes of Schiff bases is quite varied and different reactions are observed under different conditions. This helps to explain some of the apparent discrepancies observed in the literature. Thus in some cases the formation of a metal complex by a given Schiff base results in a greatly increased rate of hydrolysis. In other cases the formation of the metal complex stabilizes a different Schiff base.

The explanations advanced for this[298,299] take cognizance of the variation in the number of coordinate bonds and chelate rings. Thus, in the case of the Schiff base formed from ethylenediamine and 2-thiophenaldehyde, the metal complex is postulated not to utilize the S atoms as donors.

This results in —CH=N— linkages that are polarized to render them more susceptible to attack by water, and the resultant splitting of the ligand does not disrupt the chelate rings. This same consequence is expected if *only* the S atoms act as donors. In the case of the metal complexes of the Schiff base derived from salicylaldehyde and glycine, the coordinate bonds involve donor groups from both "parts" of the Schiff base

and the hydrolysis process is retarded by the stabilizing influence of the chelate rings.

3.8. Masking[300]

Masking by coordination may be defined as the retardation or complete suppression of a typical ligand reaction subsequent to coordination. Even before coordination compounds were clearly recognized as a separate class of substances, the suppression of some of the characteristic ligand reactions in these compounds was reported. A few of these older examples have been cited in the first chapter.

Some of the reactions of coordinated donor atoms are quite unexpected. Thus, coordinated thiol will react with alkyl bromides to form sulfonium salts. Here there are lone pairs on the donor atom in addition to the one involved in forming the coordinate bond. Their qualitative reactivity is hardly

298. D. H. Busch, *Record Chem. Progr.* (*Kresge-Hooker Sci. Lib.*) **25**, 110 (1964).
299. G. L. Eichhorn, *Federation Proc.* **20**, 40 (1961).
300. M. M. Jones, *Advan. Chem. Ser.* **62**, 229 (1967).

affected by coordination. Ammonia that has been coordinated to platinum(IV) will form N-chloro derivatives when treated with hypochlorite. The reaction involves an N—H bond rather than the lone pair. Coordinated PCl_3 will undergo hydrolysis to give coordinated $P(OH)_3$, a reaction that involves the P—Cl bonds rather than the lone pair. These examples lead to an appreciation of the fact that masking phenomena involving donor atoms are not yet so well established as are analogous phenomena with acceptor centers.

The nature of the ligand, the attacking reagent and the type of complex, as well as the nature of the accessible transition states, must all be considered in any attempt to predict the effectiveness of masking by coordination. For reactions between large molecules a transition state of very restricted geometry is often necessary. In such cases masking requirements may often be predicted by making use of a knowledge of the transition state.

Coordination has been found to have a masking action in a large number of cases. In summary, these may be divided into the following categories.

(1) *Reactions that normally involve the electron pair used to form the coordinate bond.* Here the donor atom is held in such a manner that the normal course of the reaction is no longer possible. Thus, the ammonia molecules of $[Co(NH_3)_6]^{3+}$ have lost their ability to neutralize protonic acids. Related examples are found in the resistance to oxidation found for the complexes of trialkylborons and ammonia $(R_3B:NH_3)$ and the reduction in the rate of hydrolysis of BF_3 when it is complexed, as in $F_3B:NH_3$.[301] Reactions that involve the lone pairs of trivalent Group V elements (as in R_3N, R_3P, R_3As, and R_3Sb) are usually masked when this lone pair is used to form a coordinate bond. When the donor atom is a divalent oxygen ($-\overset{..}{\underset{..}{O}}-$) or sulfur ($-\overset{..}{\underset{..}{S}}-$), the use of one of the two lone pairs will usually *not* result in complete masking. For the halides the results are similar, though their inability to undergo quaternization reactions restricts the number of useful reactions of this type. When a redox reaction proceeds via attack on the single lone pair of a ligand, coordination generally results in masking also.

(2) *Reactions for which the required ligand conformations are rendered less accessible by coordination.* Coordination usually imposes serious restrictions on the possible conformations a ligand may assume. Thus, the nearly free rotation about the carbon–carbon bond of ethylenediamine is eliminated in the complexes of this ligand in which it is present almost exclusively in the gauche conformation. The stereochemistry of larger ligands can be restricted even more drastically. Thus, coordination will almost always have a considerable effect on the entropy of activation of typical ligand reactions. As far as donor groups are concerned, rehybridization (which may occur as a conse-

301. G. Hesse, *in* "Handbuch der Katalyse" (G. M. Schwab, ed.), Vol. VI, p. 68. Springer, Vienna, 1943.

quence of coordination) will have a relatively minor role. It will result in slightly different bond angles because of the replacement of lone pair–bond pair interactions by bond pair–bond pair interactions and tend to move groups attached to the donor atom toward the donor pair.

(3) *Reactions for which coordination alters the oxidation potential of a ligand to such an extent that it is rendered thermodynamically unfavorable.* An example may be seen in the great decrease in the reactivity of iodide toward hydrogen peroxide after the iodide is coordinated to mercury(II).[302]

(4) *Reactions for which coordination changes the charge on the reactive site.* The most obvious example of this type is seen in ammines of the platinum metals where the acidity of the hydrogen atoms is greatly increased. If coordination facilitates the ionization of such hydrogens an $M-NH_3$ is changed to an $M-NH_2^-$ and the attack of another negatively charged species should be hindered, while attack by a positive species is facilitated.

(5) *Reactions for which coordination may drastically alter the character of the ligand.* In a few cases coordination results in an electron transfer process in addition to electron pair sharing. For several of the complexes of nitric oxide, evidence supports the view that one electron is transferred completely to the metal ion (reducing it to a lower oxidation state) and leaving NO^+ as the actual ligand.[303]

An appreciation of these conditions can best be seen by an examination of a number of specific reactions, including several in which masking is not found, though it might have been anticipated.

3.8.1. Masking of Ligands Towards Oxidants

The action of many inorganic oxidants (e.g., CrO_4^{2-}, H_5IO_6, Mn^{3+}, OsO_4, MnO_4^-) has been formulated as proceeding through intermediate complexes.[304] Although many of these mechanisms are subject to reinterpretation, it is found that prior coordination of the substrate ligand to some other species definitely exerts a retarding action on the normal course of the ligand oxidation. However, this retarding action has also been found in reactions where the formation of an intermediate complex by the oxidant is extremely unlikely. The coordination center used is also of some importance. If the resulting complex is inert to substitution, the masking may be complete; if it is labile the rate of reaction will usually be reduced, but not very much below that determined by the rate of dissociation of the complex.

One such masking of an oxidation reaction is seen with the oxidation of EDTA by permanganate. The rate of this reaction is reduced if the EDTA is

302. M. T. Beck, *Record Chem. Progr. (Kresge-Hooker Sci. Lib.)* **27**, 45 (1966).
303. R. J. Irving, *Record Chem. Progr. (Kresge-Hooker Sci. Lib.)* **26**, 115 (1965).
304. T. A. Turney, "Oxidation Mechanisms." Butterworth, London and Washington, D.C., 1965.

complexed to chromium(III) or bismuth(III).[304a] Derivatives of EDTA, such as hydroxyethylethylenediaminetriacetic acid (HETA) are similarly masked against oxidation by acid vanadate(V) when coordinated to chromium(III) or cobalt(III).[305] In this latter case the more stable cobalt(III) complex was found to undergo oxidation at a slower rate than the chromium(III) complex. It was also found that the rates of oxidation of $[Co(HETA)Br]^+$ and $[Co(HETA)(OH_2)]^{2+}$ were very similar. If labile complexes are present, the pH is very important in determining the relative amounts of ligand complexed as well as the effectiveness of the oxidant, most of which have rates very dependent upon pH. Because most common oxidants are used in *strongly* acidic media, inert complexes, added as such, are most suitable for demonstrating masking.

Masking can even result from coordination where the oxidant cannot possibly form stable intermediate complexes with the ligand. Ferricyanide, $Fe(CN)_6^{3-}$, is such an oxidant, yet complexing of reducing sugars with borate, masks them toward oxidation by basic solutions of $Fe(CN)_6^{3-}$.[305, 305a] In this respect ferricyanide is similar to a number of oxidants for reducing sugars, most of whose reactions can be masked to some extent by complexation of the reducing sugar with borate. Coordination also masks a number of chelating agents against the action of alkaline ferricyanide,[306] though the effect of such masking is reduced by the presence of large monatomic cations, such as Cs^+, in the reaction medium. Another example of masking towards an oxidant which does not form a stable intermediate complex is the masking of glycine towards nitrite or nitrous acid when the glycine is complexed to chromium(III).[307] Here the masking is probably steric in origin.

Our knowledge of the masking of ligand *oxidations* is limited in part by the limitations of our knowledge of the mechanisms of the normal oxidations. Until these are known in more detail masking of *oxidizing reactions* may be treated only on the basis of the empirical results, and predictions of masking effectiveness must be based on analogy with known cases.

The masking of aromatic phenols against the oxidative side reactions possible in a medium used to effect diazo coupling can be achieved via coordination. For example, the reaction of 4-diazodimethylaniline with chromotropic acid (1,8-dihydroxy-3,6-naphthalenedisulfonic acid) results in a 58% yield of the dye in which coupling has occurred at the 4-position of chromotropic acid. The dye is contaminated with by-products that arise from the concurrent oxidation of the ligand and, as a result, does not have a color of satisfactory purity. By using the calcium complex of chromotropic acid, the yield may be

304a. M. T. Beck and O. Kling, *Acta Chem. Scand.* **15**, 453 (1961).
305. M. M. Jones, D. O. Johnston, and C. J. Barnett, *J. Inorg. Nucl. Chem.* **28**, 1927 (1966).
305a. D. G. Lambert and M. M. Jones, *J. Inorg. Nucl. Chem.* **29**, 579 (1967).
306. D. G. Lambert and M. M. Jones, *J. Am. Chem. Soc.* **88**, 4615 (1966).
307. R. W. Green and K. P. Ang, *J. Am. Chem. Soc.* **77**, 5483 (1955).

increased to 90% and the dye produced has a purer color. Here coordination apparently suppresses oxidative side reactions.[308]

3.8.2. AMINO ACID REACTIONS

Masking via coordination has been found to be very useful in many of the synthetic reactions of α-amino acid molecules that bear additional functional groups. The general procedure utilizes coordination with copper(II) to tie up the carboxyl group and the α-amino group, leaving other functional groups free to react with an added reagent. In outline these reactions are of the type

The use of such reactions in preparative work has been reviewed.[309,310] An example that shows the essential features of a synthetically useful procedure is seen in the conversion of citrulline to ornithine via the copper(II) complex[311]:

A number of other examples are contained in Table V.

308. V. I. Kuznetsov, *J. Gen. Chem. USSR* (*English Transl.*) **26**, 3657 (1956).
309. R. A. Boisonnas, *Advan. Org. Chem.* **3**, 159 (1963).
310. J. F. W. McOmie, *Advan. Org. Chem.* **3**, 191 (1963).
311. A. C. Kurtz, *J. Biol. Chem.* **122**, 477 (1938); *Am. J. Med. Sci.* **194**, 875 (1937); *J. Biol. Chem.* **140**, 705 (1941).

TABLE V

SYNTHETIC REACTIONS OF α-AMINO ACIDS THAT UTILIZE MASKING VIA COORDINATION TO COPPER(II)

Amino acid	Reagent	Product	Reference
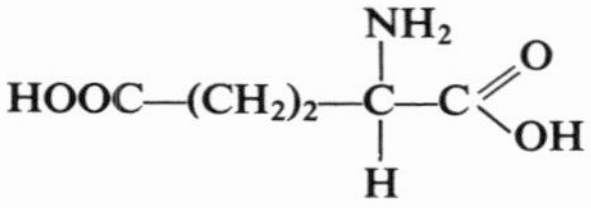 Glutamic acid $HOOC-(CH_2)_2-C(NH_2)(H)-C(=O)OH$	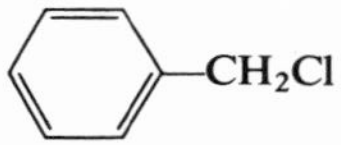 $C_6H_5-CH_2Cl$	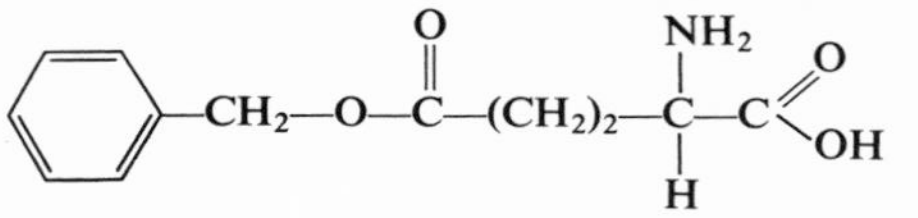 $C_6H_5-CH_2-O-C(=O)-(CH_2)_2-C(NH_2)(H)-C(=O)OH$	312
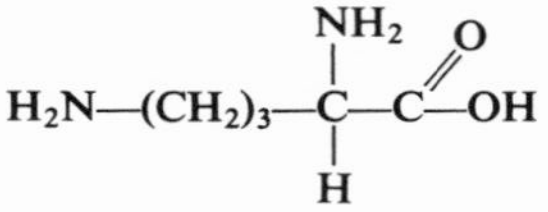 Ornithine $H_2N-(CH_2)_3-C(NH_2)(H)-C(=O)OH$	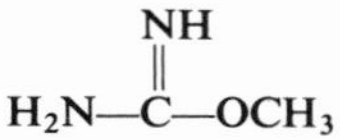 $H_2N-C(=NH)-OCH_3$	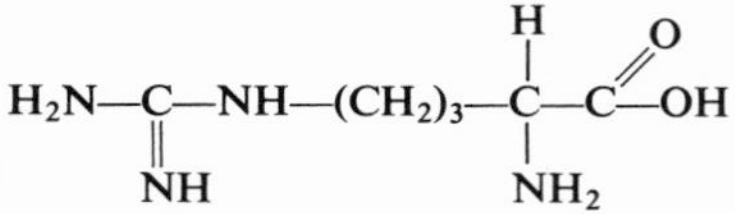 $H_2N-C(=NH)-NH-(CH_2)_3-C(NH_2)(H)-C(=O)OH$ Arginine	313
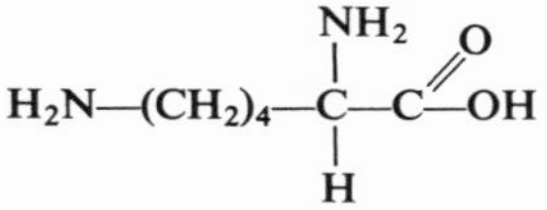 Lysine $H_2N-(CH_2)_4-C(NH_2)(H)-C(=O)OH$	$(CH_3CO)_2O$	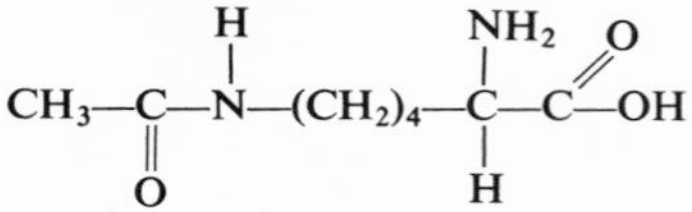 $CH_3-C(=O)-N(H)-(CH_2)_4-C(NH_2)(H)-C(=O)OH$ N-Acetyllysine	314
$H_2N-(CH_2)_x-C(NH_2)(H)-C(=O)OH$	$C_6H_5CH_2OCOCl$	$C_6H_5CH_2-O-C(=O)-NH-(CH_2)_4-C(NH_2)(H)-C(=O)OH$	315

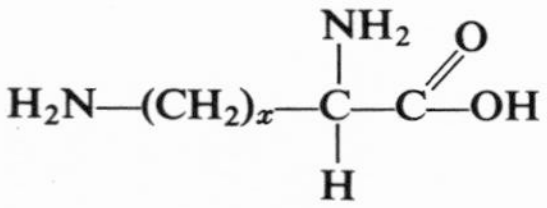

$x = 4 = $ lysine, $x = 3 = $ ornithine

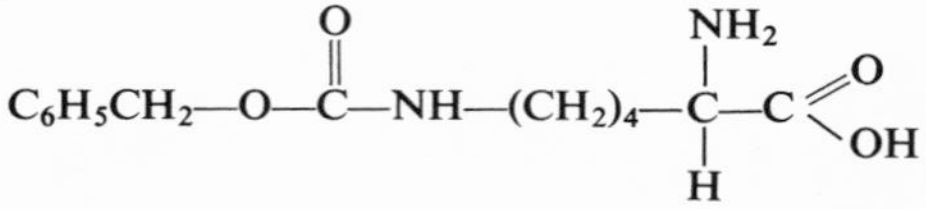

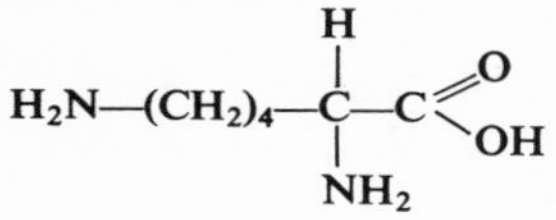

$H_2N-(CH_2)_4-\overset{\overset{H}{|}}{C}-\overset{\overset{O}{\parallel}}{C}-OH$
      NH_2

Lysine

C_6H_5NCO

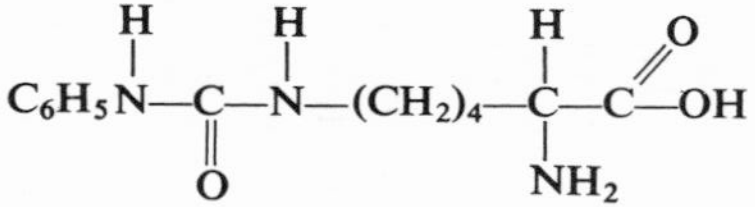

$C_6H_5N-\overset{\overset{H}{|}}{C}-\overset{\overset{H}{|}}{N}-(CH_2)_4-\overset{\overset{H}{|}}{C}-\overset{\overset{O}{\parallel}}{C}-OH$
      $\parallel$ NH_2
      O

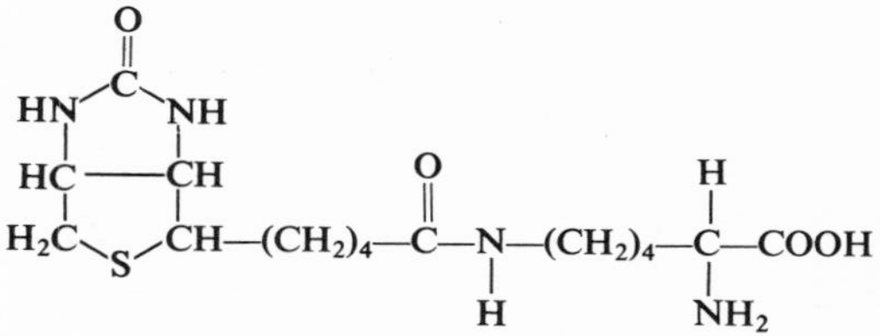

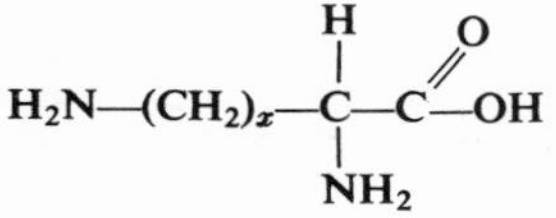

316

Biotin acid chloride

(biotin structure) $-CH-(CH_2)_4-\overset{\overset{O}{\parallel}}{C}-\overset{\overset{H}{|}}{N}-(CH_2)_4-\overset{\overset{H}{|}}{C}-COOH$
                                    NH_2

317

$H_2N-(CH_2)_x-\overset{\overset{H}{|}}{C}-\overset{\overset{O}{\parallel}}{C}-OH$
      NH_2

$x = 3,1$

KCNO

$H_2N-\overset{\overset{H}{|}}{C}-\overset{\overset{H}{|}}{N}-(CH_2)_3-\overset{\overset{H}{|}}{C}-\overset{\overset{O}{\parallel}}{C}-OH$
      $\parallel$ NH_2
      O

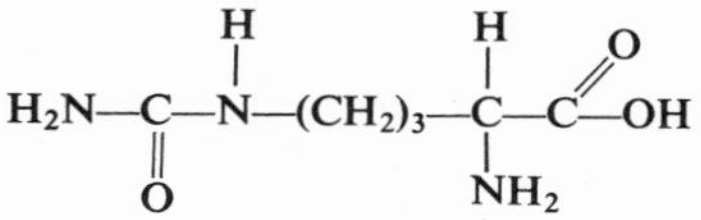

318
319

312. W. E. Hanby, S. G. Wales, and J. Watson, *J. Chem. Soc.* p. 3241 (1950).
313. F. Turba and K. H. Schuster, *Z. Physiol Chem.* (*Hoppe-Seylers*) **283**, 27 (1948).
314. A. Neuberger and F. Sanger, *Biochem. J.* **37**, 515 (1943).
315. R. L. M. Synge, *Biochem. J.* **42**, 99 (1948).
316. A. C. Kurtz, *J. Biol. Chem.* **180**, 1253 (1949). This article also describes reactions with acid chlorides (the Schotten-Baumann procedure), nitrourea, o-methylisourea salts, and S-alkylisothiouronium salts.
317. D. E. Wolf, J. Valliant, R. L. Peck, and K. Folkers, *J. Am. Chem. Soc.* **74**, 2002 (1952).
318. L. H. Smith, *J. Am. Chem. Soc.* **77**, 6691 (1955), also gives similar reactions for the synthesis of ε carbamyllysine and α-amino-γ-carbamido butyric acid.
319. A. Kjaer and P. O. Larsen, *Acta Chem. Scand.* **13**, 1565 (1959).

In the copper(II) complexes many of the diagnostic reactions of α-amino acids are also masked, such as those with fluorodinitrobenzene[320] and acetylation reagents.[314,321]

The effectiveness of the masking in these complexes appears to arise from:

(1) the considerable stability of the complex with respect to both dissociation and *exchange* reactions of the ligand and

(2) the presence of a much more reactive uncoordinated group on the ligand that consumes the added reagent before any appreciable amount can react with the momentarily dissociated α-amino groups.

A difference in the rate constants of only about 30-fold for the free and the coordinated groups is sufficient for the successful utilization of the masking action in these cases.

The utilization of ligand polarization in addition to the masking is illustrated by the reaction of copper(II) glycinate with a basic solution of acetaldehyde, to give copper(II) threoninate.[322] This is essentially a Knoevenagel condensation. The threonine is then obtained by treatment of the complex with hydrogen sulfide. The reaction is

64% yield of
Copper threoninate + copper allothreoninate

The yields obtained with tris(glycinato)cobalt(III) in this type of reaction were lower.[323] Copper glycinate and $(CH_3)_2CHCHO$, condensed similarly, give β-hydroxyleucine in good yields.[324] Serine and phenylserine can be prepared

320. T. Peters, *Biochim. Biophys. Acta* **39**, 546 (1960).
321. R. Klement, *Ber. Deut. Chem. Ges.* **66**, 1312 (1932).
322. M. Sato, K. Okawa, and S. Akabori, *Bull. Chem. Soc. Japan* **30**, 937 (1957).
323. Y. Ikutani, T. Okuda, M. Sato, and S. Akabori, *Bull. Chem. Soc. Japan* **32**, 203 (1959); see also Section 3.3.
324. Y. Ikutani, T. Okuda, and S. Akabori, *Bull. Chem. Soc. Japan* **33**, 582 (1960).

by the analogous reactions of copper glycinate with formaldehyde and benzaldehyde, respectively.[325] Aldehydes add to the copper complex of threonine to give six-coordinate complexes whose low solubility facilitates the separation of threonine from allothreonine.[326]

The reaction of glycine, in the optically active complex *levo*-glycinatobis-(ethylenediamine)cobalt(III) iodide, with acetaldehyde in the presence of sodium carbonate, resulted in a partially asymmetric synthesis of threonine.[327] The asymmetric yield was estimated at 8%. Glycinatobis-(*l*-propylenediamine)cobalt(III) chloride, when subject to the same reaction conditions, gave an asymmetric yield of only 1%.

Dwyer[328] ascribes the principal effect of the metal in these reactions to be one of providing masking by coordination, rather than activation by electronic polarization. Because direct comparison with the free ligand is difficult, this question has not yet received a direct answer in these systems.

The masking of the α-amino group in the copper complex of lysine is not always complete. Treatment of the aqueous solution of the copper complex of L- or DL-lysine with ethylene oxide resulted in the formation of both $(HOCH_2CH_2-)_2N-(CH_2)_4CH(NH_2)COOH$ and $H_2N(CH_2)_4CH(COOH)-N-(C_2H_4OH)_2$ in the relative ratio of 3 to 1. This indicates that the complex was either partially dissociated (most likely) or that the ratio of the rates of attack of the two amino groups stands as 3 : 1.[329] This is one of the few reactions where the masking of the α-amino group is incomplete in the complexes, and the mixture of products obtained here is atypical for such ligand reactions.

3.8.3. ESTERIFICATION OF FREE HYDROXY GROUP OF COORDINATED LIGANDS

Many ligands that bear a multiplicity of donor sites coordinate in such a manner that hydroxy groups remain uncoordinated. These free hydroxy groups should then be capable of reaction with various esterification reagents. Although such studies have not all been in accord, it appears to be generally true that such hydroxy groups are often extraordinarily difficult to esterify.

325. K. Okawa and M. Sato, British Patent 814,063, 1959, *Chem. Abstr.* **54**, 328g; Japanese Patent 2964, 1959, *Chem. Abstr.* **54**, 13017i; Japanese Patent 19,563, 1961, *Chem. Abstr.* **57**, 13884; German Patent 1,108,702, 1957, *Chem. Abstr.* **56**, 8836, uses copper or zinc complexes.
326. Tanabe Seiyaku Ltd., British Patents, 894,047 and 894,046; *Chem. Abstr.* **57**, 13884 (1962).
327. M. Murakami and K. Takahashi, *Bull. Chem. Soc. Japan* **32**, 308 (1959); also Japanese Patent 19,563, 1961, *Chem. Abstr.* **57**, 13884.
328. F. P. Dwyer, *in* "Chelating Agents and Metal Chelates" (F. P. Dwyer and D. P. Mellor, eds.), p. 347. Academic Press, New York, 1964.
329. O. F. Ginzburg, B. A. Porai-Koshits, and M. I. Krylova, *Puti Sinteza i Izyskaniya Protivoopukholevykh Preparatov, Tr. Simpoziuma po Khim. Protivoopukholevykh Veshchestv, Moscow*, **1960** pp. 59–65. (1962); *Chem. Abstr.* **57**, 17024.

The complications which can arise may be seen in work on N-hydroxy-ethylethylenediamine. Here[330] it was found that the oxidation of a basic mixture of a cobalt(II) salt and N-hydroxyethylethylenediamine produced primarily tris(ethylenediamine)cobalt(III). In this study, a method for preparing complexes of N-hydroxyethylethylenediamine (hereafter abbreviated as etolen) was developed based upon reactions of the type

$$[Co(NH_3)_6]Cl_3 + 3\ etolen\ \xrightarrow[\Delta]{H_2O}\ [Co(etolen)_3]^{3+} + 6NH_3 + 3Cl^-$$

Complexes with the ligand N-hydroxyethyldiethylenetriamine (hereafter abbreviated as dietolen) were prepared in a similar manner.

$$[Co(NH_3)_6]Cl_3 + 2\ dietolen\ \xrightarrow[\Delta]{H_2O}\ [Co(dietolen)_2]^{3+} + 6NH_3 + 3Cl^-$$

In both cases the cationic complexes prepared had uncoordinated hydroxyl groups and in both cases all attempts to react these with nitric acid, thionyl chloride, benzoyl chloride, or acetyl chloride failed. Because these ions have large positive charges that suppress the reaction, it was also decided to prepare analogous complexes with a lower net charge on the cation. For this purpose, $[Co(dietolen)(SCN)_3]$ and $[Co(dietolen)(NO_3)_3]$ were prepared and investigated in a similar fashion. In both cases, the complexes decomposed in the presence of the reagents, so no conclusions could be drawn. In a study involving chromium(III) complexes,[331] the complex ion bis(2-hydroxyethylimino-diacetato)chromium(III)

$$\left[\left(HO-CH_2-CH_2-N\underset{CH_2-C}{\overset{CH_2-C}{\longrightarrow}}\begin{matrix}O\\\parallel\\ _____\\ \parallel\\ O\end{matrix}\right)_2 Cr\right]^- = [Cr(HOA)_2]^-$$

was subjected to several acetylating processes, most of which failed to acetylate the free hydroxyl groups. Refluxing in a mixture of acetic anhydride and glacial acetic acid resulted in considerable decomposition, but did allow the isolation and characterization of $(H_3O)[Cr(AcOA)_2]$, the acid form of the doubly acetylated complex, which was obtained in about 25% yield. Since this ion has a negative charge, the arguments used to explain the lack of

330. W. C. Drinkard, H. F. Bauer, and J. C. Bailar, Jr., *J. Am. Chem. Soc.* **82**, 2992 (1960). The cobalt-catalyzed cleavage of N-hydroxyethylethylenediamine to ethylenediamine that occurs in the presence of oxygen has been studied in detail. See D. Huggins and W. C. Drinkard, *Advan. Chem. Ser.* **37**, 181 (1963).
331. R. A. Krause and S. D. Goldby, *Advan. Chem. Ser.* **37**, 143 (1963).

reactivity in the cobalt complexes are inadequate, at least here. Krause and Goldby discuss possible reasons for the sluggishness of these reactions. None of the proposed explanations are considered acceptable by these authors and this phenomenon presently has no satisfactory explanation.

The masking of typical hydroxyl reactions in complexes of vicinal dioximes, such as nickel(II) dimethylglyoxime, appears to arise from the formation of rather stable hydrogen bonds. The complexes which have been most thoroughly studied are those of dimethylglyoxime with nickel and palladium.

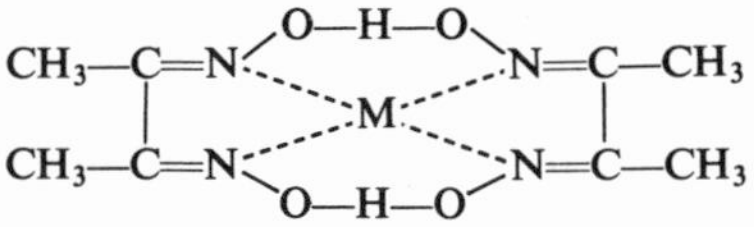

$$M = Ni(II),\ Pd(II)$$

The hydroxy groups in the nickel complex have been reported to be resistant to attack by phenyl isocyanate,[332] acetic anhydride,[333] and methylmagnesium iodide in amyl ether.[334] The infrared spectra have been interpreted to be consistent with a very short O—H—O hydrogen-bonded system.[335]

The reaction of nickel dimethylglyoxime with alkyl halides proceeds as follows[336]:

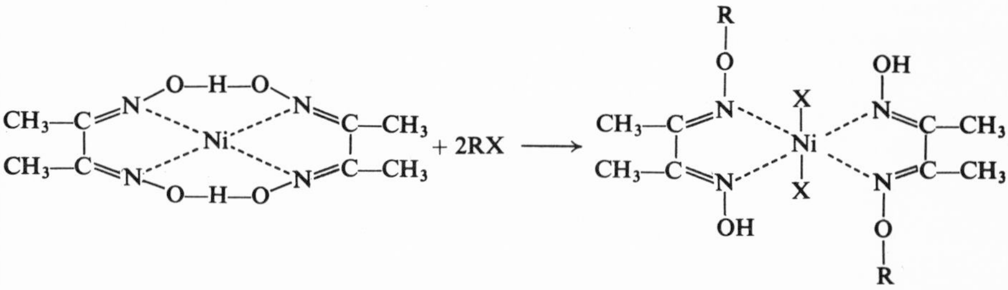

The reaction of the nickel(II), palladium(II), and platinum(II) complexes of dimethylglyoxime with acetyl chloride gives as products $[M^{II}(HDMG)Cl_2]$ and the free acetylated ligand.[337] With 2-pyridinaldoxime, the palladium(II) complex can be monoacylated while the platinum(II) complex gives a diacylated complex, $[Pt(POX—COCH_3)_2]Cl_2$ (where POX is the monovalent anion

332. L. A. Tschugaeff, *J. Chem. Soc.* **105**, 2187 (1914).
333. M. F. Barker, *Chem. News* **130**, 99 (1925).
334. O. L. Brady and M. M. Muers, *J. Chem. Soc.* p. 1599 (1930).
335. R. C. Voter, C. V. Banks, V. A. Fassel, and P. W. Kehres, *Anal. Chem.* **23**, 1730 (1951).
336. D. H. Busch, *Advan. Chem. Ser.* **37**, 15 (1963).
337. R. A. Krause, D. C. Jicha, and D. H. Busch, *J. Am. Chem. Soc.* **83**, 528 (1961). Here HDMG is the protonated form of dimethylglyoxime.

derived from 2-pyridinaldoxime). The studies of Busch and his co-workers have considerably clarified the conflicting reports on the reactions of coordinated oximes.[338-340]

Nickel dimethylglyoxime and some related complexes have also been found to react with boron compounds of the type BX_3, where X = F, CH_3-, n-C_3H_7-, n-C_4H_9-, and isobutyl.[341] The product of the reaction with BF_3 was $Ni(DMG)B_2F_4$, which was also found to form adducts with bases such as pyridine, isonitriles, and triphenylphosphine. The bis pyridine adduct is presumably octahedral and yet is diamagnetic, a rather unusual situation.

3.8.4. Reactions of Multiple Bonds in Ligands

There are many other instances in which coordination masks a ligand toward the action of normally effective reagents. In most of these, the interference is primarily based upon steric restrictions resulting from coordination. One example is the masking of coordinated olefins towards the action of bromine, which is seen in the case of $[PtCl_2(C_2H_4)]_2$.[342] This compound undergoes bromination of the double bond in the ethylene only at temperatures high enough to produce dissociation of the complex. The immediate product of the reaction with bromine is $PtCl_2Br_2(C_2H_4)$. The initial product in the chlorination of $[PtCl_2(C_2H_4)]_2$ is similarly $PtCl_4(C_2H_4)$,[343] and in the bromination of $[PtCl_2(Styrene)]_2$, one obtains $[PtCl_2Br_2(Styrene)]$.[344] Other reactions which are suppressed by coordination include the basic hydrolysis of the cyanide ion, the rearrangement of cyanate to urea in the presence of ammonium ion, and the corresponding rearrangements of thiocyanate. All these reactions involve addition to a ligand double bond, which involves the donor atom in a very direct fashion.

3.8.5. Quaternization Reactions

Both the nature of the donor atom *and* its attached groups determine whether that donor atom will undergo quaternization reactions with alkyl halides *after* coordination.

The masking of coordinated arsine toward the quaternization reaction with methyl iodide has been used to demonstrate the coordination of all of the arsenic atoms of the ligand tris(o-diphenylarsinophenyl)arsine (QAS) in its

338. E. Thilo and K. Friedrich, *Ber. Deut. Chem. Ges.* **62B**, 2990 (1929).
339. A. G. Sharpe and D. B. Wakefield, *J. Chem. Soc.* p. 496 (1957).
340. A. G. Sharpe and D. B. Wakefield, *J. Chem. Soc.* p. 3323 (1957).
341. G. Schrauzer, *Chem. Ber.* **95**, 1438 (1962).
342. J. H. Flynn and H. M. Hulburt, *J. Am. Chem. Soc.* **76**, 3396 (1954).
343. J. Chatt, *Research (London)* **4**, 180 (1951).
344. M. S. Kharasch and T. A. Ashford, *J. Am. Chem. Soc.* **58**, 1733 (1936).

complex with platinum(II).[345] This reaction is found to proceed readily with uncoordinated arsines.

The reactions of coordinated thiols have been examined in more detail. In an early report,[346] the alkylation of (2-aminoethylthio)diethylgold to give a complex sulfonium ion was found to occur quite readily.

$$
\begin{array}{c}
C_2H_5 \diagdown \quad \diagup NH_2-CH_2 \\
\qquad Au \qquad | \quad + CH_3CH_2Br \longrightarrow \\
C_2H_5 \diagup \quad \diagdown S-CH_2
\end{array}
\qquad
\begin{array}{c}
C_2H_5 \diagdown \quad \diagup NH_2-CH_2 \\
\qquad Au \qquad \underset{+}{\;} | \qquad Br^- \\
C_2H_5 \diagup \quad \diagdown S-CH_2 \\
\qquad\qquad | \\
\qquad\qquad C_2H_5
\end{array}
$$

The same complex reacts with chloramine-T to give a product in which a nitrogen has been attached to the coordinated sulfur. It was concluded that the sulfur atom of the original complex "displays the reactivity typical of an organic sulfide." In this same paper it was reported that the sulfur atom in the corresponding complex of cobalt(III) could be oxidized to the sulfone without disrupting the complex.

$$
Co \left\{ \begin{array}{c} NH_2-CH_2 \\ | \\ S-CH_2 \end{array} \right\}_3
\xrightarrow{\text{Oxidation}}
Co \left\{ \begin{array}{c} NH_2-CH_2 \\ | \\ SO_2-CH_2 \end{array} \right\}_3
$$

A kinetic study of the alkylation of coordinated thiol in $NH_2CH_2CH_2SH$ and related ligands revealed that the reaction proceeded without the breaking of the metal–sulfur bond.[347] The nucleophilicity of the coordinated sulfur was found to depend on the central metal involved, but was greater than that of the sulfur in a thiol. It was found that sulfur in such ligands did *not* react with alkyl halides when it occupied a *bridging position* between two metal atoms in a polynuclear complex.

For ligands derived from Group V and VI elements such as thiols, thioethers, amines, phosphines, and arsines, the patterns of reaction masking are dependent on the mechanism of the reactions. When the reaction involves an unshared electron pair, such as in quaternization, masking will be found when no pair of electrons is free in the complex, and will often be masked for sulfur when only one pair of electrons is free. This is also true with amines, arsines, and phosphines coordinated to a single metal atom. With thiols, when the

345. J. A. Brewster, C. A. Savage, and L. M. Venanzi, *J. Chem. Soc.* p. 3699 (1961); G. A. Mair, H. M. Belfry, and L. M. Venanzi, *Proc. Chem. Soc.* p. 170 (1961).
346. R. V. G. Ewens and C. S. Gibson, *J. Chem. Soc.* p. 431 (1949).
347. D. H. Busch, J. A. Burke, Jr., D. C. Jicha, M. C. Thompson, and M. L. Morris, *Advan. Chem. Ser.* **37**, 125 (1963).

sulfur atoms act as bridging groups between two metal ions, or with thioethers present in chelate rings, such reactions do not seem to proceed even when there is a single electron pair, ostensibly uninvolved in bonding. The two free electron pairs of the coordinated thiol group seem to be not equivalent. As a rule of thumb, a coordinated alkyl derivative of an element (Z), R_nZ will not undergo a quaternization reaction, though $R_{n-1}ZH$ which coordinates as $R_{n-1}Z^-$ will. For reactions which involve the ionization of a hydrogen from the coordinated nonmetal, coordination results in little masking. For reactions that involve expansion of the octet of the donor atom, such as occurs in the halogenation of $C_6H_5PR_2$, coordination again provides extensive and effective masking.

3.8.6. GENERAL FORMULATION OF RATE BEHAVIOR IN SYSTEMS IN WHICH COORDINATION PROVIDES MASKING

The effectiveness of masking based upon coordination is essentially the result of a drastic alteration of the rate of the reaction. One replaces the reactive ligand L, with one or more complexes ML_i, all of which undergo the reaction at a rate less than L itself. Where L participates in protonic equilibria, a further complication arises as the various species H_jL^{j+} will also have, each, a characteristic rate constant. If a reaction with a reagent R is considered, the reaction in the presence of the metal M will include

$$L + R \xrightarrow{\;k_P\;} P$$
$$HL^+ + R \xrightarrow{\;k_{HL}\;} P + H^+$$
$$\vdots \qquad\quad \vdots \qquad\qquad \vdots \quad \vdots$$
$$H_jL^{j+} + R \xrightarrow{\;k_{H_jL}\;} P + jH^+$$
$$ML_i + R \xrightarrow{\;k_{ML}\;} MP$$
$$ML_i + R \xrightarrow{\;k_{ML_i}\;} MPL_{i-1}$$

The gross rate will then be the sum of all these rates. The general trend of the rate as L is converted to ML_i will be to decrease, and this decrease is determined by the relative magnitudes of the rate constants and formation constants of the complexes. The kind of behavior which will be found may be seen by examining a simple case, carried out at constant pH (to maintain the ratio of HL to L). The relevant reactions for a system which contains a single complex are

$$HL^+ \;\rightleftharpoons\; H^+ + L \qquad K_A$$
$$M + L \;\rightleftharpoons\; ML \qquad K_1$$
$$L + R \xrightarrow{\;k_1\;} P$$
$$HL + R \xrightarrow{\;k_2\;} P$$
$$ML + R \xrightarrow{\;k_3\;} MP$$

Here the gross rate of product formation will be

$$d[P]/dt = [R]\{k_1[L] + k_2[HL] + k_3[ML]\}$$

and this can be written as

$$d[P]/dt = \{k_1 + (k_2/K_A)[H^+] + k_3 K_1[M]\}[R][L]$$

Basically, this equation shows that masking will occur when $k_3 K_1[M]$ is smaller than k_1 plus $(k_2/K_A)[H^+]$. Furthermore, the gross rate of product formation will decrease continuously as [M] increases, if the pH and the total amount of ligand are held constant. Analogous equations can be developed for systems that contain a larger number of constituents, but the general trends will be the same as long as the paths for the reaction involving the free ligand include at least one that is more important than any for the complexes. The paths involving the reaction of the free ligand may, of course, involve several that are slower than those of the complex, but masking will be noticeable if the few fast paths are suppressed by coordination.

3.8.7. THE MODERATION OF LEWIS ACID STRENGTHS

The use of coordination to moderate the action of a very vigorous Lewis acid is an additional type of masking. An example is seen in the use of the pyridine and dioxane complexes of sulfur trioxide in place of the parent compound.[348] Since the complexes used must release sulfur trioxide to other reactants, it is imperative that no reaction beyond coordination occur. Thus pyridine reacts only to give the adduct

Tertiary amines, amides, ethers, and thioethers also give this kind of adduct. Since the stability of the complex varies directly with the basic strength of the ligand, it is found that the reactivity (which is determined by the ease with which sulfur trioxide is released from the complex) is *inversely* related to the stability of the complex and hence the basic strength of the ligand. The typical reactions of sulfur trioxide (e.g., sulfonation, sulfation, and sulfamation) are also reactions of the sulfur trioxide adducts, but coordination moderates the reactivity of the sulfur trioxide and makes it easier to control the reaction.

348. E. E. Gilbert, *Chem. Rev.* **62**, 549 (1962).

3.8.8. OTHER ASPECTS

Coordination of arylalkyl ketones to aluminum chloride masks the normal reactions of the aliphatic α-hydrogens toward bromine and chlorine and allows the halogenation reaction to occur on the aromatic nucleus, rather than on the aliphatic hydrogens, as is usually observed.[349] The same procedure is effective in aromatic halogenation of the corresponding aldehydes. Aceto-phenones and propiophenones normally give phenacyl or α-halopropio-phenones in the absence of such protection. As carried out, the reaction system contains a considerable excess of aluminum chloride which also aids in the generation of a more effective halogenating agent.

Grinberg and Kats[350] studied the thermal decarboxylation of *o*-, *m*-, and *p*-aminobenzoic acids and their complexes with platinum(II). The behavior found was similar for ligand and complex except for the case of *p*-aminobenzoic acid. Here the free ligand underwent the decarboxylation, but the complex did not.

A reaction similar, in some respects, to those of α,ϵ-amino acids is the following:

This shows clearly that coordination does not mask the aldehyde oxygen toward amines.[351,352]

3.9. Macrocycle Synthesis and Coordination Templates

The considerable importance of compounds such as hemoglobin and chlorophyll has generated a great deal of interest in complexes in which a metal ion is held in the center of a large ring system, such as a cyclic tetra-pyrrole. Ring systems of this sort have been named macrocycles. For square planar complexes of copper(II), nickel(II), and palladium(II) with such macrocycles the four donor groups are held in relative positions very close to that found for the nitrogen atoms in a cyclic tetrapyrrole. This in turn has led to investigations of the use of the coordination spheres of such species as

349. D. E. Pearson, H. W. Pope, W. W. Hargrove, and W. E. Stamper, *J. Org. Chem.* **23**, 1412 (1958).
350. A. A. Grinberg and N. N. Kats, *Zh. Obshch. Khim.* **20**, 248 (1950) ; *Chem. Abstr.* **44**, 5258c.
351. P. Ray and N. N. Ghosh, *J. Indian Chem. Soc.* **26**, 144 (1949).
352. P. Ray, *J. Indian Chem. Soc.* **32**, 141 (1955).

templates to assist reactions involving the closure of linear molecules to macrocycles. Two reactions which illustrate such processes are the following:

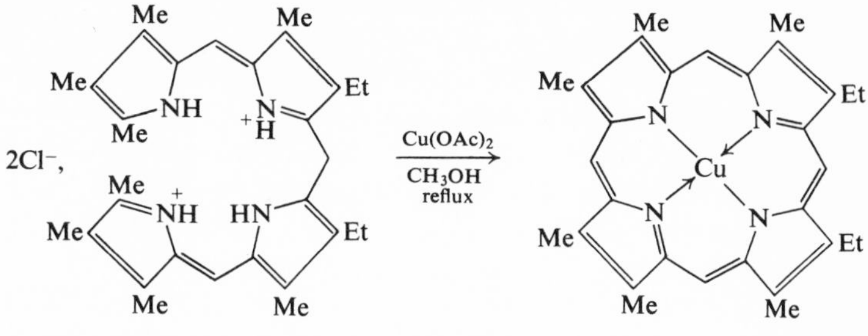

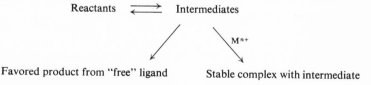

(ref. 353)

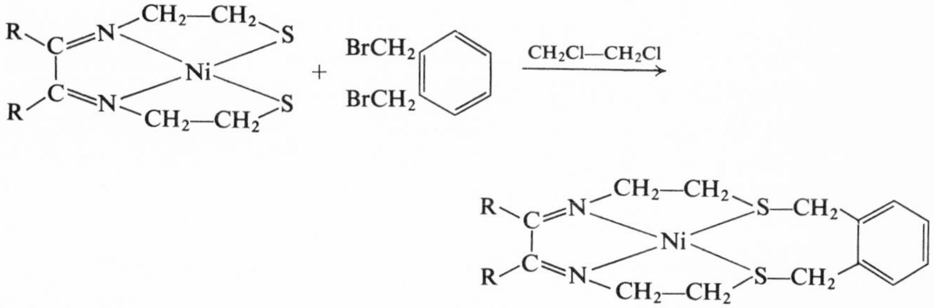

(ref. 354)

In these cases it is obvious that coordination holds the ends of a long molecule in very close proximity and facilitates a reaction giving ring closure. Comprehensive reviews of such reactions have been published.[355,356]

Following Thompson and Busch[357] we can divide the observed reactions in the "template" class into two groups. In the first group we have the consequences of a purely thermodynamic effect which may be designated an *equilibrium template reaction*. These processes are of the type

Reactants $\rightleftarrows$ Intermediates

M^{n+}

Favored product from "free" ligand   Stable complex with intermediate

353. A. W. Johnson and I. T. Kay, *J. Chem. Soc.* p. 2418 (1961); G. G. Kleinspehn and A. H. Corwin, *J. Am. Chem. Soc.* **82**, 2750 (1960).
354. M. C. Thompson and D. H. Busch, *J. Am. Chem. Soc.* **86**, 3651 (1964).
355. D. H. Busch, *Record Chem. Progr.* (*Kresge-Hooker Sci. Lib.*) **25**, 107 (1964).
356. D. St. C. Blackman and E. Markham, *Rev. Pure Appl. Chem.* **15**, 109 (1965).
357. M. C. Thompson and D. H. Busch, *J. Am. Chem. Soc.* **86**, 216 (1964).

Examples of this include the reaction of biacetyl and methylamine,[358,359] where the monomeric adduct [biacetylbis(methylimine)] can only be prepared in the form of its complexes with metal ions, as the reaction in the absence of metal ions gives a polymeric oil. Other examples include the Schiff base of salicylaldehyde and glycine which is stabilized by complex formation with metal ions,[360] and the self-condensation products of *o*-aminobenzaldehyde in the presence of nickel(II) and copper(II).[361] Reactions in this category involve a chelate system that is capable of undergoing a reversible hydrolysis and a metal ion that preferentially complexes with an intermediate (or one of a number of intermediates). Although most of the reactions of this sort studied to date involve Schiff bases, there is no reason why any reversible reaction capable of joining sections to a chain could not be effected in the same manner.

The second group of template reactions are designated *kinetic template reactions* by Thompson and Busch. These are instances in which coordination holds two or more ends of a chain ligand in a stereochemical position that favors a sequential reaction of the ends with an added reagent—the consequence being ring closure. The principal difference between these reactions and those given previously are that these are usually irreversible. Examples of this may be seen in the closure of the copper(II) tetrapyrrole system given earlier and in the closure of the nickel(II) chelate ring with 1,2-di(bromomethyl)benzene discovered by Thompson and Busch. Another example which may fit into this category is the conversion of nickel(II) dimethylglyoxime (which is a kind of a macrocycle itself) to a compound in which the bridging hydrogens are replaced by BX_2 groups.

In these products the macrocycle ring is very stable.[362,363]

The number of reactions that have been used to attain ring closure with these macrocycles is very small in comparison with the number potentially possible.

358. P. Krumholz, *J. Am. Chem. Soc.* **75**, 2163 (1953).
359. P. E. Figgins and D. H. Busch, *J. Am. Chem. Soc.* **82**, 820 (1960).
360. G. L. Eichhorn and N. O. Marchand, *J. Am. Chem. Soc.* **78**, 2688 (1956).
361. L. I. Taylor, S. C. Vergez, and D. H. Busch, *J. Am. Chem. Soc.* **88**, 3170 (1966).
362. G. N. Schrauzer, *Chem. Ber.* **95**, 1438 (1962).
363. D. Thierig and F. Umland, *Angew. Chem.* **74**, 388 (1962).

In part the reason for this lies in the preference of previous studies for precursors which could be generated by the formation of a Schiff base. As work is extended to other precursors, the number and variety of ring closure reactions available will no doubt increase.

3.10. Reactions of Coordinated Ammonia

The changes in the chemical properties of ammonia that result from coordination arise from the drawing of electronic density from the molecule towards the acceptor center. The most immediate consequence of this is an increase in the acid strength of the hydrogen atoms of the ammonia.[364] This change is most pronounced for complexes with platinum(IV), osmium(IV), gold(III), and other ions of heavy platinum-group metals.

The chemical exploitation of this change is seen in a very impressive manner in the work of Kukushkin on the reactions of coordinated ammonia with halogens.[365-371] In the initial study it was established that the chlorination of $[Pt(NH_3)_3Cl_3]Cl$ in water proceeded as follows:

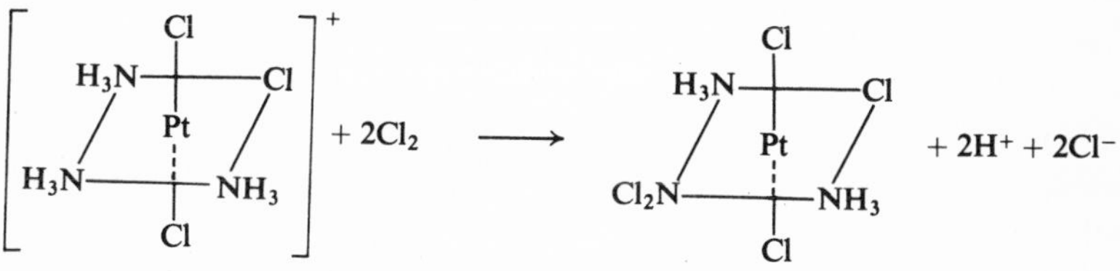

The compound containing coordinated chloramine is inclined to undergo a violent decomposition so it should be prepared only in small quantities. A number of other reactions of this same type were demonstrated, including

$$[Pt(NH_3)_5Cl]Cl_3 \xrightarrow[H_2O]{Cl_2} [Pt(NH_3)_4(NCl_2)Cl]Cl_2$$

$$[Pt(en)(Py)(NO_2)(NH_3)(Cl)]Cl_2 \xrightarrow{Cl_2} \{Pt[N-(CH_2)_2N](Py)(NO_2)(NH_3)(Cl)\}Cl_2$$

with Cl and Cl on the two N atoms and H below each.

364. F. Basolo and R. G. Pearson, "Mechanisms of Inorganic Reactions," pp. 386–394. Wiley, New York, 1958.
365. Y. N. Kukushkin, Zh. Neorgan. Khim. 2, 2371 (1957).
366. Y. N. Kukushkin, Zh. Neorgan. Khim. 4, 2460 (1959).
367. Y. N. Kukushkin, Zh. Neorgan. Khim. 5, 1943 (1960).
368. Y. N. Kukushkin, Zh. Neorgan. Khim. 6, 2451 (1961).
369. Y. N. Kukushkin and N. N. Zatsepina, Zh. Neorgan. Khim. 6, 120 (1961).
370. Y. N. Kukushkin, Zh. Neorgan. Khim. 7, 769 (1962).
371. Y. N. Kukushkin, Zh. Neorgan. Khim. 8, 817, 823 (1963).

and

$$[Pt(NH_3)_5(OH)]Cl_3 \xrightarrow{Cl_2} [Pt(NH_3)_3(NCl_2)_2Cl]Cl$$

Here there is no evidence that masking interferes in any way with these reactions. When the complexes of palladium(II) were examined for a similar reactivity, no complexes containing coordinated chloramines could be isolated.[371] The reaction of ammines of platinum(IV) with bromine can be used to introduce bromoamine in the coordination sphere, but the products are somewhat less stable than those obtained with chlorine. The general nature of the processes are similar. One example of a bromination reaction established by Kukushkin is

The reactions of halogens with [Os(en)$_3$]I$_3$ lead to products of a different nature.[372] Here the initial products were those in which the halogen attacked the anion to give ICl_2^-, IBr_2^-, and I_3^-. When the concentration of chlorine was increased or the chlorinated compound was exposed to air some further reaction occurred, but the products were not characterized.

Kukushkin's work on reactions in the inner sphere of tetravalent platinum were preceded by earlier studies of I. I. Chernyaev,[373] who showed that nitrite or hydroxylamine coordinated to platinum(II) could be reduced to coordinated ammonia. Similar studies in which the nitro group in [Pt(dien)(NO$_2$)]$^+$ was reduced to obtain [Pt(dien)(NH$_3$)]$^{2+}$ showed that the reduction could be effected polarographically, coulometrically, or by chemical means.[374] Grinberg and Gildengershel[375] reported that ethylamine (EtNH$_2$) in [Pt(NH$_2$Et)$_4$Cl$_2$]Cl$_2$ could be hydrolyzed to ethyl alcohol, leaving the nitrogen coordinated to the platinum.

Another example is found in the various platinum(II) ammines that "contain" acetonitrile. One such compound is that formed by the reaction of [Pt(CH$_3$CN)$_2$Cl$_2$] with ammonia. This gives a product whose formal composition corresponds to [Pt(CH$_3$CN)$_2$(Cl)$_2$(NH$_3$)$_2$]. For many years this was

372. G. W. Watt and J. T. Summers, *J. Am. Chem. Soc.* **88**, 431 (1966).
373. I. I. Chernyaev, *Izv. Inst. Izucheniyu Platiny i Drug. Blagorodn. Metal.* 7, 52 (1929); *Chem. Abstr.* **24**, 2684.
374. Badar-Ud-Din and J. C. Bailar, Jr., *J. Inorg. Nucl. Chem.* **22**, 241 (1961).
375. A. A. Grinberg and K. I. Gildengershel, *Dokl. Akad. Nauk SSSR* **101** (3), 491 (1955); *Chem. Abstr.* **44**, 474; *Chem. Abstr.* **49**, 12173.

considered to be an unusual complex in which platinum(II) was six-coordinated.

Other examples of this same sort are found in the products obtained in reactions such as

$$Pt(NH_3)_2Cl_2 + CH_3CN \rightarrow [Pt(CH_3CN)(NH_3)_2]Cl_2$$
$$K[Pt(NH_3)Cl_3] + CH_3CN \rightarrow [Pt(CH_3CN)(NH_3)_2Cl_2] + KCl$$

Because platinum(II) compounds of this class show chemical reactions characteristic of four-coordinate platinum(II), Lebedinsky and Golovnya[376] formulated such compounds with the ammonia bound to the acetonitrile. Compounds of this sort can be formed from starting materials containing either ammonia or acetonitrile in the coordination sphere and many related examples are known.[377] There are very few instances (if any) in which platinum(II) exhibits a coordination number other than 4 with nitrogen donor ligands, and it has recently been shown by X-ray studies[378] that the product of this reaction is [Pt(acetamidine)$_2$Cl$_2$] and that the reaction may be written

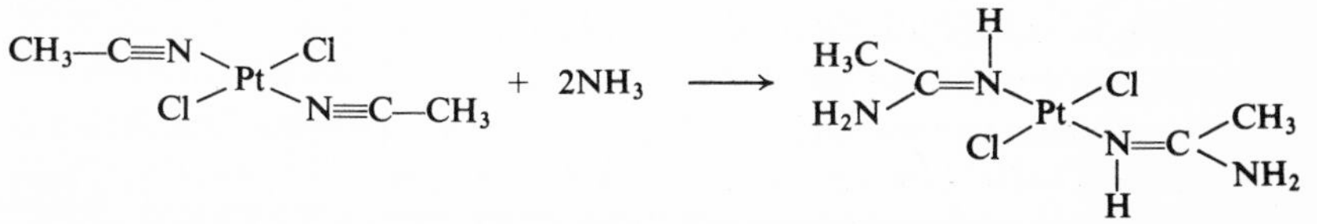

Here the coordination act accentuates the electron drift from the nitrile carbon atom and makes it more susceptible to attack by nucleophiles, in this case, ammonia. This kind of process had been essentially substantiated by chemical studies carried out previously and the formation of amidines in such reactions was suggested as early as 1951. A mechanism of this reaction which seems consistent with the known facts[379] is that of Kharitonov et al.[379]:

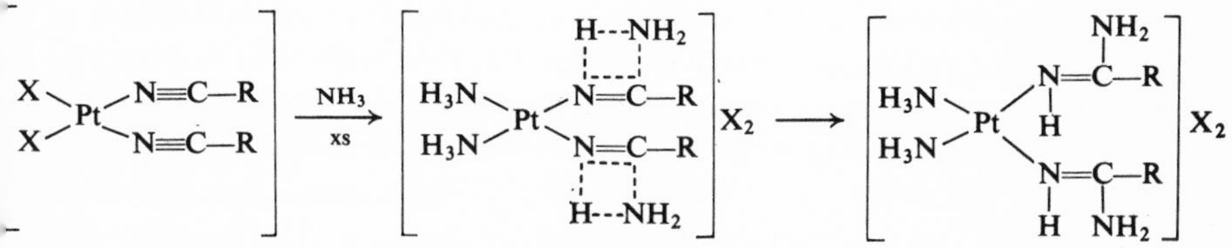

376. V. V. Lebedinsky and V. A. Golovnya, *Izv. Sektora Platiny i Drug. Blagorodn. Metal., Inst. Obshch. i Neorgan. Khim., Akad. Nauk SSSR* **16**, 29 (1939); *Chem. Abstr.* **34**, 4685.
377. Gmelins "Handbuch Der Anorganischen Chemie," 8th Ed., System No. 68, Pt. D, pp. 39, 134, 154, 211, 391. Verlag Chemie, Weinheim, 1957.
378. N. C. Stephenson, *J. Inorg. Nucl. Chem.* **24**, 801 (1962).
379. Y. Y. Kharitonov, Ni Chia-chien, and G. V. Babaeva, *Russ. J. Inorg. Chem. (English Transl.)* **7**, 513 (1962); **8**, 17 (1963), also summarizes previous work.

The displacement of the X groups from the platinum(II) does not always occur. This kind of a reaction, between a coordinated amine or nitrile and the other reactant to give an amidine, is one of considerable generality for complexes of the type $[PtX_2(N\equiv C—R)_2]$ and $[Pt(NH_3)_xX_{4-x}]$.

The reaction of deprotonated amine ligands with methyl iodide has been examined.[380] The products are the methylated amines. The overall reaction sequence is

$$[Pt(bipy)(en)]^{2+} \xrightarrow[\text{NH}_3\text{(l)}]{\text{KNH}_2} [Pt(bipy)(en-H)]^+ + NH_3$$

$$[Pt(bipy)(en-H)]^+ + CH_3I \longrightarrow [Pt(bipy)(enCH_3)]^{2+} + I^-$$

3.11. Related Effects

The number of ways in which coordination can affect ligand reactivity must include some that are very imperfectly understood at the present time as well as some yet to be discovered. Of those that are presently imperfectly under-stood, the interaction of Lewis acids with aromatic π-electron systems is one of the more important. Such interactions have been tacitly recognized for many years, though relatively little structural data is available.

Aromatic hydrocarbons act as bases towards anhydrous hydrogen halides as well as metallic halides such as $AlCl_3$, and $SbCl_3$. Thus the interaction of HCl and HBr with benzene, toluene, m-xylene, and mesitylene has been examined in n-heptane solutions and the equilibrium can be written as[381]

$$\text{ArH} \cdot \text{HX(soln.)} \rightleftarrows \text{ArH(soln.)} + \text{HX(soln.)}$$

This type of interaction is a general one for aromatic hydrocarbons and Lewis acids that are commonly used in preparative organic chemistry as coordination centers. A large number of solid adducts have been iso-lated and characterized, such as $2SbCl_3 \cdot C_6H_6$, $(CH_3)_3C_6H_3 \cdot GaBr_3$, and $Al_2Br_6 \cdot C_6H_6$.[382]

These are certainly not "coordination compounds" in the older sense of this term, though they do furnish examples which formally may be classified as such. The structural data that have been obtained on such complexes indicate that the bonding is between the aromatic system as a whole and the Lewis acid. The structures of some aluminum halide–aromatic system com-pounds have been determined, for example $Al_2Br_6 \cdot C_6H_6$,[383] where the bonding between the benzene and the Al_2Br_6 dimers is through the bromines,

380. G. W. Watt and D. G. Upchurch, *J. Am. Chem. Soc.* **87**, 4212 (1965).
381. H. C. Brown and J. J. Mechiore, *J. Am. Chem. Soc.* **87**, 5269 (1965).
382. A very comprehensive review of these compounds has been given by G. A. Olah and M. W. Meyer, *in* "Friedel-Crafts and Related Reactions" (G. A. Olah, ed.), Vol. 1, p. 710 ff. Wiley (Interscience), New York, 1963.
383. D. D. Eley, J. H. Taylor, and S. C. Wallwork, *J. Chem. Soc.* p. 3867 (1961).

but the interaction may well be a very weak van der Waal's type interaction. This compound can lose benzene very easily; traces of moisture convert it to the ionic complex $[C_6H_7]^+[Al_2Br_7]^-$. In the complex derived from benzene, copper(I) chloride, and aluminum chloride, $C_6H_6 \cdot CuAlCl_4$, the aromatic ring is bonded to the copper(I) and may be said to make it four-coordinate, with the other coordination positions occupied by chlorides of $AlCl_4^-$ groups.[384] Each copper(I) is bonded to but a single aromatic ring. This is different from the structure found in $C_6H_6 \cdot AgClO_4$,[385] where each silver(I) is bonded to two aromatic rings. The similarity between these complexes and the more stable aromatic complexes such as ferrocene is striking from a structural viewpoint. A very large number of solid complexes of silver(I) with aromatic systems have been prepared by Peyronel and his collaborators.[386] These compounds are not very stable against dissociation in the presence of solvents or reagents in general, so little can be stated about the manner in which the formation of such a complex affects the reactivity of the aromatic system.

A very closely related group of complexes are those that involve an aromatic compound, a Lewis acid halide, and a "co-catalyst"; this latter is generally a hydrogen halide, an alkyl halide, or acyl halide. An example is that formed by aluminum chloride, hydrogen chloride, and mesitylene which has the composition $[(CH_3)_3C_6H_4^+][AlCl_4^-]$ in the presence of an excess of HCl.[382] In such complexes the aromatic rings have been protonated. Structurally, of course, these compounds are very different from those obtained in the absence of the co-catalyst.

Although the arene complexes of the metals will not be considered in detail in this book, it should be noted that the cyclopentadienide anion of ferrocene and the benzene ring of bis(benzene)chromium are much *less* reactive in these complexes than they are normally, at least as far as reactivity toward electrophilic reagents is concerned.

384. R. W. Turner and E. L. Amma, *J. Am. Chem. Soc.* **85**, 4046 (1963).
385. H. G. Smith and R. E. Rundle, *J. Am. Chem. Soc.* **80**, 5075 (1958).
386. See, for example: S. Buffagni, I. M. Vezzosi, and G. Peyronel, *Gazz. Chim. Ital.* **93**, 1477 (1963), for the ninth paper in a series on these compounds.

Chapter IV CATALYSIS VIA COORDINATION

In order to possess some degree of sophistication about the use of coordination in facilitating reactions, it is necessary to examine the kinetic and thermodynamic basis for such processes, and the ways in which coordination may affect the reactivity of the attacking species (rather than the substrate).

4.1. Kinetic Classification: Effects of the Free Energy ($\Delta G^{\ddagger}$), Enthalpy ($\Delta H^{\ddagger}$), and Entropy of Activation ($\Delta S^{\ddagger}$)

The fundamental changes that allow coordination to furnish catalytic routes for reactions are variations in the ease of attainment of suitable transition states which may arise from variations in $\Delta H^{\ddagger}$, or $\Delta S^{\ddagger}$, or both for a given reaction. Such changes have been studied in relatively few cases. In the case of the coupling of diazotized p-sulfanilic acid and 8-hydroxyquinoline-5-sulfonic acid and its metal chelates, the major effect was found in the $\Delta S^{\ddagger}$ term, though $\Delta H^{\ddagger}$ also underwent changes.[1,2] These differences in $\Delta H^{\ddagger}$ and $\Delta S^{\ddagger}$ must be distinguished from *purely* thermodynamic differences that also affect the course of such reactions. One modification in the entropy term which can be anticipated is a decrease to very large negative values for $\Delta S^{\ddagger}$ for reactions in which masking is important. A $\Delta G^{\ddagger}$ change of any considerable magnitude indicates most probably that coordination is providing a new route for a reaction or is having a profound influence on the electrical charges of the species involved.

The first explanation of coordination catalysis on the basis of the $\Delta E^{\ddagger}$ changes as one passes along the reaction coordinate was given by Meerwein. A more elaborate explanation along these same lines has subsequently been

1. K. D. Maguire and M. M. Jones, *J. Am. Chem. Soc.* **85**, 154 (1963).
2. J. D. Breinig and M. M. Jones, *J. Org. Chem.* **28**, 852 (1963).

developed.[3] One may have effects that have a purely thermodynamic basis, as is shown in Figs. 1 and 2. Here the coordination process results in an additional thermodynamic stabilization of the product which may have originally been less stable (a) or unstable (b). (The figures do not indicate any change in the activation energy between the original reaction and that involving the complexed reactant.)

The kinetic effects which may ensue upon coordination are depicted in Figs. 3, 4, 5, and 6. In these cases one sees a variety of possible results, depending upon how coordination changes the character of the reactants, the reaction path, and the products.

Before proceeding, it is important to examine $\Delta G^{\ddagger}$, $\Delta E^{\ddagger}$, $\Delta H^{\ddagger}$, and $\Delta S^{\ddagger}$,[4] the relationships existing among them, and some of the information that can be gained from a more exact analysis of the factors which may underlie changes in any one of these. The basic relationships are

$$\Delta G^{\ddagger} = \Delta H^{\ddagger} - T\Delta S^{\ddagger}$$

$$\Delta H^{\ddagger} = \Delta E^{\ddagger} + P\Delta V^{\ddagger}$$

The activation energy is usually obtained from the Arrhenius relationship

$$k = A \exp(-E_a/RT)$$

where k is the rate constant; A, the pre-exponential factor; E_a, the "activation energy"; R, the gas constant; and T, the absolute temperature. An additional relationship[4] is

$$E_a \cong \Delta H^{\ddagger} + RT$$

This expression is used to obtain $\Delta H^{\ddagger}$ from the experimentally derived E_a values.

According to the absolute reaction rate theory,

$$k = \frac{\kappa \mathbf{k} T}{h} \exp\left(\frac{-\Delta H^{\ddagger}}{RT}\right) \exp\left(\frac{\Delta S^{\ddagger}}{R}\right)$$

where κ is the "transmission coefficient," the probability that the activated complex at the top of the energy barrier goes to products and $\mathbf{k}$ is Boltzmann's constant. We can approximate $\Delta S^{\ddagger}$ as

$$\Delta S^{\ddagger} = R \ln \frac{Ah}{\mathbf{k}T}$$

where A is the pre-exponential term in the Arrhenius equation and h is Planck's

3. M. M. Jones and W. A. Connor, *Ind. Eng. Chem.* **55** (9), 14 (1963).
4. These are treated in more detail in (a) K. J. Laidler, "Chemical Kinetics," 2nd Ed. McGraw-Hill, New York, 1965. (b) A. A. Frost and R. G. Pearson, "Kinetics and Mechanism," 2nd Ed. Wiley, New York, 1961.

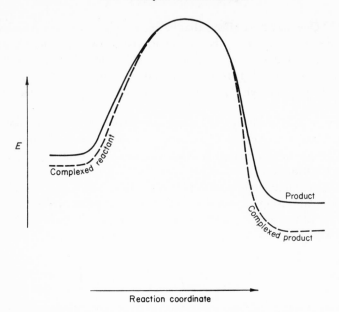

FIG. 1. Energy profile for a reaction in which product is stabilized by coordination to a greater extent than the reactant; no change in activation energy. Reaction proceeds to give product in the absence of coordination center.

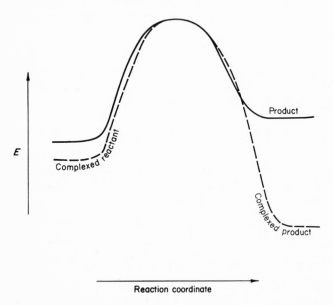

FIG. 2. Energy profile for a reaction that proceeds primarily because of the stabilization of the product by coordination; no change in activation energy.

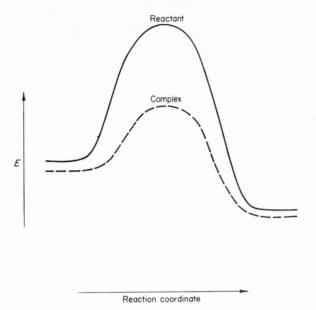

FIG. 3. Energy profile for a reaction in which the principal effect of coordination is to reduce the activation energy.

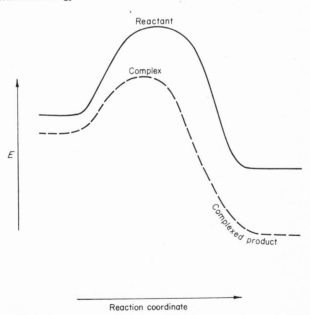

FIG. 4. Energy profile for a reaction for which coordination reduces the activation energy and stabilizes the product.

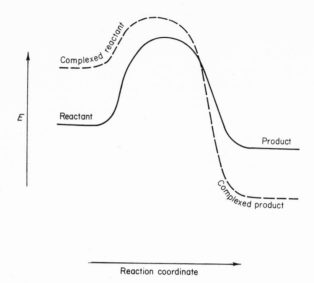

FIG. 5. Energy profile for a reaction for which coordination increases the activation energy but stabilizes the product.

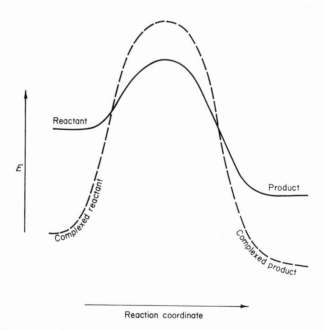

FIG. 6. Energy profile for a reaction in which coordination stabilizes both reactant and product, but also increases the activation energy.

constant. Other expressions for ΔS^{+} may be developed on the basis of detailed models, as we shall see below.

At this point it is of interest to compare ΔG^{+}, ΔH^{+}, and ΔS^{+} values for the reactions of free ligands and their complexes where such information is available. Some of these reactions are summarized in Table VI. For purposes of comparison, a decrease in the activation energy of 1 kcal/mole results in an increase in the reaction rate by a factor of about 4 at 300°K. So for n kcal the change will be of the order of 4^n. In the reactions in Table VI, the variations in the frequency factor dominate the changes which occur but do not determine them exclusively.

An examination of the complications that arise with 8-hydroxyquinoline-5-sulfonic acid shows some of the data which must be obtained to interpret the reactions of phenols. Phenols ionize to give the more reactive phenolate species; thus the temperature-dependent phenol $\rightleftarrows$ phenolate $+ H^{+}$ equilibrium will be incorporated in the apparent activation energy for the free ligand. This behavior is a common aspect of reactions of the type

$$A \rightleftarrows B^{-} + H^{+}$$
$$B^{-} + C \rightarrow P^{-}$$

The relation between A, B, and H will be through the equilibrium constant

$$K = \frac{[B^{-}][H^{+}]}{[A]}, \quad \text{or} \quad [B^{-}] = \frac{K[A]}{[H^{+}]}$$

Furthermore, since

$$\Delta G^{\circ} = -RT \ln K$$

$$K = \exp\left(-\frac{\Delta G^{\circ}}{RT}\right)$$

we can write

$$[B^{-}] = \frac{[A]}{[H^{+}]} \exp\left(-\frac{\Delta G^{\circ}}{RT}\right)$$

The rate law for the reaction between B^{-} and C will generally be of the form

$$\text{Rate} = k[B^{-}][C] = k\frac{K[A]}{[H^{+}]}[C]$$

For phenols, the equilibrium constant K is small and the rate data will generally be based upon measured changes in [A]. Since both k and K are temperature-dependent, a kinetic study of a sort which actually measures the rate in the form

$$\text{Rate} = \frac{k'}{[H^{+}]}[A][C]$$

TABLE VI

ACTIVATION PARAMETERS FOR SOME REACTIONS OF COORDINATED AND FREE LIGANDS

Substrate	Reaction	Reference	E_a (kcal)	A (sec^{-1})	$\Delta H^{\ddagger}$ (kcal)	$\Delta S^{\ddagger}$ (eu)	$\Delta G^{\ddagger}$ (kcal)
8-Hydroxyquinoline-5-sulfonic acid (as phenolate)	Coupling^a with p-diazosulfanilic acid	1	19.3	9.7×10^{17}	18.7	+23.8	11.6
Zn(II) complex of above	Same as above	1	13.4	7.7×10^{8}	12.8	−17.7	18.1
8-Hydroxyquinoline-5-sulfonic acid	Mercuration	5	13.6	5×10^{7}	13.0	−25.0	20.5
Cu(II) complex of above	Mercuration	5	19.0	9.6×10^{12}	18.4	−6.9	20.5
8-Hydroxyquinoline-5-sulfonic acid	Iodination	6, 7	16.7	3.9×10^{13}	16.1	+3.7	15.0
Rh(III) complex of above	Iodination	7	17.7	3.2×10^{8}	17.1	−19.6	23.6
Aniline	Bromination	8	12.2	3.4×10^{13}	11.6	+1.4	12.0
[Co(en)$_2$(NH$_2$C$_6$H$_5$)(H$_2$O)]$^{2+}$	Bromination	8	10.2	4.3×10^{6}	9.4	−30.4	18.5

^{a} These reactions occur only for the *phenolate* form of the ligand.

5. N. K. Chawla and M. M. Jones, *Inorg. Chem.* **3**, 1549 (1964).
6. C. Bostic, Ph.D. Thesis, Univ. of Arizona, Tucson, Arizona, 1963.
7. R. C. McNutt, Ph.D. Thesis, Vanderbilt Univ., Nashville, Tennessee, 1967.
8. N. K. Chawla, D. G. Lambert, and M. M. Jones, *J. Am. Chem. Soc.* **89**, 557 (1967).

will give k' values whose temperature dependence includes that of both k and K. This problem is commonly encountered in the literature and is worth considering in more detail. The nominal relations between the real and the apparent rate constants can be developed as follows: since

$$k' = kK$$

and

$$k' = A' \exp\left(-\frac{E'_a}{RT}\right) = A \exp\left(-\frac{E_a}{RT}\right) \exp\left(-\frac{\Delta G^\circ}{RT}\right)$$

then, on taking logarithms

$$\ln A' - \frac{E'_a}{RT} = \ln A - \frac{E_a}{RT} - \frac{\Delta G^\circ}{RT}$$

Since the temperature dependence of k' is used to determine E' from a plot of $\ln k$ vs. $1/T$, we can see that

$$E'_a = E_a + \Delta G^\circ$$

Consequently, it is necessary to know ΔG° for the preequilibrium step in order to derive E_a from data in which its presence has been explicitly or implicitly ignored.

One would anticipate that coordination of a ligand would result in a change of the steric factor of any of its reactions, simply by virtue of the effect of the metal ion on the surface contour that the molecule presents to its environment. From collision theory, one can express the rate constant for a second-order reaction as

$$k = PZ \exp(-E_a/RT)$$

where

$$Z = n_1 n_2 \left(\frac{\sigma_1 + \sigma_2}{2}\right)^2 \left[\frac{8\pi RT(M_2 + M_1)}{M_1 M_2}\right]^{1/2}$$

is the number of collisions between two different molecules per second. Here the n's are the numbers of molecules per cubic centimeter, the σ's are the molecular diameters, and the M's are their molecular weights. The factor P can be used to explain certain abnormalities of a given reaction and is often referred to as the steric factor. For ambient conditions of temperature and pressure, Z will have a value in the neighborhood of 10^{28} collisions per cubic centimeter per second. Conversion of this value to the customary units of moles, liters, and seconds gives a frequency factor of the order of 10^{11} liter mole^{-1} sec^{-1}.

Although the major factor governing the rates of bimolecular reactions is the activation energy, the variations in the pre-exponential factor can also result in drastic changes in rates. In comparing ligand reactivity in and out of complexes, a number of serious problems arise. The first of these is encountered when we have a situation such as that found with phenols, where the form usually coordinated is the *anion* derived from the phenol. This will, of necessity, be more reactive toward electrophilic reagents than the protonated form, the phenol. This means that the reactivity of the ligand in the complex must be compared to its uncomplexed behavior *in both forms*. In the vast majority of cases, aromatic ligands that possess *good donor groups* are so enormously activated that their rates in many of their characteristic reactions are extremely large. When this problem is avoided by using aliphatic amines, it is found that the reactivity of the aliphatic portion of the ligand is usually too slight to be utilizable in comparative kinetic studies. Use of pyridine or its derivatives (such as orthophenanthroline) presents a situation similar to the problem encountered with phenol because of the ease with which the ligand can be protonated. The net result of these difficulties has been a serious paucity of good, comparable kinetic data for both the free and the complexed ligand in a given system. The ideal situation is one such as is found with aniline, namely, the reactions of the free ligand are well characterized, and complexation occurs without the loss of a proton by the ligand. Unfortunately, the number of aniline complexes suitable for such studies is limited. A single case, the bromination of $[Co(en)_2(NH_2C_6H_5)(H_2O)]^{3+}$ has been examined in detail.[9] Here the bromination reaction (at 25°C) has a second-order rate constant of 1.44×10^{-1} mole^{-1} sec^{-1}, but that of free aniline is about 3×10^{10} mole^{-1} sec^{-1}. Attempts to study the iodination rate of aniline in $[Pd(NH_2C_6H_5)_4]^{2+}$ led merely to ligand substitution.

4.1.1.   A MODEL FOR ENTROPY OF ACTIVATION CHANGES

When a positively charged metal ion becomes attached to an organic ligand, a new substrate is generated that has a different net charge. For ionic or polar reactions this will directly affect the electrostatic interactions involved in the formation of the transition state. It is possible to make qualitative statements concerning the expected results for attack by both positively charged reagents (electrophilic attack) and by negatively charged reagents (nucleophilic attack). The increase of the positive charge on the substrate will make the entropy of activation increase for electrophilic substitution (formation of the activated complex will be *more* difficult) and will make the entropy of activation decrease for nucleophilic substitution (formation of the activated complex will occur more readily). These arguments can be put on a quantitative basis using arguments given in detail by K. J. Laidler.[10]

9. N. K. Chawla, D. G. Lambert, and M. M. Jones, *J. Am. Chem. Soc.* **89**, 557 (1967).
10. K. J. Laidler, "Reaction Kinetics," Vol. II, pp. 6–18. Macmillan (Pergamon), New York, 1963.

The essential points lie in the calculation of the free energy change resulting solely from electrostatic interactions. The free energy of activation will contain a term of the type

$$\Delta G_{es}^{\ddagger} = \frac{NZ_A Z_B}{\epsilon d_{AB}}$$

where $\Delta G_{es}^{\ddagger}$ represents this electrostatic interaction, Z_A and Z_B are the charges on the ions forming the transition state, ϵ is the dielectric constant of the medium, and d_{AB} is the separation distance of the centers of these charges. Then

$$\Delta S_{es}^{\ddagger} = -\left(\frac{\partial \Delta G_{es}^{\ddagger}}{\partial T}\right)_P = \frac{NZ_A Z_B}{\epsilon d_{AB}}\left(\frac{\partial \ln \epsilon}{\partial T}\right)_P$$

If only Z_A and Z_B are considered to change in going from the reaction of the free ligand to that of the complex ligand we can write this simply as

$$\Delta S^{\ddagger} = FZ_A Z_B$$

where F is a numerical factor determined by the nature of the solvent and d_{AB} (for water at ambient temperature F is -10). The change in $\Delta S^{\ddagger}$ on forming a complex with a metal ion of $+Z_M$ charge can be written as

$$\Delta\Delta S^{\ddagger} = F(Z_A + Z_M)Z_B - FZ_A Z_B$$

$$\Delta\Delta S^{\ddagger} = FZ_M Z_B$$

The magnitude and sign of this term will depend on (1) the solvent and (2) the charge on the attacking species Z_B. Since $(\partial \ln \epsilon/\partial T)_P$ is negative for all solvents, so will F be also always negative. Since Z_M is positive, Z_B will determine whether the entropy of activation changes to more negative or more positive values on coordination. If Z_B is also positive

$$\Delta\Delta S^{\ddagger} = -F(Z_M)(Z_B) = -FZ_M Z_B$$

and the $\Delta S^{\ddagger}$ value will change to more negative values and this will make the attainment of the transition state more difficult. If Z_B is negative

$$\Delta\Delta S^{\ddagger} = (-F)(Z_M)(-Z_B) = +FZ_M Z_B$$

and the $\Delta S^{\ddagger}$ value will be shifted to more positive values, and this will make the attainment of the transition state easier.

The actual situation in complexes may be expected to involve changes in d_{AB}, which, however, are very difficult to estimate. If the electrostatic changes in $\Delta G^{\ddagger}$ are the only ones responsible for the difference in the reaction rates of the free and the complexed ligand, the ratio of the rate constants may be estimated as follows:

$$k_f = \frac{\kappa kT}{h} \exp\left(\frac{-\Delta G^{\ddagger}_{nes}}{RT} - \frac{Z_A Z_B e^2}{\epsilon d_{AB} kT}\right)$$

$$k_c = \frac{\kappa kT}{h} \exp\left[\frac{-\Delta G^{\ddagger}_{nes}}{RT} - \frac{(Z_A + Z_M)Z_B e^2}{\epsilon d_{AB} kT}\right]$$

Here $\Delta G^{\ddagger}_{nes}$ represents the contribution to $\Delta G^{\ddagger}$ from terms other than the electrostatic ones. From these expressions the ratio k_c/k_f may be found to be

$$\frac{k_c}{k_f} = \frac{\exp[-(Z_A + Z_M)Z_B e^2/\epsilon d_{AB} kT]}{\exp[-Z_A Z_B e^2/\epsilon d_{AB} kT]}$$

Since

$$\ln k_c = \frac{-(Z_A + Z_M)Z_B e^2}{\epsilon d_{AB} kT} + C$$

$$\ln k_f = -\frac{Z_A Z_B e^2}{\epsilon d_{AB} kT} + C$$

so

$$\ln \frac{k_c}{k_f} = -\frac{Z_M Z_B e^2}{\epsilon d_{AB} kT}$$

Here again the nature of the effect is determined primarily by the charge on Z_B. If Z_B is negative the right-hand side term will be positive and $k_c > k_f$; if Z_B is positive then $k_c < k_f$. The value used for ϵ has an enormous effect on the numerical values obtained.

Other models may be used for this process which may be more realistic for certain reactions. For the single sphere activated complex of Laidler and Eyring,[11] a more complicated expression is obtained

$$\ln \frac{k_c}{k_f} = -\frac{e^2}{2\epsilon kT}\left[\frac{Z_M^2 + 2Z_A Z_M + 2Z_B Z_M}{r_{\ddagger}} - \frac{2Z_A Z_M + Z_M^2}{r_A}\right]$$

When $r_{\ddagger} = r_A$, this expression reduces to the one given above. Here $r_{\ddagger}$ is the radius of the activated complex, which is assumed to be the same for the free ligand and the complex. If this assumption cannot be made, the expression becomes much more complicated. An analogous, but much more complicated expression can be derived from the expressions given by Kirkwood.[12] Unfortunately more realistic models give expressions correspondingly more difficult to test.

One general result which can be obtained from any of these models is that the effect of coordination on the rate of reactions of this sort is such that the

11. K. J. Laidler and H. Eyring, *Ann. N.Y. Acad. Sci.* **39**, 303 (1940).
12. J. G. Kirkwood, *J. Chem. Phys.* **2**, 351 (1934).

difference in rates between the free and the complexed ligand will *increase* significantly as the dielectric constant of the solvent decreases. Thus a reaction whose rate in water is changed to only a small extent by coordination should show an increasing effect as we pass to solvents of lower dielectric constant, such as methanol, ethanol, or dioxane. If solvent molecules are involved in the formation of the activated complex such a trend may be overshadowed by other factors. The effect of increasing the temperature will be to bring the rates relatively closer, using the models given.

4.2. Coordination Equilibrium and Catalysis

There are a number of instances in which the formation of a complex or a chelate stabilizes a product and leads to its formation in much larger amounts than would occur in the absence of the coordination center. These are generally reactions of the sort

$$A + B \rightleftarrows C; \quad K = [C]/[A][B]$$

then

$$M + C \rightleftarrows MC$$

where M is a coordination center (acceptor), often followed by

$$MC \rightleftarrows MC(\text{solid})$$

The perturbation that coordination introduces into these systems can be assigned to the following factors:

(1) The increase in the enthalpy of the system arising from the formation of coordinate bonds in the complex MC.

(2) The change in the entropy of the system from this reaction.

(3) The lattice energy or heat of solution of the solid complex MC, when it is precipitated as a pure solid from the reaction media.

A detailed consideration of each of these individual terms will show how such effects may be estimated in a given case.

4.2.1. ENTHALPY CHANGES

If M (which may be a Lewis acid such as $AlCl_3$) can form a bond to C *without* breaking other bonds, the enthalpy change here will be

$$\Delta H_1 = \Delta H(\text{M—C})$$

where $\Delta H(\text{M—C})$ is the enthalpy of formation of the M—C bond.

If, in order to form a bond to C, M must break other bonds previously formed, then the enthalpy change here will be

$$\Delta H_1 = \Delta H(\text{M—C}) - \sum_i \Delta H(\text{M—X}_i)$$

where M—X_i are the bonds which must be broken. In aqueous solution this term is of considerable magnitude, since the bonds between a metal ion and water must be broken and the hydration energies of most cations are high.

4.2.2. ENTROPY CHANGES

For a reaction in which the original coordination center may contain solvent molecules (q), the reaction may be written as

$$\text{M(q)}_x + \text{C} \rightleftarrows \text{MC} + x\text{q}$$

and the entropy change for this reaction is given by

$$\Delta S' = S^{\circ}_{\text{MC}} + xS_{\text{q}}^{\circ} - S^{\circ}_{\text{M(q)}_x} - S_{\text{C}}^{\circ}$$

When one allows S°_{MC} to represent the product complex whether solid or liquid, one then has an equation that gives the additional entropy change arising from the solid. In most cases the $S^{\circ}_{\text{M(q)}_x}$ term may be estimated from equations such as those of Powell and Latimer[13]

$$S^{\circ}_{298} = \tfrac{3}{2}R \ln (\text{atomic weight}) - \frac{270Z}{(r + x)^2} + 37$$

where Z is the numerical charge on the ion, r is its crystal radius, and x is 2.00 for positive ions and 1.00 for negative ions. Other equations which are available may be used or one may use the tables of Latimer and Jolly.[14]

4.2.3. LATTICE ENERGIES AND HEATS OF SOLUTION

If a lattice energy term is involved in the formation of an ionic solid by the product, this term will generally be of very considerable magnitude whose accurate estimation is not easy. If a neutral complex is formed it will have a heat of solution (ΔH_s) of the order of 10–15 kcal/mole.[15]

By combining the above terms, one can estimate $\Delta G'$, or the free energy change arising from the introduction of the coordination center into the reaction system. This is

$$\Delta G' = \Delta H_1 - \Delta H_s - T\Delta S'$$

13. R. Powell and W. M. Latimer, *J. Chem. Phys.* **19**, 1139 (1950).
14. W. M. Latimer and W. L. Jolly, *J. Am. Chem. Soc.* **75**, 1548 (1953).
15. M. M. Jones, J. L. Wood, and W. R. May, *J. Inorg. Nucl. Chem.* **23**, 305 (1961); M. M. Jones, A. T. Davila, J. E. Hix, Jr., and R. V. Dilts, *J. Inorg. Nucl. Chem.* **25**, 369 (1963).

or

$$\Delta G' = \Delta H(\text{M—C}) - \sum_i \Delta H(\text{M—X}_i) - \Delta H_s - T\{S^\circ_{\text{MC}} + xS_q^\circ - S^\circ_{\text{M(q)}_x} - S_C^\circ\}$$

In a general way it can be seen that coordination will be especially useful in reactions in which product formation is favored by

(a) High M—C bond energies. This will increase as the number of chelating rings increase.

(b) Low M—X_i bond energies.

(c) Large enthalpies of solution for the product complex. Thus the use of a large counterion of the same charge as the product complex ion should lead to a larger ΔH_s and greater product formation.

(d) Large values of S°_{MC}, again a factor that increases as the number of chelate rings increase.

(e) Large values of xS_q° or small values of $S'_{\text{M(q)}_x}$ or S_C°. These terms can be manipulated by change of solvent, or cation used as coordination center. The desired product C usually must be assumed to be subject to only very slight variations in its other properties, such as bond energies of bonds not changed in the process.

The amount of experimental data available on systems of this kind is quite limited, though one very thorough study is available. This is on the Gatterman-Koch aldehyde synthesis,[16, 17] which can be written as

$$C_6H_6 + CO \xrightarrow{\text{HCl, AlCl}_3} C_6H_5CHO:AlCl_3$$

The nominal reaction is

$$C_6H_6 + CO \rightarrow C_6H_5CHO$$

A calculation of the free energy change for this reaction showed that it probably *did not proceed in the absence of complex formation*. At 298°K, ΔG° for the reaction without complex formation was estimated to be +2.06 kcal with a corresponding yield of benzaldehyde of 2% and an equilibrium constant of 31.6×10^{-3} for the reaction. The free energies of formation of benzaldehyde complexes with stannic chloride, aluminum chloride, ferric chloride, and antimony trichloride were all found to be negative (−7.6, −2.4, −2.0, and −1.3 kcal/mole, respectively) with a corresponding change in ΔG° for the reaction to more negative values. For stannic chloride, which forms the complex $SnCl_4(C_6H_5CHO)_2$, the equilibrium constant at 298°K was estimated at 3.6×10^5 and the corresponding yield of benzaldehyde 100%. In these cases, the entropy change on complexation does not favor the reaction as the values are all negative. The principal factor assisting the formation of the

16. H. Campbell and D. D. Eley, *Nature* **154**, 85 (1944).
17. M. H. Dilke and D. D. Eley, *J. Chem. Soc.* p. 2601, 2613 (1949).

benzaldehyde complex is the very considerably negative enthalpy changes that occur when the complexes are formed.

The use of coordination to stabilize very reactive unsaturated hydrocarbons is also possible, as may be seen in another reaction, presumably of this same sort, the stabilization of tetramethylcyclobutadiene in its complex with nickel(II) chloride.[18]

$$\begin{array}{c}H_3C\\H_3C\end{array}\underset{\underset{CH_3}{\mid}}{\overset{\overset{CH_3}{\mid}}{\square}}\begin{array}{c}Cl\\Cl\end{array} + Ni(CO)_4 \xrightarrow[\substack{ether}]{\substack{Benzene\\acetone}} \begin{array}{c}H_3C\\H_3C\end{array}\square\begin{array}{c}CH_3\\CH_3\end{array}\cdots\mid\cdots\cdots NiCl_2 + 4CO$$

4.3. The Activation of Small Molecules

One very important aspect of ligand reactivity is the surprising generality of the coordination process as a means of *activating* small molecules for *further reaction*.[19] This catalysis or activation can be effected by a wide variety of Lewis acids, not all of which are equally effective. On surveying these reactions one is struck by the common patterns involving the activation of small molecules via coordination in the generation of electrophilic reagents, free radicals, and even nucleophilic reagents.

4.3.1. GENERAL PRINCIPLES

When any molecule is brought close to a positive ion the molecule suffers a certain amount of electronic polarization. In many cases this is merely a distortion of the electronic distribution toward the positive ion. When the molecule and the positive ion form a coordinate bond, the resultant distortion of the electronic cloud assumes a more permanent status which may result in very considerable changes in the rates of many reactions which such a molecule undergoes. Two aspects of this phenomenon are (a) the ways in which the electronic distribution of a ligand is affected by coordination and (b) how a large number of the resulting reactivity changes can be brought into a systematic arrangement.

As noted earlier, the consequences of the electronic polarization that ensues upon coordination were first studied systematically by Meerwein,[20-24] who

18. R. Criegee, *Angew. Chem. Intern. Ed. English* **1**, 522 (1962).
19. M. M. Jones, *J. Chem. Educ.* **41**, 493 (1964).
20. H. Meerwein, *Schriften Konigsberg. Gelehrten Ges. Naturw. Kl.* **3**, 129 (1927).
21. H. Meerwein, *Ann. Chem. Liebigs* **455**, 227 (1927).
22. H. Meerwein, *Marburger Sitzber.* **65**, 119 (1930).
23. H. Meerwein and H. Maier-Huser, *J. Prakt. Chem.* **134**, 51 (1932).
24. H. Meerwein and G. Hinz, *Ann. Chem. Liebigs* **484**, 1 (1931).

centered his attention on organic ligands. He showed how the coordination of the hydroxy group of an organic acid to a Lewis acid resulted in a large increase in the dissociation constant of the acid. This was explained as a consequence of the depletion of electrons from the hydrogen–oxygen bond which facilitated the release of a proton from the oxygen.

Weak acid   Strong acid

In considering the net effect of coordination on the ligand electron density, it is necessary to examine the three types of coordinate bonds and their effects on their electron density. For a simple coordinate bond of the usual sort, a σ-bond, there will be a depletion of electrons from the ligand. Both electrons of the bond are furnished by the ligand and undergo a displacement toward the metal. For a complex that also contains π-bonds between the metal and the ligand, the situation will be more complicated. Some π-bonds are formed using electrons from filled d orbitals of the metal, which are shared with empty ligand orbitals. This will reduce the net charge transferred from the ligand to the metal. If, however, a π-bond is formed in which electrons are donated *from* suitable ligand orbitals to empty metal orbitals, this will accentuate the depletion of charge from the ligand. The occurrence of π-bonding with ligand donation may well be involved to a slight extent in the activation of molecular halogens by species such as $AlCl_3$. Most of the complexes utilized in organic chemistry for halogenation, Friedel-Crafts reactions, and the like involve predominantly σ-type coordinate bonds.

It is thus expected that the coordination of a small molecule will distort its electron density pattern to produce significant, and hopefully, useful changes in its reactivity. The molecules which will be considered here are frequently found to be nonpolar or weakly polar species *prior* to coordination. Coordination of these smaller molecules increases their polarity and allows more reactive ionic, ion pair,[25] or highly polarized species to be generated. Some typical examples are listed in Table VII.

It is generally found that coordination results in an increase in the polarity of the ligand–acceptor system, though in some cases stereochemical arrangements may result in a small or zero net dipole for the complex as a whole.* The coordinate bond itself always possesses a considerable dipole moment, which often can be very large.

* Section 5.2.6 contains a more detailed discussion of this point.

25. J. L. Cotter and A. G. Evans, *J. Chem. Soc.* p. 2988 (1959).

TABLE VII

ACTIVATION OF SMALL MOLECULES VIA POLARIZATION

Original molecule	Reactive species generated

Electrophile produced

Cl_2 Cl^+ or $\overset{\delta+}{Cl}\!-\!\overset{\delta-}{Cl}$

Br_2 Br^+ or $\overset{\delta+}{Br}\!-\!\overset{\delta-}{Br}$

$ClCN$ CN^+ or $\overset{\delta+}{NC}\!-\!\overset{\delta-}{Cl}$

H_2O $\overset{\delta+}{H}\!-\!\overset{\delta-}{OH}$

$RCOCl$ RCO^+, $\overset{\delta+}{RC}\!=\!\overset{\delta-}{O}$ or $\overset{\delta+}{R}\!-\!\underset{\underset{O}{\|}}{C}\!-\!\overset{\delta-}{Cl}$, with Cl below first structure

R_3CCl $R_3C^+ + Cl^-$ or a less polar form

$H_2C\!=\!CH_2$ $\overset{\delta+}{H_2C}\!=\!\underset{\delta-}{CH_2}$

$C\!\equiv\!O$ $\overset{\delta+}{C}\!\equiv\!\overset{\delta-}{O}$

NO_2Cl NO_2^+

$HNO_3(HONO_2)$ NO_2^+

$NOCl$ NO^+

NH_2OH NH_2^+

NH_2OSO_3H NH_2^+

Free radical generated

N_2 N_2^- (?)

O_2 O_2^-

H_2O_2 $HO\cdot$

N_2H_4 $NH_2\cdot$

Nucleophile generated

H_2 H^-

$C\!\equiv\!O$ $\overset{\delta-}{C}\!\equiv\!\overset{\delta+}{O}$

The actual formation of stable, isolable coordination compounds is *not* a necessary condition which must be met before coordination can be assigned a catalytic role in a reaction. For example, the mercuric(II) and silver(I) ions and analogous species which have a considerable tendency to coordinate halogen can accelerate the removal of halogen from both inorganic[26,27] and organic[28] systems.

$$[Co(NH_3)_5Br]^{2+} + Hg^{2+} + H_2O \rightarrow [Co(NH_3)_5(H_2O)]^{3+} + HgBr^+$$
$$RCl + Hg^{2+} \rightarrow R^+ + HgCl$$

26. F. A. Posey and H. Taube, *J. Am. Chem. Soc.* **79**, 255 (1957).
27. M. D. Alexander and D. H. Busch, *J. Am. Chem. Soc.* **88**, 1130 (1966).
28. S. Oae and C. A. VanderWerf, *J. Am. Chem. Soc.* **75**, 5037 (1953).

These reactions are assumed to proceed through an unstable intermediate in which the halogen is bonded to two other atoms. Some of these have been studied in detail and a very thorough kinetic study has been carried out on the reaction of mercuric nitrate with some primary and secondary alkyl bromides.[29] The silver ion also has been shown to be capable of participating in similar reactions.[30-32]

One factor that always must be taken into consideration is the steric interaction with the acceptor species. Thus a small highly charged monatomic ion will usually not present the same opportunity for steric hindrance to a reaction as antimony trichloride. The amount of information available on the way these steric effects may arise is extensive, but except for boron acceptors, this is somewhat unorganized. Ideally one would hope to estimate the role of the acceptor species in changing the frequency factor and activation energy of the reaction. This can be done qualitatively *only* when the course of the reaction has been thoroughly characterized kinetically.

The mode of activation via coordination may vary considerably. In many cases it occurs by means of an increase in the polar character of an electrophilic reagent to give a more effective attacking species. In other cases, the bond weakening resulting from coordination is the critical step. Coordination subsequently allows the bond to be broken more readily by a third reagent, as in the splitting of coordinated ethers. In any event, the electronic configuration of the metal ion appears to be of somewhat lesser significance than its charge and radius in such reactions. The formation of π-bonds with the ligand, which generally involves back-donation of electrons by the metal, is a secondary factor that appears to be either indispensable, as in the metal carbonyls and their reactions, or impossible to sort out from other factors, as in the majority of complexes.

A principle stated explicitly by Nyholm[33] and of use in many of these cases is that an increase in the number of donors around a central metal ion leads to a lower charge shared by each with the metal. This approximate rule can be used to estimate the variation in the reactive sites of a complex as the coordination number is changed as well as the relative reactivity of complexes with various metal-to-ligand ratios. An example can be seen in the explanation of the catalytic activity of zinc dialkyldithiocarbamates and their amine adducts on the disproportionation of diethyl trisulfide.[34] In this case the sulfur atoms

29. O. T. Benfey, *J. Am. Chem. Soc.* **70**, 2163 (1948).
30. C. Prevost, *Compt. Rend.* **236**, 288 (1956).
31. N. Kornblum, R. A. Smiley, H. E. Ungnade, A. M. White, B. Taub, and S. A. Herbert, *J. Am. Chem. Soc.* **77**, 5528 (1955).
32. W. D. Emmons and A. F. Ferris, *J. Am. Chem. Soc.* **75**, 2257 (1953).
33. R. S. Nyholm, *Proc. Chem. Soc.* p. 279 (1961).
34. G. M. C. Higgins and B. Savile, *J. Chem. Soc.* p. 2812 (1963).

of the coordinated ligand act as a nucleophilic catalytic center. The complexes are of the type $Zn(SCSNR_2)_2$ and they undergo addition reactions with suitable nitrogen bases.

$$Zn(SCSNR_2)_2 + :N{\Large\gtrless} \longrightarrow {\Large\gtrless}N:Zn(SCSNR_2)_2$$

The reaction examined was the disproportionation

$$2EtS-S-S-Et \rightleftarrows Et_2S_4 + Et_2S_2$$

The zinc complex catalyzes this reaction, presumably because the $3d$ electrons on its sulfur atoms allow them to act as nucleophiles in the following reaction sequence (where Y: is the nucleophilic sulfur):

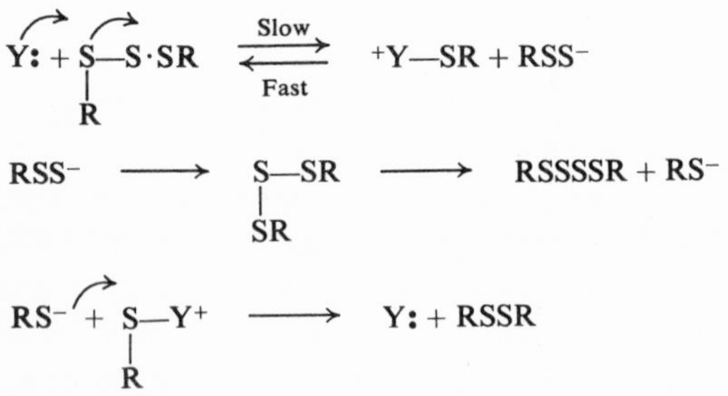

$$Y: + \underset{\underset{R}{|}}{S}-S\cdot SR \underset{\text{Fast}}{\overset{\text{Slow}}{\rightleftarrows}} {}^+Y-SR + RSS^-$$

$$RSS^- \longrightarrow \underset{\underset{SR}{|}}{S}-SR \longrightarrow RSSSSR + RS^-$$

$$RS^- + \underset{\underset{R}{|}}{S}-Y^+ \longrightarrow Y: + RSSR$$

Thus the zinc dialkyldithiocarbamates and piperidine, when used separately, are rather weak catalysts for the reaction, but taken together they are much more effective. When the coordination number of the zinc(II) is increased to five or six by the addition of an amine such as piperidine, the nitrogen atoms of the base aid in the neutralization of the charge of the zinc(II). Consequently the metal ion releases electronic charge to the sulfur atoms of the ligand, which then become more strongly nucleophilic.

When the reactant molecule (i.e., the molecule on which it is desired to carry out the substitution reaction) is also capable of forming complexes, then the Lewis acid must be added in a much larger than catalytic quantity so that some catalytically active amount remains free after the complexation equilibrium is attained. Numerous examples based on this rationale have been observed where large molar ratios of Lewis acid to substrate are utilized. These include the Fries reaction,[35] the Friedel-Crafts reactions of aromatic acid anhydrides,[36] ketones, aldehydes, and the like, as well as the "swamping

35. A. H. Blatt, *Org. Reactions* 1, 342 (1942).
36. E. Berliner, *Org. Reactions* 5, 229 (1949).

catalyst effect" in aromatic halogenation.[37-39] The kinetic pattern of these reactions was first studied by Olivier in 1914. He examined the reaction of aromatic sulfonyl chlorides with benzene in the presence of varying amounts of aluminium chloride.[40]

It was found that the rate of the reaction increased slowly with increasing mole ratio of aluminum chloride to sulfonyl chloride as long as all the sulfonyl chloride was not complexed. After a sufficient amount of aluminum chloride was added to complex all of the substrate, the rate of the reaction increased very rapidly with further additions of aluminum chloride. This same behavior is found in many other reactions and results from the fact that the catalysis proceeds via the generation of an electrophilic species, which requires that the Lewis acid react with the poorer of two donors in the systems. The activation will then occur in an appreciable amount only after the coordination sites of the better donor are effectively saturated. In such cases, the dissociation of the complex formed with the better donor may occur to such an extent that it furnishes some catalyst for the generation of the attacking species. In such a situation the relation between the mole ratio of reactants and the rate constant need not show a discontinuity at an integral value, although it frequently will.

4.3.2. THE GENERATION OF ELECTROPHILES

The generation of electrophilic species is facilitated by the coordination act when it polarizes a ligand in such a manner that it puts a partial net positive charge on a suitable atom. The general reaction types are of the sort

$$M + :A:B \rightarrow M:A:^- + B^+$$

and

$$M + :A:B \rightarrow M:\overset{\delta-}{A}:\overset{\delta+}{B}$$

Here M is any Lewis acid and A and B may be the same or different. Of direct interest under this heading are the closely related mechanisms in which compounds such as ferric chloride, aluminum chloride, and boron trifluoride catalyze the chlorination and bromination of aromatic compounds. The

37. D. E. Pearson and H. W. Pope, *J. Org. Chem.* **21**, 381 (1956).
38. D. E. Pearson, W. W. Hargrove, J. K. T. Chow, and B. R. Suthers, *J. Org. Chem.* **26**, 789 (1961).
39. B. R. Suthers, P. H. Riggins, and D. E. Pearson, *J. Org. Chem.* **27**, 447 (1962).
40. S. C. J. Olivier, *Rec. Trav. Chim.* **33**, 91, 244 (1914).

reaction of chlorine and ferric chloride is postulated to lead to more reactive species either by cleavage of the chlorine–chlorine bond,

$$:Cl:Cl: + FeCl_3 \rightleftarrows :Cl:^+ + FeCl_4^-$$

or by rendering the bond more polar,

$$:Cl:Cl: + FeCl_3 \rightleftarrows :\overset{\delta+}{Cl}-\overset{\delta-}{Cl}:FeCl_3$$

Either process leads to a predicted increase in the amount of positive halogen in the system and it is this positive halogen that is considered to be the effective halogenating agent in such systems. This explanation of the catalytic activity of metal halides in such systems was first proposed by Pfeiffer and Wizinger[41-43] and has since been extended to a large number of analogous reactions. All of the halides that are effective catalysts for halogenation are known to form halo anions of the sort required by such a mechanism. Ferric chloride also catalyzes the aromatic iodination by ICl.[44]

The activation of a molecule like a halogen or a pseudohalogen should show a certain specificity for the metal halide which parallels the acceptor tendencies of the metal halide. Thus, thiocyanogen, $(SCN)_2$, *should* be activated by species that have a marked tendency to coordinate to SCN^-. Here one would expect the Hg^{2+} would be a much more effective catalyst than $AlCl_3$. However, only $AlCl_3$ and $Al(SCN)_3 \cdot 2(C_2H_5)_2O$ have been studied as catalysts.[45]

The activation of molecular iodine can be effected by treatment of a solution of iodine with a silver salt. The process that occurs here is

$$:I:I: + Ag^+ \rightarrow :I^+ + Ag:I: \downarrow$$

The positive iodine can be isolated in the form of complexes with pyridine or dipyridyl if these reagents are present in the reaction mixture.[46] The same process may also be used with other halogens or pseudohalogens, though such an activation process is usually not so necessary in effecting electrophilic substitutions with them.[47] This type of reaction also furnishes a procedure for generating reactive carbonium ions from alkyl halides or various halogen

41. P. Pfeiffer and R. Wizinger, *Ann. Chem. Liebigs* **461**, 138–139 (1928).
42. P. Pfeiffer, *Angew. Chem.* **42**, 907 (1929).
43. C. C. Price, *Chem. Rev.* **29**, 37 (1941).
44. R. M. Keefer and L. J. Andrews, *J. Am. Chem. Soc.* **78**, 5623 (1956).
45. E. Soderback, *Acta Chem. Scand.* **8**, 1851 (1954).
46. J. Kleinberg, "Unfamiliar Oxidation States and Their Stabilization," p. 37. Univ. of Kansas Press, Lawrence, Kansas, 1950.
47. Bromine has been activated for the preparation of bromo-substituted benzoic acids by the use of Ag_2SO_4 in H_2SO_4: P. B. D. DeLaMare and J. H. Ridd, "Aromatic Substitution," p. 110. Butterworth, London and Washington, D.C., 1959.

compounds.[30,48] The general reaction for such cases is

$$RX + Ag^+ \rightarrow R^+ + AgX$$

and both R and X can be varied widely. The prime requirement is that AgX be insoluble. A variation of this may be found in reactions of the type

$$RX + AgZ \rightarrow RZ + AgX$$

e.g.,

$$RSO_2Cl + AgSR' \rightarrow RSO_2SR' + AgCl$$

The use of both silver(I) and mercury(II) ions to assist the removal of a halide ion from an alkyl halide has been studied extensively.[28-32,49-51] The rate law found for such a reaction is determined by whether or not coordination plays a role in the activated complex.[52] Although these reactions may be carried out with cations other than silver(I), only mercury(II) is widely used in similar reactions. This is a result of the greater insolubility of the silver compounds that are formed, compared to those of other cations [e.g., lead(II)], and their correspondingly greater effectiveness.

Spectrophotometric studies on the behavior of such species as trityl chloride, $(C_6H_5)_3CCl$, in the presence of various Lewis acids[53] show that these reagents assist ionization by reactions of the type

$$ZnCl_2 + (C_6H_5)_3CCl \rightleftharpoons (C_6H_5)_3C^+ + ZnCl_3^-$$

The kinetic study of the Friedel-Crafts synthesis of benzophenone from the benzoyl chloride–aluminum chloride complex[54] and benzene showed that the reaction of $[C_6H_5COCl \cdot AlCl_3]$ was quite slow in the absence of any additional aluminum chloride (above that required to form the complex), but became considerably more rapid when further aluminum chloride was added.[55] This indicates that the reactions of acyl halides are probably more complex than those of trityl chloride.

The exact nature of the complexes formed by aluminum chloride with acyl halides are a point of some controversy. Cook[56] has presented evidence which

48. L. P. Hammett, "Physical Organic Chemistry," p. 138, 153. McGraw-Hill, New York, 1940.
49. K. A. Burke and F. G. Donnan, *J. Chem. Soc.* **85**, 555 (1904).
50. N. Kornblum, R. A. Smiley, R. K. Blackwood, and D. C. Iffland, *J. Am. Chem. Soc.* **77**, 6269 (1955), and other papers in this series.
51. N. Kornblum, L. Fishbein, and R. A. Smiley, *J. Am. Chem. Soc.* **77**, 6261 (1955).
52. M. B. Nieman, G. V. Maksimova, and Y. M. Shapovalov, *Dokl. Akad. Nauk SSSR* **85**, 1289 (1952); *Chem. Abstr.* **47**, 388.
53. M. Baaz, V. Gutman, and J. R. Masagner, *Monatsh. Chem.* **92**, 582, 590 (1961); V. Gutman, M. Baaz, and O. Kunz, *Monatsh. Chem.* **93**, 1162 (1962).
54. W. A. Ridell and C. R. Noller, *J. Am. Chem. Soc.* **52**, 4365 (1930).
55. H. Ulich and P. Fragstein, *Ber. Deut. Chem. Ges.* **72**, 620 (1939).
56. D. Cook, *Can. J. Chem.* **37**, 48 (1959).

shows that

$$CH_3—\underset{\underset{Cl}{|}}{C}{=}O : AlCl_3 \quad \text{and} \quad [CH_3CO^+][AlCl_4^-]$$

may both be present in a solvent of high dielectric constant such as nitro-benzene ($\epsilon = 36.1$) but only the first form is present in a solvent of low dielectric constant such as chloroform ($\epsilon = 5.05$). In solid $C_6H_5COCl \cdot AlCl_3$, the aluminum is coordinated to the oxygen with the rather short Al—O distance of 1.84 Å.[57]

Although there are a large number of well-characterized complexes in which the nitrosyl group is a ligand, the information on their reactions is quite scattered. The reactions of pentacyanonitrosylferrate(II), $Fe(CN)_5(NO)^{2-}$, with compounds containing an active methylene group have been studied in some detail.[58-60] Such reactions transform the active methylene group into an oxime.

$$Fe^{II}—NO + \overset{\backslash}{\underset{/}{C}}H_2 + OH^- \;\rightarrow\; Fe^{II}—(N\overset{|}{\underset{\underset{O}{\|}}{—}C}—H) + H_2O$$

$$Fe^{II}—(N\overset{|}{\underset{\underset{O}{\|}}{—}C}—H) + H_2O \;\rightarrow\; Fe^{II}(H_2O) + H—\overset{\backslash}{C}{=}NOH$$

This reaction does not seem to be reported for NO or NO^+. The coordinated NO here also gives characteristic reactions with sulfides.

Because of the lability of the hydrogen atoms of water even prior to coordina-tion, effects of coordination on the reactivity of water are usually quantitative differences in equilibrium constants rather than qualitative ones. One well-established phenomenon is the increase of the acidic nature of water when it is coordinated. This result was noted and studied in detail by the early 1930's.[61] Subsequent studies have been concerned primarily with quantitative deter-mination of the equilibrium constants,[62] rather than resultant changes in the reactivity patterns of water.

A striking example of the reaction of a coordinated ligand is to be seen in the chlorination of coordinated ammonia as reported by Kukushkin in studies

57. S. E. Rasmussen and N. C. Broch, *Chem. Commun.* p. 289 (1965).
58. H. E. Williams, "Cyanogen Compounds," 2nd Ed., pp. 244 ff. Arnold, London, 1948.
59. N. V. Sidgwick, "The Chemical Elements and Their Compourds," pp. 1345–1346. Oxford Univ. Press (Clarendon), London and New York, 1950.
60. J. H. Swinehart and W. G. Schmidt, *Inorg. Chem.* **6**, 232 (1967).
61. F. Reiff, *Z. Anorg. Allgem. Chem.* **208**, 321 (1932).
62. L. G. Sillén, *Quart. Rev. (London)* **13**, 146 (1959).

of a variety of ammines.[63] The general types of reaction were found to be

$$X_5—Pt—NH_3 + Cl_2 \rightarrow X_5—Pt—NH_2Cl + HCl$$

$$X_5—Pt—NH_2Cl + Cl_2 \rightarrow X_5—Pt—NCl_2^- + H^+ + HCl$$

In some cases the complexes in which further substitution had occurred were found to be very easily prepared. This further reaction with chlorine to give di- and trichloramine is one that ammonia itself undergoes if the pH is sufficiently low.[64,65] Coordination also appears to stabilize the various chloramines, especially toward thermal decomposition. From the conditions of polarization to which the coordinated ammonia is subject, one would expect that the nominal replacement of H^+ by Cl^+ would proceed *more* readily in the complex. From such data as is on hand this seems to be the case. It is also of interest to note that the transformation of $[Pt(NH_3)_5Cl]Cl_3$ into $[Pt(NH_3)_3(NCl_2)_2Cl]$ increases the acid strength of the hydrogens which are still bonded to the nitrogen.

The aluminum-chloride-catalyzed aminations of aromatic systems by hydroxylamine, NH_2OH,[66,67] or hydroxylamine-O-sulfonic acid[68,69] are more clear-cut examples of activation via coordination. Typical reactions include

$$NH_2OH + ArH \xrightarrow{AlCl_3} ArNH_2 + H_2O$$

$$NH_2OSO_3H + ArH \xrightarrow{AlCl_3} ArNH_2 + H_2SO_4$$

When a molecule or anion is incorporated as a ligand into a complex with a positive ion, the ligand will suffer a depletion of electronic charge and will be more electrophilic in nature than it was prior to coordination. Although such a species may be difficult to think of as an electrophilic *reagent*, rather than a substrate, it is important to note that such a species is always more susceptible to attack by nucleophiles after coordination. Examples involving larger organic molecules have been collected by Bender.[70] Bender lists these reactions,

63. Y. N. Kukushkin, *Zh. Neorgan. Khim.* 7, 769 (1962), and other papers in this journal by the same author. These reactions have previously been examined in some detail towards the end of Section 3.9.
64. E. Colton and M. M. Jones, *J. Chem. Educ.* 32, 485 (1955).
65. R. S. Drago, *J. Chem. Educ.* 34, 541 (1957).
66. C. Graebe, *Ber. Deut. Chem. Ges.* 34, 1778 (1901).
67. G. F. Jaubert, *Compt. Rend.* 132, 841 (1901).
68. P. Kovacic and R. P. Bennett, *J. Am. Chem. Soc.* 83, 221 (1961).
69. P. Kovacic and J. L. Foote, *J. Am. Chem. Soc.* 83, 743 (1961).
70. M. Bender, *Advan. Chem. Ser.* 37, 19 (1963).

many of which are considered in detail elsewhere in this book in an impressive array:

"... the hydrolysis of carboxylic acid esters, carboxylic acid amides, phosphate esters, phosphonate esters, halophosphates, pyrophosphates and Schiff bases, carboxylation and decarboxylation reactions, the hydrogenation and hydration of unsaturated systems, olefin-forming elimination reactions, transaminations, aldol condensations, and nucleophilic displacement reactions."

The activation of unsaturated molecules via coordination has also been both widely used and thoroughly studied.[71] Perhaps the best known example is the Smidt reaction (commonly designated "the Wacker Process" by industrial chemists) for the preparation of acetaldehyde from ethylene. The steps in this process are

$$C_2H_4 + PdCl_2 + H_2O \rightarrow C_2H_4O + Pd + 2HCl$$
$$Pd + 2CuCl_2 \rightarrow PdCl_2 + 2CuCl$$
$$2CuCl + \tfrac{1}{2}O_2 + 2HCl \rightarrow 2CuCl_2 + H_2O$$

The overall reaction is thus

$$C_2H_4 + \tfrac{1}{2}O_2 \rightarrow C_2H_4O$$

Coordination of olefins to palladium facilitates attack by nucleophiles; the initial step in the reaction of olefin–palladium chloride complexes with water is the attack of water on the complex.[72] The overall mechanism can be described by the equation

$$PdCl_4^{2-} + C_2H_4 \rightleftarrows [PdCl_3C_2H_4]^- + Cl^-$$
$$[PdCl_3C_2H_4]^- + H_2O \rightleftarrows [PdCl_2(H_2O)C_2H_4]^- + Cl^-$$
$$[PdCl_2(H_2O)(C_2H_4)]^- + H_2O \rightleftarrows [PdCl_2(OH)(C_2H_4)]^- + H_3O^+$$
$$[PdCl_2(OH)C_2H_4)] \rightarrow Pd^0 + HCl + CH_3CHO, \text{ followed by regeneration}$$
$$\text{of } PdCl_4^{2-}$$

The activation of other kinds of unsaturated molecules is also possible, as can be seen from the example [73]

71. J. Smidt, W. Hafner, R. Jira, R. Sieber, J. Sedlmeier, and A. Sabel, *Angew. Chem. Intern. Ed. English* **1**, 80 (1962); E. W. Stern and M. L. Spector, *Proc. Chem. Soc.* p. 370 (1961); E. W. Stern, *Proc. Chem. Soc.* p. 111 (1963); J. Tsuji, H. Takahashi, and M. Morikawa, *Tetrahedron Letters* **49**, 4387 (1965); R. Jira, J. Sedlmeier, and J. Smidt, *Ann. Chem.* **693**, 99 (1966); A. Aguilo, *Advan. Organometal. Chem.* **5**, 321 (1967).
72. P. M. Henry, *J. Am. Chem. Soc.* **88**, 1597 (1966).
73. G. Schrauzer, *Angew. Chem.* **75**, 250 (1963); G. Schrauzer, *J. Am. Chem. Soc.* **81**, 5310 (1959), gives further reactions.

The number of such reactions is very large indeed and is the basis of much industrial chemistry developed in large measure from the studies of Reppe and his collaborators.[74] A recently reported reaction of a slightly different sort is the silver-ion-catalyzed isomerization of *cis*-4-maleylacetoacetate and maleylacetone to their trans isomers.[75]

The species that have the greatest tendency to form coordinate bonds to olefins are Cu^+, Ag^+, Pd^{2+}, Pt^{2+}, and their immediate neighbors in the periodic table (especially Os, Ir, Ru, and Rh in their low oxidation states). These are the species most commonly involved in the catalysis of the reactions of olefins. Platinum(IV) is not commonly useful though it is capable of effecting some reactions, e.g.,[76]

$$RCH{=}CHR' + PtF_6^{2-} + H_2O \rightarrow RCOCH_2R' + Pt^{2+} + 4F^- + 2HF$$

One point upon which a certain amount of controversy exists is the detailed description of the nature of the complex which is formed between a Lewis acid (an electron-pair-deficient species) and an unsaturated hydrocarbon, such as ethylene or benzene, and subsequently is responsible for the increased reactivity.[77] These complexes may be either σ- or π-complexes. A σ-complex is one in which a σ-bond is formed between the electron-deficient species and the aromatic ring or olefin. In the case of strong protonic acids this leads to carbonium ions derived from the aromatic systems. In such σ-complexes one finds that the proton is bound to one specific carbon atom of the aromatic system.

Intermediate formed
by attack of X^+ on C_6H_6,
a σ-complex

σ-Complex
produced by
reaction of C_6H_5Z,
HF, and SbF_5

(A σ-complex of an olefin is customarily called a carbonium ion.) In π-complexes the bonding between the two constituents is presumably less localized and involves the entire aromatic ring or the unsaturated system as a whole. These species are similar in many respects to the olefin complexes of the platinum metals in which the platinum is bonded in such a fashion that the

74. W. Reppe *et al.*, *Ann. Chem.* **560**, 1, 93, 104 (1948); **582**, 1, 38, 72, 87, 116, 133 (1953).
75. C. T. Kisker and D. I. Crandall, *Tetrahedron* **19**, 701 (1963).
76. R. D. W. Kemmitt and D. W. A. Sharp, *J. Chem. Soc.* p. 2567 (1963).
77. E. Berliner, *Progr. Phys. Org. Chem.* **2**, 253 (1964).

center of the ethylenic linkage is in a square plane with the other three groups bonded to the metal.

Representation of π-complex formed as an intermediate in the reaction of an olefin and an electron-pair-deficient species E

Representation of π-complex formed as an intermediate in the attack of C_6H_6 by X^+

Included in the class of the π-complexes are also the molecular compounds such as quinhydrone, picrates, and as a limiting case compounds such as bis(benzene)chromium(0).

The activation of a large number of organic systems of the type RCOCl or ROR is possible if such species are coordinated to suitable Lewis acids. Such processes are an integral part of the Friedel-Crafts acylation reaction. In recent years the reactive intermediates in a large number of aromatic hydrocarbon–Lewis acid systems have been isolated and characterized by Olah and his collaborators. The activation presumably proceeds by way of a carbonium ion.

$$RCOCl + AlCl_3 \rightarrow RCO^+ + AlCl_4^-$$

In the case of the toluene–boron trifluoride–hydrogen fluoride system, a reactive carbonium salt has been isolated that is formed in the reaction[78]

$$\text{(structure)} + HF + BF_3 \longrightarrow \text{(structure)} \; BF_4^-$$

The cation formed is not an intermediate in an acylation reaction but is given as an example of one of the types of carbonium ion which may be formed from aromatic species in strongly acidic media. The use of Friedel-Crafts-type catalysts has been widely exploited in the activation of unusual species. Thus cyanogen chloride, ClCN, interacts with aluminum chloride to produce a species $CNCl, AlCl_3$ that ionizes to give CN^+ and $AlCl_4^-$ (possibly as an ion pair) and which reacts with benzene to produce benzonitrile.[79]

$$\text{(benzene)} + ClCN + AlCl_3 \longrightarrow \text{(benzonitrile, CN)} + HCl + AlCl_3$$

78. G. A. Olah and S. J. Kuhn, *J. Am. Chem. Soc.* **80**, 6535, 6541 (1958); G. A. Olah, ed., "Friedel-Crafts and Related Reactions," Vol. I, Chapt. II. Wiley (Interscience), New York, 1963.
79. A. A. Woolf, *J. Chem. Soc.* p. 252 (1954).

A similar effect is produced by ferric chloride. Analogous reactions occur when nitrosyl chloride interacts with a suitable Lewis acid to produce the nitrosonium ion, NO^+, as in [80]

$$NOCl + FeCl_3 \rightarrow NO[FeCl_4]$$

Nitryl chloride, NO_2Cl, and nitryl fluoride behave similarly to yield the nitronium ion, NO_2^+, and a complex anion [81].

$$NO_2F + BF_3 \rightarrow NO_2[BF_4]$$

A somewhat more unusual example is the reaction of arsenic trichloride with chlorine in the presence of aluminum chloride.[82] This gives a salt of the tetrachloroarsonium ion, $AsCl_4^+$.

$$AsCl_3 + Cl_2 + AlCl_3 \rightarrow [AsCl_4][AlCl_4]$$

The $AsCl_4^+$ species should be an electrophilic reagent, though information on this point is presently unavailable.

4.3.3. The Generation of Free Radicals

When coordination creates circumstances favorable to the *complete* transfer of electrons, free radicals of considerable reactivity may be generated. This is often found with iron, copper, and manganese complexes because of the ease with which the central ion can assume various oxidation states. The coordination act can catalyze processes in which ligands are reduced as well as oxidized.

The activation of molecular nitrogen by what may well be a coordination process is involved in the fixation of this element from the air by certain microorganisms. The N_2 molecule is isoelectronic with the CO molecule and would be expected to form complexes with suitable coordination centers, i.e., those capable of forming π-bonds with such a ligand. It is well established that compounds of both molybdenum and iron are essential to the fixation of atmospheric nitrogen. There are at present no unequivocal proofs that coordination *can activate* molecular nitrogen, however. According to one report,[83] *nitrogen* is capable of oxidizing hemoglobin (Fe^{2+}) to hemiglobin (Fe^{3+}), and hydrogen can reverse this process. The hemoglobins used were obtained from soybean nodules and presumably are those involved in nitrogen fixation. The elementary steps possible in the fixation of atmospheric nitrogen by lower organisms can, in principle, involve either oxidation or reduction. Present evidence favors a reduction of the nitrogen and a sequence for the

80. J. R. Partington and A. L. Whynes, *J. Chem. Soc.* p. 1952 (1948); J. Lewis and D. B. Sowerby, *J. Chem. Soc.* p. 1617 (1957).
81. G. Olah, S. Kuhn, and A. Mlinko, *J. Chem. Soc.* p. 4257 (1956).
82. L. Kolditz and W. Schmidt, *Z. Anorg. Allgem. Chem.* **296**, 188 (1958).
83. P. B. Hamilton, A. L. Shug, and P. W. Wilson, *Proc. Natl. Acad. Sci. U.S.* **43**, 297 (1957).

iron-containing nitrogen-fixing enzyme, nitrogenase, involving such a reduction has been proposed[84] and is

$$\text{nitrogenase Fe}^{2+} + N_2 \rightleftarrows \text{nitrogenase Fe}^{3+} + N_3^{3-} \xrightarrow{\text{H}_2\text{O}}$$
$$\text{nitrogenase Fe}^{3+}(OH^-) + NH_3$$

The equilibrium constant for the nitrogenase–N_2 dissociation reaction has been estimated independently by several workers and is of the order of 0.02 atm.[85]

Volpin and his co-workers have demonstrated that elementary nitrogen may be reduced to a fixed form (ultimately ammonia) by processes involving organometallic complexes.[86-90] They showed that elementary nitrogen was fixed by mixtures of anhydrous chromium(III) chloride and ethylmagnesium bromide or of $(\pi\text{-}C_5H_5)_2TiCl_2$ and ethylmagnesium bromide. Subsequent examination of the behavior of systems containing transition metal complexes and organometallic compounds showed most of them to be capable of reducing elementary nitrogen, the most effective being derived from $Ti(OC_2H_5)_4$ or $VO(C_5H_7O_2)_2$.

The direct production of complexes of molecular nitrogen is possible via at least two routes. The first involves the reduction of $RuCl_3$ or $RuCl_3(OH)$ with zinc in the solvent tetrahydrofuran, with the entire system under nitrogen pressure.[91] The solid product was not isolated but was characterized by means of its spectra and its similarity with the spectra of the material obtained by Allen and Senoff described below. The second route is by direct reactions of the type

$$\text{CoH}_3(PPh_3)_3 + N_2 \rightleftarrows \text{CoH}(N_2)(PPh_3)_3 + H_2$$

84. J. E. Carnahan and J. E. Castle, *J. Bacteriol.* **75**, 121 (1958); J. E. Carnahan, L. E. Mortensen, H. F. Mower, and J. E. Castle, *Biochim. Biophys. Acta* **38**, 188 (1960); J. E. Carnahan and J. E. Castle, *Ann. Rev. Plant Physiol.* **14**, 125–136 (1963). See also R. W. Hardy, E. Knight, Jr., and E. K. Jackson, *Biochem. Biophys. Res. Commun.* **23**, 409 (1966) and *Chem. Eng. News* Jan. 30, p. 32 (1967).

85. H. Takahashi, S. Taniguchi, and F. Egami, *in* "Comparative Biochemistry" (M. Florkin and H. S. Mason, eds.), Vol. V, p. 140. Academic Press, New York, 1963.

86. M. E. Volpin and V. B. Shur, *Dokl. Akad. Nauk SSSR* **156**, 1102 (1964), *Chem. Abstr.* **61**, 8933; *Vestn. Akad. Nauk SSSR* **34** (1), 51 (1965), *Chem. Abstr.* **63**, 228; M. E. Volpin and V. B. Shur, *Nature* **209**, 1236 (1966).

87. M. E. Volpin, V. B. Shur, and L. P. Bichin, *Izv. Akad. Nauk SSSR Ser. Khim.* No. 4, 720 (1965); *Chem. Abstr.* **63**, 1244.

88. M. E. Volpin, M. A. Ilavtovskaya, E. I. Larikov, M. L. Khidekel, Y. A. Shvetsov, and V. B. Shur, *Dokl. Akad. Nauk SSSR* **164** (2), 331 (1965); *Chem. Abstr.* **63**, 15840.

89. A. Yamamoto, S. Kitazume, L. S. Pu, and S. Ikika, *Chem. Commun.* p. 79 (1967) have reported the reaction $\text{Co(acac)}_3 + 3\text{AlEt}_2(\text{OEt}) + 3PPh_3 + N_2 \rightarrow [(Ph_3P)_3CoN_2]$.

90. A. Misono, Y. Uchida, and T. Saito, *Bull. Chem. Soc. Japan* **40**, 700 (1967) reported a similar study using isobutylaluminum as the reductant.

91. A. E. Shilov, A. K. Shilova, and Y. G. Borodko, *Kinetika i Kataliz* **7**, 768 (1966).

where the equilibria can be shifted back and forth at will.[92] The indirect production of such complexes has been reported in somewhat greater detail. The reactions reported were

$$RuCl_3 \cdot xH_2O + N_2H_4 \cdot H_2O \rightarrow [Ru(NH_3)_5N_2]^{2+}$$

(ref. 93)

(ref. 94)

The ability of platinum hydride complexes to interact with compounds analogous to elementary nitrogen in some respects has also been demonstrated.[95] An example is

Subsequent reduction of the compound leads to the corresponding hydrazine.

The activation of molecular oxygen by coordination is well established in both biochemical and inorganic systems. The cations that are especially active in this respect possess two qualifications: they can form π-bonds and they can give up an electron to the oxygen. They include Fe(II), Mn(II), Co(II), Cu(I), and related transition metal ions. These reactions are almost invariably free radical reactions. Their initiation may involve the reaction of oxygen with either a hydrated metal ion or a complex containing other ligands.[96-98] In

92. A. Sacco and M. Rossi, *Chem. Commun.* p. 316 (1967).
93. A. D. Allen and C. V. Senoff, *Chem. Commun.* p. 621 (1965); the structure of the dichloride of this cation has been reported by F. Bottomley and S. C. Nyburg, *Chem. Commun.* 897 (1966) to be one in which a central octahedrally coordinated ruthenium is surrounded by five NH_3 groups and one N_2 group bound to the ruthenium at one end. See also: A. D. Allen, F. Bottomley, R. O. Harris, V. P. Reinsalu, and C. V. Senoff, *J. Am. Chem. Soc.* **89**, 5595 (1967) and D. E. Harrison and H. Taube, *J. Am. Chem. Soc.* **89**, 5706 (1967).
94. J. P. Collman and J. W. Kang, *J. Am. Chem. Soc.* **88**, 3459 (1966); J. P. Collman, M. Kubota, J.-Y. Sun, and F. Vastire, *J. Am. Chem. Soc.* **89**, 169 (1967).
95. G. W. Parshall, work reported in *Chem. Eng. News* Jan 30, p. 34 (1967).
96. D. Huggins and W. C. Drinkard, *Advan. Chem. Ser.* **37**, 181 (1963).
97. D. L. Leussing and T. N. Tischer, *Advan. Chem. Ser.* **37**, 216 (1963).
98. S. Fallab, *Chimia (Aarau)* **16**, 189 (1962).

biochemical systems coordination of molecular oxygen to various complexes such as iron-containing respiratory enzymes[99] and analogous systems is important in activating molecular oxygen for various oxidation reactions including those in which H_2O, H_2O_2, or oxidized organic compounds are the products. The enzymes that produce H_2O or H_2O_2 are called oxidases; those in which the oxygen is directly incorporated into an oxidized organic product are called oxygenases.[100]

It is possible to effect hydroxylation reactions of many systems, and thus the incorporation of oxygen in an organic product, by the use of the Udenfriend reagent.[101, 102] The essential ingredients of this system are a buffer, a suitable substrate, ascorbic acid, a suitable metal complex, and oxygen. A suitable substrate may be an aromatic, heterocyclic, or aliphatic compound. A suitable metal complex is Fe(II)–EDTA. The steps involved are an initial oxidation of ascorbic acid to give monodehydroascorbic acid and hydrogen, both as radicals, and the subsequent interaction of these with oxygen and then with the substrate. Thus, when aniline is used as the substrate, the products include p- and o-aminophenol; pyrene is converted to 3-hydroxypyrene.[103] This system is rather similar to the nonenzymic decarboxylation reaction of methionine in the presence of a buffer, ferrous ion, ascorbic acid, and EDTA.[104] The principal difference between the nonenzymic and the enzymic reaction of this sort is that the nonenzymic reactions show a much lower degree of stereospecificity.

The formation of metal complexes with O_2 and their subsequent reaction with substrates has been supported by evidence obtained in studies of autoxidation reactions.[105] This involves the formation of a species such as $Co^{2+} \cdot O_2$ or analogous complexes with organic ligands which have been known for some time.[106, 107] These are to be distinguished from cases in which the oxidizing power of a higher oxidation state is used and subsequently regenerated by oxidation with atmospheric oxygen. Common cases of this latter sort involve Cu^{2+} as an oxidant.

99. O. Warburg, "Heavy Metal Prosthetic Groups and Enzyme Action," Chapts. VI, VII, VIII. Oxford Univ. Press (Clarendon), London and New York, 1949.
100. O. Hayaishi, ed., "Oxygenases," p. 6. Academic Press, New York, 1962.
101. S. Udenfriend, C. T. Clark, J. Axelrod, and B. B. Brodie, *J. Biol. Chem.* **208**, 731, 741 (1958).
102. J. H. Green, B. J. Ralph, and P. J. Schofield, *Nature* **195**, 1309 (1962).
103. F. Dewhurst and G. Calcutt, *Nature* **191**, 808 (1961).
104. M. Mazelis, *Nature* **189**, 305 (1961).
105. N. Uri, *in* "Autoxidation and Antioxidants" (W. O. Lundberg, ed.), Vol. 1, p. 97. Wiley (Interscience), New York, 1961.
106. A. E. Martell and M. Calvin, "Chemistry of the Metal Chelate Compounds," pp. 337 ff. Prentice-Hall, Englewood Cliffs, New Jersey, 1952.
107. L. H. Vogt, H. M. Faigenbaum, and S. E. Wiberley, *Chem. Rev.* **63**, 269 (1963).

The behavior of hydrogen peroxide is somewhat different from most of the other molecules mentioned, as the usual result of the activation of this molecule is its decomposition.

$$2H_2O_2 \xrightarrow{M^{2+}} 2H_2O + O_2$$

This reaction has been examined by a large number of investigators. A more interesting situation is one in which the hydrogen peroxide is activated for attack on other species. Many of these reactions, involving catalysts such as horseradish peroxidase, have been developed by B. C. Saunders and his students.[108-110] In some cases these enzyme-catalyzed reactions furnish remarkably effective and specific synthetic routes. The activation of both hydrogen peroxide and organic peroxides can frequently be effected by Fe^{2+} or some other metal ion. Here the essential process is the generation of reactive hydroxyl radicals or their equivalent.

$$H_2O_2 + Fe^{2+} \rightarrow HO\cdot + FeOH^{2+}$$

Such processes are of distinct synthetic utility.[111]

Although one might expect to find certain similarities between the behavior of hydrazine and hydrogen peroxide, these are presently known mostly for the metal-ion-catalyzed decompositions of these species. There appears to have been no obvious exploitation of a "Fenton's reagent" based on hydrazine rather than hydrogen peroxide.[112] The reduction of chlorate by hydrazine, however, is found to be catalyzed by both silver and copper salts and by osmic acid.[113]

Carbonic anhydrase (also called carbonate dehydratase) is an enzyme that catalyzes the reaction

$$H_2CO_3 \rightarrow H_2O + CO_2$$

It may thus be said to activate carbonic acid. The enzyme is a constituent of red cells and is inactivated by typical ligands which are good donors toward iron(III) such as cyanide and azide.[114]

108. B. C. Saunders and G. H. R. Watson, *Biochem. J.* **46**, 629 (1950).
109. A. G. Holmes-Siedle and B. C. Saunders, *Chem. Ind. (London)* p. 164 (1959).
110. B. C. Saunders, A. G. Holmes-Siedle, and B. P. Stark, "Peroxidase." Butterworth, London and Washington, D.C., 1964.
111. S.-O. Lawesson and G. Sosnovsky, *Svensk Kem. Tidskr.* **75**, 343 (1963).
112. P. Pascal, "Traite de Chemie Minerale," Vol. 10, p. 556. Masson, Paris, 1959.
113. Ref. 112, p. 557; N. P. Keier, G. K. Boreskov, V. V. Rod, A. P. Terentiev, and E. G. Rukhadze, *Kinetika i Kataliz* **2**, 509 (1961), *Chem. Abstr.* **58**, 5082.
114. M. Dixon and E. C. Webb, "Enzymes," 2nd Ed., pp. 338, 453, 643, 644. Academic Press, New York, 1964.

4.3.4. THE GENERATION OF NUCLEOPHILES

Coordination can lead to the formation of reactive nucleophiles under two conditions. The first occurs in the case where coordination ties up the only pair of electrons available, as with H_2. In this respect the behavior of hydrogen is unique. The hydrogen molecule *has* only *two* electrons; if these are used to form a coordinate bond the products will be a proton (solvated) whose behavior is of lesser interest, and a coordinated hydride ion that is the center of a novel type of reactivity. The second type of reactive nucleophile is found with ligands whose usual coordination involves bonding in which the back-donation of electrons from the metal is more important than the formation of the normal, σ-type coordinate bond. This may occur with carbon monoxide.

The activation of molecular hydrogen via coordination or processes in which metals split the hydrogen molecule has been very thoroughly studied by J. Halpern and his students.[115] Complexes of the more usual sorts may also be used as catalysts for such reactions. The ions $[Co(CN)_5]^{3-}$ and $[Co(NH_3)_5Cl]^{2+}$ have been found to catalyze hydrogenation of a number of inorganic and organic species including the reductive amination of α-keto acids[116-118]; chromium(III) stearate catalyzes the reduction of cyclohexene,[119] and the reaction product of triethylaluminum and nickel(II) 2-ethylhexanoate catalyzes the hydrogenation of many organic compounds, presumably via a nickel(0) hydride.[120] Some of these reactions, but not all, go via coordinated hydride. Reactions subjected to kinetic study by Halpern and his group in which simple aquo ions are involved as activators were found in almost all cases to involve heterolytic splitting of hydrogen as the rate-determining step if a suitable substrate was present.[121]

The changes in the reactivity of carbon monoxide that arise upon coordination can be seen in the reactions of the metal carbonyls. It should be recalled that carbon monoxide has only a small dipole moment ($\mu = 0.1$ D) in the free state; coordination will tend to make this larger and hence will assist polar reactions. The enormous number of reactions of this sort that are known prevents a complete listing, but the oxo process, the homologation reaction, and carbon monoxide insertion are typical of these.

Oxo reaction (also called hydroformylation)

$$CH_2{=}CH_2 + CO + H_2 \xrightarrow{\ H[Co(CO)_4]\ } CH_3CH_2CHO$$

115. J. Halpern, *Advan. Catalysis* **11**, 301 (1959); J. Halpern, *J. Phys. Chem.* **63**, 398 (1959).
116. S. W. Weller and G. A. Mills, *Advan. Catalysis* **8**, 163 (1956) (a review).
117. M. Murakami and J.-W. Kang, *Bull. Chem. Soc. Japan* **35**, 1243 (1962).
118. J.-C. Lauer, *Ann. Chim. (Paris)* **10**, 301 (1965) (a review).
119. V. A. Tulupov, *Zh. Fiz. Khim.* **36**, 1617 (1962); *Chem. Abstr.* **57**, 14471.
120. S. J. Lapporte and W. R. Schuett, *J. Org. Chem.* **28**, 1947 (1963).
121. J. F. Harrod, S. Ciccone, and J. Halpern, *Can. J. Chem.* **39**, 1372 (1961); M. T. Beck, I. Gimesi, and J. Farkas, *Nature* **197**, 73 (1963).

Homologation reaction

$$CH_3-\underset{\underset{CH_3}{|}}{\overset{\overset{CH_3}{|}}{C}}-OH \xrightarrow[CO, H_2]{H[Co(CO)_4]} CH_3-\underset{}{\overset{\overset{CH_3}{|}}{C}}=CH_2 \rightarrow$$

$$(CH_3)_3CCH_2OH + CH_3-\underset{\underset{CH_3}{|}}{CH}-CH_2CH_2OH$$

Carbon monoxide insertion reaction[122]

$$CH_3Mn(CO)_5 + CO \rightarrow CH_3COMn(CO)_5$$

A survey of a number of these has been published.[123] The activation of carbon monoxide by coordination is a widely useful method for the preparation of many kinds of organic compounds and new types of reactions are being discovered continually. A further example is the carboxylation of alkali halides or sulfates.

$$RX + CO + R'OH + Base \xrightarrow{[Co(CO)_4]^-} RCOOR' + (HBase)X$$

This reaction proceeds through the acyl cobalt carbonyls, $RCOCo(CO)_4$.[124] Aluminum chloride can also assist in the activation of carbon monoxide in some reactions.[125] From the examples that have been presented it is apparent that coordination may furnish a very useful process in the activation of a large number of molecules. It must be emphasized that the known examples by no means exhaust the possible situations where coordination can act in this way.

4.4. Stereoselective Coordination Catalysis

When a metal ion is coordinated to an asymmetric species (which is generally present as a chelate ring), it is found that ligand substitution reactions of the other coordination positions do not usually occur to give equal amounts of substitution for both components of a pair of optically isomeric ligands. The most common example of this is found in reactions in which a mixture of (+) and (−) forms of a chelating agent (such as propylenediamine) are used to prepare a cobalt(III) complex containing three chelate rings. In such cases the final complexes are often found to contain the (+) or the (−) forms of the chelating agent, but not both.[126] This kind of reaction has been studied by

122. F. Calderazzo and F. A. Cotton, *Inorg. Chem.* 1, 30 (1962).
123. I. Wender, H. W. Sternberg, R. A. Friedel, S. J. Metlin, and R. E. Markby, *U.S. Bur. Mines, Bull.* No. 600 (1962).
124. R. F. Heck and D. S. Breslow, *J. Am. Chem. Soc.* 85, 2779 (1963).
125. E. W. Crandall, C. H. Smith, and R. C. Horn, *J. Org. Chem.* 25, 329 (1960).
126. R. D. Gillard and H. M. Irving, *Chem. Rev.* 65, 603 (1965); J. H. Dunlap and R. D. Gillard, *Advan. Inorg. Chem. Radiochem.* 9, 185 (1966).

Bailar and by Dwyer and by the students of each of them. The degree of stereospecificity varies from case to case. In the reactions of some asymmetric complexes it may be large (i.e., only one of a pair of enantiomorphs being taken up by the asymmetric complex). In other cases it may be almost non-existent. Some examples are (pn = propylenediamine; PDTA = propylene-diaminetetraacetic acid)

$$cis\text{-}[Co(-pn)_2Cl_2]Cl + (\pm)pn = L(-)\text{-}[Co(-pn)_3]^{3+}$$

(ref. 127)

$$(-)[Co(+PDTA)]^- + (\pm)pn = D(+)[Co(+pn)_3]^{3+}$$

(ref. 128)

Where more stable bonds may be formed, it *is* possible to prepare complexes containing both (+) and (−) forms, and in recent years much effort has been expended in refining the information available on such systems.

It has been shown[129] that earlier work of Jaeger and his collaborators on *trans*-1,2-cyclopentanediamine complexes (upon which much later work was developed) was in error with respect to the structures of the complexes involved, but the subsequent work has borne out many of these ideas and provided additional experimental examples. The subsequently developed systems often exhibited the kind of stereospecificity that Jaeger thought that he had found.

The stereospecificity of many metal-activated enzymes appears to be of this sort. The basic enzyme structure is itself asymmetric. Coordination of a metal to this will usually result in a very high degree of stereoselectivity for coordination to the remaining positions in the coordination sphere of the metal. The stereospecificity of these enzymes may also arise in a more direct manner from the asymmetric structure of the enzyme itself.

It is important to emphasize that the stereoselectivity of the coordination act is only rarely an exclusive or absolute stereospecificity. Since its basis is in the small free energy differences of the sorts that arise from interatomic interactions in different conformations, one might speak more accurately of the *relative selectivity* of the coordination center. It is well to recall that a free energy difference of 1 kcal between two different isomeric forms means an equilibrium constant of 5.5 in favor of the more stable form. This means that an equilibrium mixture will contain 84.7% of the more stable form and 15.4% of the less stable form. The free energy differences responsible for the stereoselectivity of ligand replacement reactions are rarely greater than 10 kcal.

The kind of stereoselectivity which may be found in complexes is illustrated by the preparation of L-[carbonatobis(1-propylenediamine)]cobalt(III)

127. A. D. Gott and J. C. Bailar, Jr., *J. Am. Chem. Soc.* **74**, 4820 (1952).
128. H. M. Irving and R. D. Gillard, *J. Chem. Soc.* p. 5266 (1960).
129. J. E. Phillips and D. J. Royer, *Inorg. Chem.* **4**, 616 (1965).

iodide.[130] Here the cobalt(III) complex was prepared by the oxidation of cobalt(II) in a suitable medium containing *l*-propylenediamine. Slow crystallization of the iodide from water allowed the preparation of the pure L form as a solid. In solution the D and L forms are in equilibrium and the removal of the less soluble L form (as its iodide) allows the equilibrium to shift so that more of the L form is generated.

There are a large number of cases of this sort of behavior and the literature has been critically summarized by Sargeson.[131] Sargeson gives an especially well-documented presentation of the degree of stereoselectivity for a given reaction and the factors that determine this. He also presents some reactions that clearly indicate that the formation of complexes containing both *d* and *l* isomers of a bidentate ligand will occur and, that when the complexes that result are inert, these materials can be readily isolated and characterized. One such reaction is

$$[Pt(l\text{-pn})(Cl_4)] + 2(d\text{-pn}) \xrightarrow{\text{DMF}} [Pt(l\text{-pn})(d\text{-pn})_2]Cl_4$$

The product here gives only two isomers, D and L with the ratio of *l*-pn to *d*-pn of 1 to 2.

The coordination behavior of labile complexes is normally such that equilibrium mixtures are obtained in which all of the constituents are present. There are energy differences between the different possible isomers and these presumably govern the selectivity of such equilibria.[132]

Another type of stereoselectivity which may be found is in the reaction of asymmetric reducing agents with asymmetric oxidizing agents. This type of stereoselectivity is related to that involving ligand replacement because many such redox reactions require prior coordination of the reactants. It is possible to prepare an asymmetric oxidizing agent, such as Fehling's solution, by using either the *d* or the *l* form of tartaric acid to form the basic complex with copper(II). Such reagents are found to react at different rates with the *d* and *l* isomers of sugars. Thus, Fehling's solution prepared from *d*-tartaric acid reacts at different rates with the *d* and *l* forms of altrose, a sugar. Similar differences in rates are found for the *d* and *l* forms of other sugars, such as arabinose.[133] There is a further aspect of such reactions which is of considerable interest: the rate of reaction of the *d*-tartrate with *l*-altrose is the same as that of the *l*-tartrate reagent with *d*-altrose. The *d–d* pairs and *l–l* pairs also have the same rates.

130. F. P. Dwyer and T. E. MacDermott, *Inorg. Chem.* **2**, 871 (1963).
131. A. M. Sargeson, *in* "Chelating Agents and Metal Chelates" (F. P. Dwyer and D. P. Mellor, eds.), pp. 183–235. Academic Press, New York, 1964.
132. W. E. Bennett, *J. Am. Chem. Soc.* **81**, 246 (1959); J. H. Ritsma, G. A. Wiegers, and F. Jellinek, *Rec. Trav. Chim.* **84**, 1577 (1965).
133. N. K. Richtmeyer and C. S. Hudson, *J. Am. Chem. Soc.* **58**, 2540 (1936).

4.4.1. CONFORMATIONAL ANALYSIS

When the bonding of chelating agents to a central metal occurs, there are a number of requirements on the conformations of the chelating rings and their bonded groups.[134, 135] These arise because of the different interaction energies of the nonbonded groups in the different conformations and the varying coordinate bond energies as the bonded groups are moved. The estimation of these is called "conformational analysis" and is of considerable interest because such knowledge enables the prediction of which of the possible conformations will be the most stable, and from this, which ligand conformation will be the one present for attack by an external reagent. Since the conformation will often determine the relative ease of attack, this information is of potential utility in gauging how this particular stereochemical factor will affect the reactivity of the free vs the coordinated ligand.

The estimation of the energy differences between the different conformations is based upon the consideration of the energies of the different types of interactions.[136-138] The method of Corey and Sneen uses known interatomic distances and bond angles for most of the atoms and then calculates the remainder by vector analysis. When a solution using normal bond angles and interatomic distances is not possible, a reasonable solution is obtained by the use of two conditions: (1) the total distortion in all angles should be as small as possible and (2) the various angles should be distorted to approximately the same extent. The orientation of the donor atoms about the central atom can be taken to be approximately the same as that found when the donor atoms are not present in chelate rings. The conformations of the chelate rings are what is to be established and this is done using the techniques developed for flexible carbocyclic rings. The results for an ethylenediamine–metal chelate ring are the following:

$$M \overset{N}{\underset{N}{\diagdown}} \overset{\theta}{\diagup} C \overset{H}{\underset{H}{\diagdown}} H \qquad \theta = 48.8°; \ NCoN = 86.2°$$

The hydrogen atoms on adjacent carbon atoms are almost completely staggered. The chelate ring is also comparable to the cyclohexane ring in that the substituents on the carbon atoms are of the axial or the equatorial type.

----- , equatorial substituent

——— , axial substituent

134. E. L. Eliel, N. L. Allinger, S. J. Angyal, and G. A. Morrison, "Conformational Analysis." Wiley (Interscience), New York, 1965.
135. M. Harnack, "Conformational Theory." Academic Press, New York, 1965.
136. E. J. Corey and J. C. Bailar, Jr., J. Am. Chem. Soc. 81, 2620 (1959).
137. D. H. R. Barton and R. C. Cookson, Quart. Rev. (London) 10, 44 (1956).
138. E. J. Corey and R. A. Sneen, J. Am. Chem. Soc. 77, 2505 (1955).

With cyclohexane, and presumably such chelate rings as well, the axial orientation for groups larger than hydrogen is one of higher energy (less stable) than the equatorial orientation.

The estimation of the relative energies of different conformations can also be effected by the use of the method of Mason and Kreevoy.[139] This is based on the use of potential functions for van der Waals' interactions between nonbonded atoms. Such van der Waals' interactions are responsible for about half of the rotational barriers about a carbon–carbon bond, with the remainder being attributed to electrostatic interactions of the charge distributions in the chemical bonds.

One of the principal bases for prediction of the preferred conformations is that large substituents on the chelate ring tend to be in *equatorial* positions. When the chelate ring is linked to a carbocyclic ring in the ligand, the conformation of the carbocyclic ring itself must be first established and the most stable form of it will generally be present in the complex. It should be noted that the actual conformation is determined by the differences of a fairly large number of relatively small energy terms that include nonbonded interactions of H atoms on the carbon, nitrogen, phosphorus, or other atoms in the chelate rings and electrostatic interactions between H atoms of amino or hydroxy donor groups.

Conformational analysis should prove useful in the analysis of the stereo-specificity of the reactions of coordinated ligands.

4.4.2. STEREOSPECIFIC POLYMERIZATION

A stereospecific polymerization is one carried out in such a manner that the steric course of the addition of each unit to the basic structure follows a regulated path. When such a path is identical for every unit added one has an *isotactic* polymer in which the orientation of each unit is the same. When every other unit follows the same path, with adjacent units being added in an enantiomeric process, one has a *syndiotactic* polymer. If the path of such a reaction is not controlled in this respect, the addition of each unit occurs in a random manner insofar as the steric course of the reaction is concerned. The resultant polymers are termed *atactic*.[140]

The type of stereoregular polymerization that is most obviously dependent upon coordination chemistry is that discovered by K. Ziegler. "Ziegler catalysis" effects the low-pressure room temperature polymerization of ethylene and other suitable olefins under the influence of an appropriate

139. E. A. Mason and M. M. Kreevoy, *J. Am. Chem. Soc.* **77**, 5808 (1955).
140. Reviews and summaries: E. L. Eliel, "Stereochemistry of Carbon Compounds," pp. 446–453. McGraw-Hill, New York, 1962; G. Natta and I. Pasquon, *Advan. Catalysis* **9**, 2 (1959); C. E. H. Bawn and A. Ledwith, *Quart. Rev. (London)* **16**, 361 (1962); J. K. Stille, *Chem. Rev.* **58**, 541 (1958); V. D. Gupta and R. B. Beevers, *Chem. Rev.* **62**, 665 (1962); H. L. Williams, *Record Chem. Progr. (Kresge-Hooker Sci. Lib.)* **23**, 243 (1962).

catalyst. The original catalyst was prepared by mixing hexane or heptane solutions of titanium tetrachloride and triethylaluminum to form a dark insoluble precipitate. This and its supernatant solution are used as the catalyst. The catalyst contains a lower oxidation state of titanium and an organo-aluminum grouping of some sort. It has subsequently been shown that the titanium tetrachloride may be replaced by a halide or an ester of a transition metal of the titanium, vanadium, or chromium family. The triethylaluminum may be replaced by simple or mixed aryl or alkyl compounds of the elements of Groups I, II, and III. The catalysts produced using different starting materials can vary enormously in their effectiveness.

The olefins that undergo stereospecific polymerization in the presence of these catalysts include simple olefins such as ethylene, propylene, styrene, and dienes, as well as many of their derivatives. When the olefin contains a polar group that is a potential electron pair donor, the catalysts are usually in-effective. For example, ester and nitrile groups render olefins not susceptible to such a polymerization (e.g., methyl acrylate and acrylonitrile). This is presumably related to the removal of the coordination centers active as polymerization catalysts by prior reaction with these donor groups. It is quite probable that such compounds can be subjected to stereospecific poly-merization if the interfering donor groups are first coordinated to some suitable coordination center.

The polymerization process presumably involves complexes containing structures of the sort

$$\underset{R}{\overset{R}{\diagdown}}Al\underset{Cl}{\overset{R}{\diagup}}\underset{Cl}{\overset{Cl}{\diagup}}Ti\underset{Cl}{\overset{Cl}{\diagup}}$$

The reaction is very obviously related to an insertion-type reaction found for aluminum trialkyls at elevated temperatures. This is often referred to as an "aufbau" reaction and is of the type

$$R_3Al + CH_2{=}CH_2 \rightarrow R_2Al{-}CH_2{-}CH_2{-}R$$

Such reactions can proceed by further insertions at any of the aluminum–carbon bonds; however, they do *not* occur with dimeric aluminum alkyls. The mixed dimeric aluminum–titanium complexes contain a titanium species which can presumably coordinate to olefins via its empty d orbitals.

The number of detailed mechanisms which have been suggested for this important kind of polymerization is very large. Although many of them contain common features they differ in the detail they present and in the relative importance they assign to the solid and the dissolved catalytic species which are present.

The mechanism of Natta and his co-workers involves the aufbau mechanism on a mixed complex.

A mechanism based on the aufbau reaction on a bivalent titanium species has been proposed[141] and involves the following steps:

$$ClTi[C_2H_4]_n \cdot R + C_2H_4 \;\rightarrow\; Cl\!-\!Ti\!-\![C_2H_4]_n \cdot R \;\rightarrow\; ClTi[C_2H_4]_{n+1}R, \text{ etc.}$$
$$\vdots$$
$$CH_2\!=\!CH_2$$

Bivalent titanium appears to be a reasonable choice and would be formed by the reduction of titanium tetrachloride by the aluminum alkyl. The few bivalent titanium compounds known at the present time have a coordination number of six and an octahedral stereochemistry.

A much more detailed mechanism has been given by Cossee,[142] who regards the reaction as one that occurs on the surface of the insoluble reduction product generated in the preparation of the catalytic mixture. An active center with a Ti—R linkage forms a π-bond with the olefin that then adds across the Ti—R bond in an insertion reaction. Cossee has developed the stereochemical details of his mechanism in great detail.

A final type of mechanism which has been suggested for the Ziegler catalysis is the ion pair mechanism.[143]

$$AlR_3 + TiCl_3 \;\rightarrow\; RTiCl_2 + AlR_2Cl$$
$$AlR_2Cl + RTiCl_2 \;\rightarrow\; [TiCl_2^+][AlR_3Cl^-] \xrightarrow{\;CH_2=CH_2\;}$$
$$[TiCl_2^+][AlR_3Cl^-] \;\rightarrow\; [TiCl_2 \cdot CH_2CH_2^+][AlR_3Cl^-] \;\rightarrow$$
$$\vdots$$
$$CH_2\!=\!CH_2$$
$$TiCl_2 \cdot CH_2CH_2R + AlR_2Cl \;\rightarrow\; [TiCl_2^+][AlR_2(CH_2CH_2R)Cl^-], \text{ etc.}$$

141. D. B. Ludlum, A. W. Anderson, and C. E. Ashby, *J. Am. Chem. Soc.* **80**, 1380 (1958).
142. P. Cossee, *Trans. Faraday Soc.* **58**, 1226 (1962); see also E. J. Arlman, *J. Catalysis* **5**, 178 (1966).
143. H. Uelzman, *J. Org. Chem.* **25**, 671 (1960); G. Bier, *Kunststoffe* **48**, 354 (1958).

Most of these mechanisms are compatible with the facts known about these reactions. It is quite possible to combine features of each to obtain combinations that are also feasible.

It should be noted that the aufbau reactions of the aluminum alkyls

$$AlR_3 + CH_2{=}CH_2 \rightarrow R_2Al{-}CH_2{-}CH_2{-}R$$

are closely analogous (in at least some formal aspects) to the insertion reactions of alkyl metal carbonyls, such as that found with methylmanganese carbonyl.

$$CH_3{-}Mn(CO)_5 + CO \rightarrow CH_3{-}\underset{\underset{O}{\|}}{C}{-}Mn(CO)_5$$

In each case a species capable of forming π-bonds to a transition metal is incorporated into a metal alkyl in such a way that the metal–carbon bond of the metal–alkyl linkage is broken and is replaced by a bond between the metal and the π-bonding species. In the case of the carbonyl insertion reaction, it is known that one of the carbonyl groups already bonded to the metal is placed between the metal and the alkyl group.[144] It is possible to write a mechanism for the Ziegler polymerization analogous to that used for the carbon monoxide insertion reactions, though the detailed testing of such a mechanism seems not yet to have been carried out. The analogy here leads[144] one to suspect the generality of the following type of reaction:

$$Z_yMR_x + \Pi \rightarrow Z_yR_{x-1}M{-}\Pi{-}R$$

where M is a metal, R is an alkyl group, and Π is a species capable of π-bonding. So far this reaction has been established for $\Pi = CO$ and C_2H_4. Since there are a large number of other potential π-bonding species that are also unsaturated, it is expected that many more reactions of this type will be discovered in the future.

4.5. Mixed Complexes

The participation of mixed complexes in catalytic processes may occur in many different ways. In at least some of these, the mixed complexes possess an effectiveness markedly superior to simple complexes of rather similar composition. One of the features of mixed complexes that makes them especially suitable is the way in which they can hold two or more potentially reactive ligands in close proximity. This is a prominent feature in reactions such as Ziegler catalysts, hydrolysis of α-substituted esters, and in a large number of the reactions already described.

144. R. F. Heck, in "Mechanisms of Inorganic Reactions," pp. 179–211. Am. Chem. Soc. (R. F. Gould, ed.) Washington, D.C., 1964.

The behavior of such mixed complexes can often be quite surprising. Vaska and his co-workers[145, 146] have shown how iridium complexes, such as $[IrCl(CO)(Ph_3P)_2]$, can be transformed into hydrido complexes by reaction with hydrogen.

$$[Ir^ICl(CO)(Ph_3P)_2] + H_2 \xrightarrow{25°C} [Ir^{III}H_2Cl(CO)(Ph_3P)_2]$$

This complex is also capable of acting as an oxygen carrier when dissolved in benzene or toluene.

$$[IrCl(CO)(Ph_3P)_2] + O_2 \rightleftharpoons [Ir(O_2)Cl(CO)(Ph_3P)_2]$$

The structure of the oxygen complex has been determined[147] and is found to contain either a five- or a six-coordinate iridium and an O_2 species, as shown,

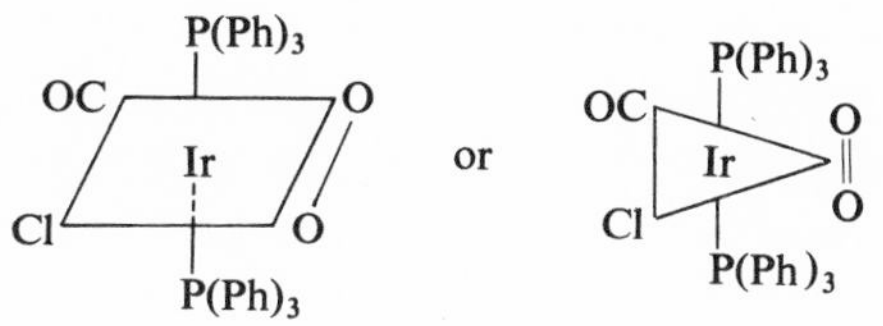

The structure and properties of this mixed complex suggest that it may serve as a model for a large number of such systems that are involved in the transport of H_2 or O_2.

This same complex also undergoes a reversible reaction with carbon monoxide.[148]

$$[IrCl(CO)(Ph_3P)_2] + CO \underset{k_1}{\overset{k_2}{\rightleftharpoons}} [(CO)IrCl(CO)(Ph_3P)_2]$$

There is thus some similarity between the coordinating properties of the complex $[IrCl(CO)(Ph_3P)_2]$ and complexes such as hemoglobin. The reaction with carbon monoxide, however, is rapidly reversible with the iridium complex, and oxygen can displace carbon monoxide from it with greater ease than is the case with hemoglobin. The equilibrium constant for the carbonylation reaction given above is 1.91×10^5 liter mole^{-1}; k_2 is 43.4 liter mole^{-1} sec^{-1},

145. L. Vaska, *J. Am. Chem. Soc.* **83**, 756 (1961); L. Vaska and J. W. DiLuzio, *J. Am. Chem. Soc.* **83**, 2784 (1961); S. S. Bath and L. Vaska, *J. Am. Chem. Soc.* **85**, 3500 (1963); L. Vaska, *Science* **140**, 809 (1963); L. Vaska and J. W. DiLuzio, *J. Am. Chem. Soc.* **84**, 679 (1962); L. Vaska and R. E. Rhodes, *J. Am. Chem. Soc.* **87**, 4970 (1965).
146. L. Vaska and D. L. Catone, *J. Am. Chem. Soc.* **88**, 5324 (1966).
147. J. A. Ibers and S. J. LaPlaca, *Science* **145**, 920 (1964); S. J. LaPlaca and J. A. Ibers, *J. Am. Chem. Soc.* **87**, 2581 (1965).
148. L. Vaska, *Science* **152**, 769 (1966).

and so k_1 is 2.27×10^{-4} sec^{-1}. Complexes of this sort also add HCl, HBr, SO$_2$, NO$_2$, H$_2$S,[147] alky halides,[149] hydrosilanes,[150] and even N$_2$.[151]

The great flexibility that mixed complexes allow arises from the fact that changes in ligands about a given coordination position can result in enormous changes in the donor atom specificity of that position. This results from changes in both the σ- and π-bonding ability of that position. Nyholm[33] has emphasized that the charge distribution about the central atom is dependent upon *all* of the donor atoms as these all participate in the process of bringing the central atom to a state of electroneutrality. For donor atoms of a given type, the net charge transferred per donor to the central ion decreases as the number of donors increases. Fallab has shown how the catalytic effectiveness of iron complexes in the decomposition of hydrogen peroxide is extremely dependent upon the donor groups.[152] When iron complexes are examined in which four of the coordination positions are occupied by pyrrole groups, it is found that variations in the fifth ligand can lead to changes in the rate constant of several orders of magnitude. Thus hemoglobin and catalase result in very different rates of decomposition of hydrogen peroxide, even though each contains its iron bonded to four pyrrole nitrogens in a plane with one or two additional groups bonded in axial positions. Judging from the enormous number of natural iron-containing catalysts that are based upon this kind of a structure, it would seem to be an ideal basis for systematic studies. Hemoglobin is known to bind not only oxygen, carbon monoxide, and nitric oxide, but also a number of other π-bonding species such as ethylene, nitrosobenzene, azide, and isonitriles. The reactivity of such coordinated species must be modified to at least some extent by this coordination, but no *in vitro* applications of this seem to have been exploited. Of the other potentially useful metallo-porphyrin complexes, only those of vanadium and manganese seem to be used in nature. It should be recalled that variation in the structures of such materials must result in two kinds of variations in properties if the materials are to be effective catalysts. First, the acceptor response properties to suitable ligands must be changed and, secondly, the redox properties of the system must be altered. For this reason natural pyrroles presumably are concentrated among those metals that exhibit two or more oxidation states not too widely separated in redox potential. On this basis, the first row transition metals which are most suitable are vanadium, manganese, and iron. It should also be recalled that most natural systems have been developed by a process of evolution which probably *began* with very simple systems that had the desired properties to a small extent.

149. R. F. Heck, *J. Am. Chem. Soc.* **86**, 2796 (1964).
150. A. J. Chalk and J. F. Harrod, *J. Am. Chem. Soc.* **87**, 16 (1965).
151. J. P. Collman and J. W. Kang, *J. Am. Chem. Soc.* **88**, 3459 (1966).
152. S. Fallab, *Chimia (Aarau)* **16**, 189 (1962).

The role of mixed complexes that are labile is of enormous importance in many biologically critical systems. Since many parts of living organisms are maintained at a pH not very far removed from neutrality, any transition metal ions nominally present in the free state will be partly hydrolyzed to hydroxy species of the types $M(OH)_z$ or $M_m(OH)_y$. These will then form further coordinate bonds with other donor species present. The resultant hydroxy complexes may have *very* different catalytic properties than the simple aquo species from which they are derived. Basic complexes of this sort have been proposed as the essential substrate in the oxidative deamination of amino acids.[153]

The interaction of two different ligands in the same complex is very clearly seen in the catalytic hydrolysis of 8-acetoxyquinoline-5-sulfonic acid (A) by the zinc complex with the pyridinecarboxaldoxime anion (B).[154]

(A)   (B)

In this reaction a mixed complex is first formed that contains (A) and (B); the acetyl group is then rapidly transferred to the oxygen of the oxime and is then hydrolyzed at a somewhat slower rate. The overall rate is still more rapid than the uncatalyzed hydrolysis of (A). The oxygen of the oximate anion, when in the mixed complex, is in a position to attack the acetyl group of (A). The mechanism of this reaction is very similar to that of enzymes that catalyze acyl transfer reactions, i.e., the acyl group is first transferred to a nucleophilic group on the enzyme and then hydrolyzed off the enzyme.

The mixed complexes that have been used as oxidation catalysts have not yet been put on a really systematic basis. The essential ingredients are a transition metal ion with easily accessible adjacent oxidation states, a multidentate chelating agent, oxygen, and often a suitable reducing agent, such as ascorbic acid. The interactions in these systems are indeed complex. Thus ascorbic acid accelerates the oxygenation of the cobalt(II)–glycylglycine

153. J. Nyilasi, *Acta Chem. Acad. Sci. Hung.* **21**, 235 (1959); **34**, 229 (1962); **35**, 465 (1963); **38**, 261 (1963).
154. R. Breslow and D. Chipman, *J. Am. Chem. Soc.* **87**, 4196 (1965).

complex and the cobalt(II)–glycylglycine complex accelerates the autoxidation of ascorbic acid.[155] The behavior of many systems in which autoxidation reactions occur shows similar patterns of interdependent reactions. This apparently results from the interdependence of the chain of free radical reactions upon which the overall reaction is dependent.

One problem that frequently renders the elucidation of mixed complex systems extremely difficult is the accurate evaluation of the species present. With inert complexes, this can occasionally be solved by the isolation and characterization of the species present. With labile systems the difficulty is normally rendered severe because the system is undergoing reaction while any attempt is made to determine its *equilibrium* properties. When only one complex is present, its composition and concentration may often be estimated with reasonable certainty by a method of successive approximations. When several complexes are present, they will usually differ considerably in their catalytic activity and the kinetic behavior of the system will then be dependent upon the distribution of the complexes present. In such systems the accuracy with which the successive stability constants can be obtained will then determine how well the kinetic behavior can be related to the types and amounts of the various complexes present. In general, the precision with which successive stability constants can be determined for a given metal–ligand system ML_n falls off as n increases, so, the accuracy with which K_1 can be determined is greater than that for K_2, which in turn is greater than that of K_3, etc. Where two or more ligands are involved in a system of mixed complexes, the accuracy is certainly no better. One is thus faced with a dilemma. If such a catalytically active system is to be studied in detail, the accurate determination of the relevant equilibria require that the ligand reaction be slow, i.e., that the system be a poor catalyst. If, on the other hand, we are interested in experiments to determine the system of maximum catalytic effectiveness, we must be willing to accept estimates of equilibrium constants that are often *quite* poor. In cases in which the product of the reaction (e.g., the amino acid produced by the hydrolysis of amino acid esters) is a better complexing agent than the initial reactant, these difficulties are compounded by the continual removal of the catalytically active metal as the reaction proceeds.

One way of eliminating some of the difficulties that arise in such a situation is to ignore the formation of any complex between the catalyst and the substrate when formulating any explicit rate of equilibrium expressions. This has been done in several of the instances cited earlier. It is often the only solution to this problem when the complex with the substrate has a very short life. Such a procedure has the unfortunate result of providing energies of activation and frequency factors that are *composites* of two or more terms, as has been shown

155. M. T. Beck and S. Gorog, *Acta Univ. Szeged. Acta Phys. Chem.* **4**, Suppl. 62 (1958) (Symposium volume).

earlier. Ultimately, the development of more accurate and rapid relaxation methods for studying such problems will provide data of the sort required for the proper solution of such problems.

It must be noted that mixed complexes are often involved in reactions when the requirement that the ligands be mixed is probable, though not rigorously proven. The most obvious complexes of this sort are the ones utilized in organic chemistry that contain an organic ligand bound to a metallic or non-metallic coordination center whose other coordination positions are occupied by halide ions. Thus the widely used complexes of $AlCl_3$, BF_3, $SnCl_4$, and the like are all of this type. The important features present in such complexes are (1) a small, highly charged central ion that possesses very considerable polarizing power and (2) a group of ligands derived from highly electronegative species that will suffer polarization to a relatively slight extent. The net result of these two factors is that the additional organic ligand will generally suffer a very considerable degree of polarization and provide a significant fraction of the electronic charge needed by the central ion to achieve a state of near electroneutrality. When the halide groups are replaced by other, more polarizable ligands, especially organic ones, the catalytic power of the coordination centers is generally drastically reduced. This is especially apparent in derivatives of these elements such as alkoxides or carboxylate complexes. When the ligands are too electronegative to allow the formation of a covalent bond, one also obtains catalytically inactive species that are generally ionic solids such as aluminum fluoride or sulfate. The presence of the proper combinations of ligands in these mixed complexes is thus also critical to their proper catalytic function.

In summary, it is to be noted that mixed complexes are very important in catalytic phenomena in large measure because of the wide variation in properties which can be achieved with them. To a less frequent extent they function to bring reactive species together, within the coordination sphere. It is not convenient to treat all mixed complexes at the same point because there are often more salient and important features of such complexes which form the basis for their activity. Thus the fact that the central metal ion has certain redox properties, bonds well to π-bonding ligands, or is very small, may be more important than the fact that it is present in a mixed complex. In a similar manner, the fact that coordination polarizes a ligand can often be more important than the fact that the ligand is present in a mixed complex.

4.6. Acidity Functions for Coordination Centers

When a reaction is catalyzed by a metal ion or other coordination center that functions primarily by virtue of its acidity, it is very helpful to have some measure of the acidity in the reaction medium. This problem has been solved in part for protonic catalysis by the development of various kinds of acidity functions, the first of which is the pH, and the second, the acidity function of Hammett.[156] The Hammett acidity function, which is defined for the transfer of a proton to a neutral base (B) has the form

$$H_0 = -\log\left(\frac{a_{H^+} f_B}{f_{BH^+}}\right)$$

where a_{H^+} is the activity of hydrogen ion and the f's are activity coefficients. When the proton transfer is to a charged base a different acidity function must be defined in terms of a charged species B. The function H_0 reduces to the simple pH function in dilute aqueous solutions. For many reactions H_0 is found to be correlated with the rate in much the same manner as the pH is in dilute aqueous systems.

The extension of these ideas to certain types of coordination compounds may be seen in the work of Perrin and Westheimer[157] on the mercuration of benzene. A function Hg_0 was defined as

$$Hg_0 = -\log hg_0 = -\log\left(\frac{a_{Hg^{++}} f_S}{f_{SHg^{++}}}\right)$$

where S is an aromatic hydrocarbon which reversibly forms a σ-complex, SHg^{2+}. These authors proposed that the rates of mercuration of aromatic systems should be correlated approximately by the Hg_0 function.

For reactions catalyzed by metal ions, complexes, or neutral Lewis acids, especially when examined in a nonaqueous solvent or when run in the presence of a high concentration of coordination centers, an analogous expression can be used to obtain a measure of the activity of these solutions capable of quantitative expression. By analogy with the Hammett acidity function, we can define an acidity function $M_{i,j,k}$ for the species in such systems as

$$M_{i,j,k} = -\log\left[\frac{(a_{M(L)_j^{+i}})(f_{B^k})}{(f_{[M(L)_j B]^{i+k}})}\right]$$

Here i is the charge on $M(L)_j$, j is the number of ligands coordinated to M which gives the effective Lewis acid in the system, B is the substrate species upon which the Lewis acid is acting, and k is the electrical charge on B; i and k may have negative or positive values or zero, j can be zero or have positive values. All the L's need not be identical. $M_{i,j,k}$ can be measured in the same manner as that used to establish H_0 in many cases.

This type of function should prove to be especially useful in introducing some regularity in the organization of the rates of aromatic reactions when the

156. L. P. Hammett, "Physical Organic Chemistry," pp. 267–281. McGraw-Hill, New York, 1940.
157. C. Perrin and F. H. Westheimer, J. Am. Chem. Soc. 85, 2777 (1963).

substrate is also a donor species. In many of these reactions the rate is quite slow when the ratio of Lewis acid to substrate is small. As this ratio increases, the rate increases slowly. When the point of the stoichiometric ratio (usually one Lewis acid per donor group) is passed, however, the rate of the reaction increases at a very rapid rate with further amounts of Lewis acid. (When the initial complex is unstable the rate will increase prior to the stoichiometric point.) In these cases the Lewis acid functions in two ways: as an ordinary acceptor center and as a catalyst. The initial Lewis acid is largely consumed by reaction with the donor centers,

$$M + L \rightleftarrows ML; \quad K_i = \frac{[M][L]}{[ML]}$$

so $[M] = K_i[ML]/[L]$. In these cases K_i, the instability constant of the complex, is often small so $[M]$ increases only slowly until ML is completely formed, i.e., all the L is tied up as ML. Once this point is passed the amount of free catalytically active M will increase directly as the excess M increases (and so will $M_{i,j,k}$). The second step in such a reaction can be the weaker interaction of M with say an acyl halide to generate a carbonium ion. The rate will then be directly proportional to the amount of active species. Plots of $\log k$ vs $M_{i,j,k}$ should be straight lines when the $M_{i,j,k}$ proper to the reaction type is used.

These functions do not possess the generality of the Hammett acidity function as the properties of the specific Lewis acids and bases enter into their definitions. They should be approximately independent of B, when bases of the same types (sterically and electronically) are considered in a series of reactions. It must be noted that the customary identification of concentrations and activities may lead to very serious errors in concentrated nonaqueous solutions of neutral Lewis acids.

4.7. Photochemical Reactions

Because of the readiness with which many metal ions and their complexes absorb light of both visible and ultraviolet wavelengths, one would suspect that coordination would be capable of furnishing a means of making a potentially photoreactive ligand more strongly absorbent, or of making such ligands absorbent in a region in which they normally show no absorption. When the properties of the metal–ligand system are properly matched, one may enhance charge transfer processes and generate reactive free radicals. This phenomenon has been amply demonstrated in the systems which contain ferric ions and oxidizable species such as iodide, thiocyanate, and bromide. Less well known, but just as well established are those systems based on cobalt(III) complexes of the type $[Co(NH_3)_5X]^{2+}$, in which the absorption of light leads to an electron transfer process when the oxidation potential of the

X is in a suitable range. General references to photochemical reactions are given in refs. 158–166.

The assistance which coordination may furnish to photochemical activation is thus primarily by means of changes in the absorption spectra and redox properties of coordination centers of the transition and inner transition series ions. The basic process here is one in which light is absorbed by the complex or central ion (whose energy levels have been perturbed by the coordination process) to give an activated species that breaks down into a free radical derived from the coordinated anion or molecule and a complex that contains the metal in an oxidation state lower by one unit than that initially present. Examples of such processes include the following:

$$FeBr^{2+}(aq) + h\nu = Fe^{2+}(aq) + Br\cdot$$
$$[Co(NH_3)_5I]^{2+} + h\nu = [Co(NH_3)_5]^{2+} + I\cdot$$
$$Ce(H_2O)_x^{4+} + h\nu = Ce^{3+}(aq) + H^+ + OH\cdot \qquad \text{(ref. 167)}$$

The free radicals that result from this activation process can then react with suitable substrates in the system or they can be used to initiate chain reactions such as the polymerization of unsaturated organic compounds.

When processes of this sort are easily reversible, as in the ferrous–ferric system, they should provide a means of catalyzing reactions when the two reactants can be brought together more readily after one of them has assumed a radical form. If one of the species also is capable of oxidizing the metal back to its original oxidation state, it should be possible to use such metal complex systems for catalytic purposes. As an example, consider the photochemical bromination of isopentane. This proceeds slowly via bromine radicals to give *tert*-amyl bromide. Since ferric bromide complexes undergo the charge transfer absorption to generate bromine radicals, the addition of ferric bromide to such a reaction mixture should lead to catalysis, because the

158. N. Uri, *Chem. Rev.* **50**, 375 (1950).
159. F. Basolo and R. G. Pearson, "Mechanisms of Inorganic Reactions," (2nd ed.) pp. 654–666. Wiley, New York, 1967.
160. G. S. Hammond and N. J. Turro, *Science* **142**, 1541 (1963). A general review of organic photochemistry.
161. A. Schönberg, "Präparative organische Photochemie." Springer, Berlin, 1958.
162. C. R. Masson, V. Boekelheide, and W. A. Noyes, Jr., *in* "Technique of Organic Chemistry" (A. Weissberger, ed.), Vol. II, p. 257. Wiley (Interscience), New York, 1956.
163. J. G. Calvert and J. N. Pitts, Jr., "Photochemistry." Wiley, New York, 1966.
164. E. Rabinovitch and R. L. Belford, "Spectroscopy and Photochemistry of Uranyl Compounds." Macmillan (Pergamon), New York, 1964.
165. "Advances in Photochemistry" (W. A. Noyes, Jr., G. S. Hammond, and J. N. Pitts, Jr., eds.). Wiley (Interscience), New York, 1963 (first of a series).
166. A. W. Adamson, *Advan. Chem. Ser.* **49**, 237 (1965) and the discussion following this on pp. 248–257.
167. T. J. Sworski, *J. Phys. Chem.* **67**, 2858 (1963).

bromine present is capable of reoxidizing any ferrous iron formed. A similar process should be possible for iodinations and thiocyanations of such compounds.

An example in which coordination is fundamental to a photochemical decomposition is found in the uranyl oxalate actinometer. When the amount of oxalic acid in the system is much greater than that of the uranyl salt, the over-all reaction is simply

$$(COOH)_2 \xrightarrow[UO_2^{2+}]{h\nu} CO_2 + CO + H_2O$$

When the molar ratio of oxalate to uranyl ion is less than unity, reduction of the uranium(VI) to uranium(V) occurs.[168] The photochemical decomposition of oxalate complexes of iron(III) and cobalt(III) proceeds with the reduction of two metal ions for each oxalate ion oxidized.[169] Here the initial photoreaction is one in which an electron is transferred from a coordinated oxalate anion to the central ferric ion.

The sensitizing action of iron(III) on the photoreaction of iodine and hydroxycarboxylic acids (such as citric, tartaric, lactic, and mandelic) has been attributed to the formation of complexes.[170] The proposed mechanism involved the photoreaction of the iron(III) complex to give a radical or radical–ion intermediate with reducing powers that subsequently reacts to reduce the ferric ion or iodine.

This kind of reaction is of the general type

$$M^{x+} \cdots L \xrightarrow{h\nu} M^{(x-1)+} + L\cdot$$

and is well established for many transition element complexes which contain the element in a high oxidation state. The generality of these reactions for acidopentamine cobalt(III) complexes with readily oxidized ligands has been emphasized by Adamson.[171] With ligands resistant to oxidation, the reaction for cobalt(III) complexes is one of photoaquation.

A reaction of another sort is found for many hydrated ions, where the central cation is *oxidized* photochemically. In these processes one observes

$$M^x(OH_2)_y \xrightarrow{h\nu} \{M^{x+1}(OH_2)^-\}$$

with the subsequent formation of free radicals ($H\cdot$) by interaction with protons

168. G. K. Rollefson and M. Burton, "Photochemistry and the Mechanism of Chemical Reactions," pp. 381–382. Prentice-Hall, Englewood Cliffs, New Jersey, 1939.
169. C. A. Parker and C. G. Hatchard, *J. Phys. Chem.* **63**, 22 (1959); C. A. Parker, *J. Phys. Chem.* **63**, 26 (1959).
170. G. V. Bakore and S. D. Rhardwaj, *Proc. Natl. Inst. Sci. India* **A29** (1), 90 (1963); *Chem. Abstr.* **60**, 154.
171. A. W. Adamson, *Discussions Faraday Soc.* **29**, 163 (1960).

from the solvent. In many such systems there is considerable evidence that a hydrated electron is the primary product of such photolytic reactions.

$$M^x(OH_2)_y \xrightarrow{h\nu} M^{x+1}(OH_2)_y + e(H_2O)_z^-$$

The hydrated electron then reacts with reducible species present in the solution.[172]

For some cations that are readily reducible, the water, rather than the metal ion, serves as the source of the liberated electron.

$$M^x(OH_2)_y \xrightarrow{h\nu} M^{x-1}(OH_2)_y{}^+ \xrightarrow{OH^-} M_{aq}^{x-1} + OH\cdot$$

A reaction of a different sort is the copper(I)- and copper(II)-sensitized photochemical reaction of peresters with ethers. Here a copper complex of the perester is formed in which the O—O bond is more readily dissociated to give reactive free radicals.[173] A typical reaction effected in this manner is

$$(C_2H_5)_2O + (CH_3)_3COOCCH_3 \xrightarrow[h\nu]{Cu^+ \text{ or } Cu^{2+}} \underset{\substack{| \\ O \\ | \\ C_2H_5}}{CH_3-C}\overset{H}{\underset{}{\;}}-O-\overset{O}{\underset{}{C}}-CH_3 + (CH_3)_3COH$$

In the photolysis of ceric ammonium nitrate in glacial acetic acid,[174] a variety of products is obtained. These include carbon dioxide, nitromethane, nitric acid, methanol, methyl nitrate, methane, and methyl acetate. The steps invoked to explain these products are an initial absorption of light to give an activated species

$$[Ce(IV)NO_3^-(HOOCCH_3)] + h\nu \rightleftarrows [Ce(IV)NO_3^-(HOOCCH_3)]^*$$

The next steps involve the decomposition of this activated species

$$[Ce(IV)(NO_3^-)(HOOCCH_3)]^* \begin{cases} Ce(III) + HONO_2 + CH_3CO_2 \quad (a) \\ \\ Ce(IV)NO_3^- + CO_2 + CH_4 \quad (b) \end{cases}$$

172. A comprehensive survey of the reactions of the hydrated electron and solvated electrons may be found in E. J. Hart, ed., "Solvated Electron," Advan. Chem. Ser. 50 (1965).
173. G. Sosnovsky, J. Org. Chem. 28, 2934 (1963).
174. T. W. Martin, A. Henshall, and R. C. Gross, J. Am. Chem. Soc. 85, 113 (1963); T. W. Martin, R. E. Rummel, and R. C. Gross, J. Am. Chem. Soc. 86, 2595 (1964); T. W. Martin, J. M. Burk, and A. Henshall, J. Am. Chem. Soc. 88, 1097 (1966).

TABLE VIII

PHOTOCHEMICAL PREPARATIONS

Reaction[a]	Wavelength (Å)	Quantum yield	Reference
$XArCr(CO)_3 + D \rightarrow XArCr(CO)_2D + CO$	2000–4500 Å with 3660 and 4005 Å peaks	—	175
$C_5H_5Mn(CO)_3 + D \rightarrow C_5H_5Mn(CO)_2D + CO$	Same as above	~1	176
$Cr(CO)_6 \rightarrow Cr(CO)_5 + CO$	Same as above	~0.4	177
$Fe(CO)_5 + 3AcacH \rightarrow Fe(Acac)_3 + 1.5H_2 + 5CO^b$	UV	—	178
$Cr(H_2O)_6^{3+} + SCN^- \rightarrow Cr(H_2O)_5SCN^{2+} + H_2O$	4000–5750	~1×10^{-4}	179
$\overset{*}{Mn}(CO)_6 + CO \rightarrow Mn(CO)(CO)_5 + CO$	3660	0.12–0.23	180
$W(CO)_6 + xCH_3CN \rightarrow W(CO)_{6-x}(CH_3CN)_x + xCO$	—	—	181
$PhH + \frac{1}{2}O_2 \xrightarrow{Fe^{3+},\ Cu^{2+}} PhOH + Ph_2 + 2H\cdot$	3130	0.13	182
$PhCOOH + \frac{1}{2}O_2 \xrightarrow{Fe^{3+}} HOPhCOOH$	3650	—	183, 184
$RH,\ etc. \xrightarrow{CuCl_2}$ Halogenated products, etc.	—	—	185
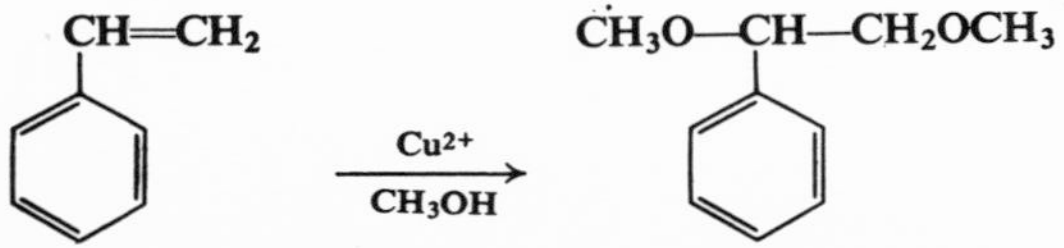	2537	—	186

TABLE VIII—*continued*

PHOTOCHEMICAL PREPARATIONS

Reaction[a]	Wavelength (Å)	Quantum yield	Reference
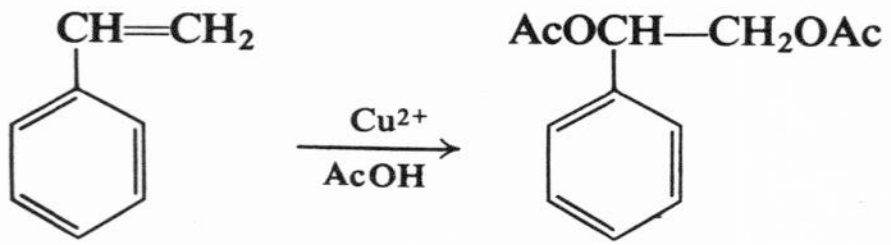 CH=CH$_2$ (phenyl) $\xrightarrow[\text{AcOH}]{\text{Cu}^{2+}}$ AcOCH—CH$_2$OAc (phenyl)	2537	—	186

[a] Here D indicates donor molecule (Lewis base).

[b] Acac = CH$_3$C=CHC—CH$_3$, with O⁻ and O.

175. W. Strohmeier and H. Hellmann, *Chem. Ber.* **96**, 2859 (1963).
176. W. Strohmeier, C. Barbeau, and D. von Hobe, *Chem. Ber.* **96**, 3254 (1963).
177. W. Strohmeier and K. Gerlach, *Chem. Ber.* **94**, 398 (1961).
178. J. C. Goan, C. H. Huether, and H. E. Podall, *Inorg. Chem.* **2**, 1078 (1963).
179. A. W. Adamson, *J. Inorg. Nucl. Chem.* **13**, 275 (1960).
180. W. Strohmeier and R. Muller, *Z. Physik. Chem. (Frankfurt)* **28**, 112 (1961).
181. G. R. Dobson, M. F. A. El Sayed, I. W. Stolz, and R. K. Sheline, *Inorg. Chem.* **1**, 526 (1962).
182. J. H. Baxendale and J. Magee, *Trans. Faraday Soc.* **51**, 205 (1955).
183. H. G. C. Bates and N. Uri, *J. Am. Chem. Soc.* **75**, 2754 (1953).
184. J. Saldick and A. O. Allen, *J. Am. Chem. Soc.* **77**, 1388 (1955).
185. J. K. Kochi, *J. Am. Chem. Soc.* **84**, 2121 (1962).
186. S. Murai and S. Tsutsumi, *Bull. Chem. Soc. Japan* **39**, 198 (1966).

and finally other steps involve the reactions of these species among themselves and the starting materials to give other products. Because of the special nature of the initial photodecomposition of the $[Ce(IV)(NO_3^-)(HOOCCH_3)]$ complex, reaction (a) above is described as a ligand photooxidation–reduction sensitization and (b) as a ligand photosensitization. They are unusual in that all of the constituents of the mixed complex are activated for potential reaction and the energy transfer subsequent to absorption of the photon is unimolecular (i.e., within the complex).

The use of photochemical methods often provides a very convenient route to new complexes. Some of the most striking applications of this sort are seen in the syntheses of various metal carbonyls and their derivatives that contain coordinated olefins or aromatic compounds. Some of these are listed in Table VIII together with other photochemical syntheses of more typical complexes.

The photochemical catalytic isomerization of olefins is found to occur in the presence of iron dodecacarbonyl $[Fe_3(CO_{12})]$.[187] Thus 1-octene can be converted to a variety of isomeric materials when it is irradiated in the presence of iron dodecacarbonyl in light petroleum. The mechanism proposed for this process involves the initial formation of $Fe(CO)_4$, which then coordinates to the olefin to give a complex similar to that formed with ethylene: $C_2H_4 \cdot Fe(CO)_4$. The complexed olefin then undergoes a rearrangement and subsequently is released as the complex undergoes a slow decomposition.

The use of π-complexes of olefins as photochemical catalysts provides some easy routes to certain products derived from olefins.[188] The cuprous chloride complex with cyclooctadiene catalyzes the photochemical conversion of 1,5-cyclooctadiene to tricyclo[3.3.0.0]octane.

The irradiation (2537 Å) of 1,3-butadiene in ether, in the presence of cuprous chloride, leads to a 30% yield of cyclobutene; in the absence of cuprous chloride this reaction was not observed. The reactions of this sort show a considerable degree of specificity on the π-complex present, as the use of

187. M. D. Carr, V. V. Kane, and M. C. Whiting, *Proc. Chem. Soc.* p. 408 (1964).
188. R. Srinivasan, *J. Am. Chem. Soc.* **85**, 3048 (1963).

1,5-hexadiene with the cuprous chloride π-complex with 1,5-octadiene did not lead to isomerization of the 1,5-hexadiene.

The importance of photochemical reactions involving metal complexes in biology is enormous, and a special journal has been established which is largely devoted to this area. This is *Photochemistry and Photobiology*, a journal that contains data on a large number of rather complex systems, in many of which metal ions play a significant role, e.g., the photooxidation of ascorbic acid by a manganese–flavin–catalase system.[189] These are largely outside of the scope of the present work.

4.8. The Catalysis of Homogeneous Hydrogenations

The brief treatment of the activation of molecular hydrogen in Section 4.3 gives only a superficial notion of the amount of work that has been carried out on this type of reaction. Much of it has resulted in empirical information that has been recast into a more detailed structural and mechanistic framework only more recently.

Homogeneous "hydrogenation" (actually more exactly a catalytic reduction) in aqueous solution was recognized in early studies of the reaction of elementary hydrogen with aqueous solutions of some easily reduced metal salts. This was found to result in the reduction of the metal ion in many cases. Thus ions derived from elements below hydrogen in the electromotive series can often be reduced to the free element by the high-pressure hydrogenation of their aqueous solutions, and some of these reactions occur at room temperature. For other ions, the reduction may be merely to a lower, but still positive oxidation state.[190] The fact that these species can be reduced from homogeneous solution by hydrogen implies that they are potentially capable of catalyzing homogeneous hydrogenations by acting as or furnishing intermediates which can reduce other species that are not as capable of entering into a direct interaction with elemental hydrogen.

One of the first reports of the homogeneous catalysis by metal salts of the reduction of substrates by hydrogen was made by Calvin.[191] He found that *p*-benzoquinone could be reduced by hydrogen in quinoline solutions when

189. H. M. Habermann and H. Gaffron, *Photochem. Photobiol* **1**, 159 (1962).
190. For some early uses of palladium and platinum complexes as catalysts for homogeneous reactions, see E. K. Rideal and H. S. Taylor, "Catalysis in Theory and Practice," pp. 192 ff. Macmillan, New York, 1919. The cases cited involve reduction to a colloidal form of the element. The direct hydrogenation of metal salts may be found in earlier literature. Thus 2 *N* CuCl$_2$ can be reduced with hydrogen at 100 atm to give CuCl: V. Ipatieff, *Ber. Deut. Chem. Ges.* **44**, 3452 (1911). A large number of related reactions are cited in the volumes of Gmelin's Handbuch that deal with the metals below hydrogen in the electromotive force series.
191. M. Calvin, *Trans. Faraday Soc.* **34**, 1181 (1938).

various copper salts and complexes were also present in solution. The most effective catalysts were found to be cupric acetate and bis(salicylaldehydato)-copper(II). Solutions of these copper(II) compounds react with hydrogen in an autocatalytic reaction that proceeds until most of the copper has been reduced to the cuprous state. This part of the process was found to be very greatly affected by the presence of small amounts of aniline, which was present as an impurity in the quinoline. This initial step was found to be markedly accelerated by the aniline.

The mechanism proposed for the catalytic hydrogenation (reduction) of the substrate p-benzoquinone in the presence of copper(I) and quinoline(Q) was the following (Cu^I represents cuprous acetate):

$$Cu^I + Q \; \underset{}{\overset{}{\rightleftharpoons}} \; Cu^IQ$$

$$Cu^IQ + H_2 \; \underset{k_1'}{\overset{k_1}{\rightleftharpoons}} \; Cu^IQH_2$$

$$Cu^IQH_2 + 2Su \; \overset{k_2}{\longrightarrow} \; Cu^IQ + 2SuH$$

$$Cu^IQH_2 + Cu^IQ \; \overset{k_3}{\longrightarrow} \; 2Cu^0 + 2Q + 2HAc$$

where $k_2 > k_1' > k_1 > k_3$ (here Su represents *one* equivalent of the reducible substrate). In a later paper[192] this mechanism was altered to accommodate the fact that dimeric forms of the copper complexes, $(Cu^IQ)_2$ and $(Cu^IQ)_2H_2$, were suspected to be present in these solutions.

Although this system has been subjected to extensive study,[193-201] its properties are more like those of a *redox* catalyst than a *hydrogenation* catalyst. Thus its general behavior is what might be expected for a system in which the effective reductant is the cuprous ion.*,[200]

* The Cu^IH complexes present in these systems are not effective hydrogenation catalysts under ambient conditions. Apparently analogous complexes, when promoted by the presence of cadmium, can catalyze the hydrogenation of carboxylic acids to alcohols in a heterogeneous system at elevated temperatures and pressures. See H. W. van der Linden, B. Stouthamer, and J. C. Vlugter, *Chem. Weekblad* **60**, 254 (1964), *Chem. Abstr.* **61**, 9691f; B. J. Stouthamer and J. C. Vlugter, *J. Am. Oil Chemists' Soc.* **42**, 646 (1965).

192. M. Calvin, *J. Am. Chem. Soc.* **61**, 2230 (1939).
193. W. K. Wilmarth, M. K. Barsh, and S. S. Dharmatti, *J. Am. Chem. Soc.* **74**, 5035 (1952).
194. W. K. Wilmarth and M. K. Barsh, *J. Am. Chem. Soc.* **75**, 2237 (1953).
195. M. Calvin and W. K. Wilmarth, *J. Am. Chem. Soc.* **78**, 1301 (1956).
196. W. K. Wilmarth and M. K. Barsh, *J. Am. Chem. Soc.* **78**, 1305 (1956).
197. S. Weller and G. A. Wells, *J. Am. Chem. Soc.* **75**, 769 (1953).
198. L. W. Wright and S. Weller, *J. Am. Chem. Soc.* **76**, 3345 (1954).
199. L. Wright, S. Weller, and G. A. Mills, *J. Phys. Chem.* **59**, 1061 (1955).
200. M. Parris and R. J. P. Williams, *Discussions Faraday Soc.* **20**, 240 (1960).
201. W. J. Downing and P. E. Potter, *Proc. Chem. Soc.* p. 244 (1960).

Homogeneous hydrogenations by transition metal complexes of the sort that have been widely used may be ascribed tentatively to Yuji Shibata and his co-workers, E. Matsumoto and M. Iguchi (translated as Iguti in earlier issues of *Chemical Abstracts*). Shibata and Matsumoto[202] reported that [Pd(en)Cl$_2$] accelerated the reduction of quinone by hydrogen. In more detailed studies, Iguchi reported[203] that unstable rhodium(III) complexes (such as [Rh(NH$_3$)$_5$(OH$_2$)]Cl$_3$ with replaceable water and [Rh(NH$_3$)$_4$Cl$_2$]Cl with replaceable chloride) accelerated the reduction of quinone by hydrogen, but substitution-inert complexes (such as [Rh(NH$_3$)$_6$]Cl$_3$ and [Rh(en)$_3$]Cl$_3$) did not. He also found that rhodium chloride catalyzed the reduction of quinone, fumaric acid, methylene blue, sodium nitrite, and hydroxylamine. In a later paper, Iguchi[204] reported his observations on the reaction of hydrogen with potassium cobaltous cyanide. He found that half a mole of hydrogen was taken up per cobalt atom and reported methylamine as a reduction product from the cyanide.

The nature of these reactions has been worked out in greater detail as the types of interaction which hydrogen may exhibit with metal ions have been worked out in greater detail. A major step was the acceptance of the fact that the hydride anion, H:$^-$, can function as a ligand in the complexes involved in such catalytic processes. The characterization of the borohydride ion, BH$_4$$^-$, which contains such ligands and is indeed a fair reducing agent (though *not* generated under the conditions utilized in homogeneous hydrogenations), assisted this development considerably.[205] The hydride complexes of the transition elements are of a related type, but the isolated complexes have certain stabilizing ligands present, such as phosphines, carbon monoxide, cyanide, and other high ligand field strength ligands with pi bonding (back-donating) characteristics. These compounds can often be formed from hydrogen-containing organic compounds, as well as by direct reaction with molecular hydrogen. Some of the reactions that have been used to prepare hydrido complexes are

$$Co_2(CO)_8 + H_2 \xrightarrow[\text{pressure}]{\Delta} 2HCo(CO)_4$$

(ref. 206)

202. Y. Shibata and E. Matsumoto, *Nippon Kagaku Zasshi* **60**, 1173 (1939); *Chem. Abstr.* **34**, 1582.

203. M. Iguchi, *Nippon Kagaku Zasshi* **60**, 1787 (1939); *Chem. Abstr.* **34**, 1937.

204. M. Iguchi, *Nippon Kagaku Zasshi* **63**, 634 (1942); *Chem. Abstr.* **41**, 2975.

205. Lithium aluminum hydride can function as a catalyst for the homogeneous hydrogenation of 2-pentyne and conjugated dienes to monoolefins at 190°C and 800–1400 psi of H$_2$ in tetrahydrofuran [L. H. Slaugh, *Tetrahedron* **22**, 1741 (1966)]. Here the reaction proceeds by a succession of steps in which the olefin adds on LiAlH$_4$ to give an intermediate metal alkyl which then undergoes hydrogenolysis.

206. J. Chatt, *Proc. Chem. Soc.* p. 318 (1962). This is a review with references to other reviews as well as the original literature.

$$RhCl_3 \xrightarrow[\text{[(C}_6\text{H}_5)_2\text{P(C}_2\text{H}_5)]}{\text{C}_2\text{H}_5\text{OH}} \{RhHCl_2[P(C_2H_5)(C_6H_5)_2]_3\}$$

(ref. 207)

$$RhCl_3[As(C_6H_5)_2CH_3]_3 \xrightarrow{\text{H}_2\text{PO}_3} \{RhHCl_2[As(C_6H_5)_2CH_3]_3\}$$

(ref. 208)

$$[(C_2H_5)_3P]_2PtCl_2 \xrightarrow[\text{tetrahydrofuran}]{\text{LiAlH}_4} [(C_2H_5)_3P]_2PtHCl$$

(ref. 209)

$$Rh^{3+} + CN^- \xrightarrow[\text{in H}_2\text{O}]{\text{NaBH}_4} [HRh(CN)_5)]^{3-}$$

(ref. 209)

$$\{Pt[P(C_2H_5)_3]Cl_2\}_2 \xrightarrow[\text{OH}^-]{\text{C}_2\text{H}_5\text{OH}} HPt[P(C_2H_5)_3]_2Cl$$

(ref. 209)

$$2RhS + H_2O + 9CO + 4Cu \xrightarrow[\text{pressure}]{\Delta} 2HRh(CO)_4 + CO_2 + 2Cu_2S$$

(ref. 209)

$$2[Co(CN)_5]^{3-} + H_2 \rightleftharpoons 2[HCo(CN)_5]^{3-}$$

(ref. 210)

Although these reactions exhibit some similarities to those in which simple metal ions (such as Ag^+, Hg_2^{2+}, Hg^{2+}, and Cu^{2+}) and their complexes react with hydrogen, the properties of the products are quite different. Following Simandi and Nagy,[211] we can differentiate between *redox* catalysts and *hydrogenation* catalysts. Thus silver(I) and the other species cited are redox catalysts. They function in the presence of suitable reducible substrates (such as $Cr_2O_7^{2-}$ or Ce^{4+}) and allow hydrogen to function as a reducing agent towards such oxidants. The hydrogenation catalysts facilitate the hydrogenation of double bonds and are quite different in structure and composition from the redox catalysts. Of the hydrogenation catalysts, the pentacyanocobaltate(II) ion has been studied the most thoroughly. The mechanism by which $[HCo(CN)_5]^{3-}$ hydrogenates unsaturated organic molecules is dependent apparently upon the substrate to some extent. Thus Kwiatek and his

207. A. Sacco and R. Ugo, *Chim. Ind.* (*Milan*) **45**, 1096 (1963); *Chem. Abstr.* **60**, 15411.
208. J. Lewis, R. S. Nyholm, and G. K. N. Reddy, *Chem. Ind.* (*London*) p. 1386 (1960).
209. M. L. H. Green, *Angew. Chem.* **72**, 719 (1960), a review.
210. (a) N. K. King and M. E. Winfield, *J. Am. Chem. Soc.* **80**, 2060 (1958); **83**, 3366 (1961); (b) B. DeVries, *J. Catalysis* **1**, 489 (1962); (c) G. A. Mills, S. Weller, and A. Wheller, *J. Phys. Chem.* **63**, 403 (1959); (d) J. Kwiatek, I. L. Mador, and J. K. Sezler, *J. Am. Chem. Soc.* **84**, 304 (1962); *Advan. Chem. Ser.* **37**, 201 (1963); (e) J. Bayston, N. K. King, and M. E. Winfield, *Advan. Catalysis* **9**, 312 (1957); (f) S. W. Weller and G. A. Mills, *Advan. Catalysis* **7**, 163 (1956); (g) M. Iguchi, *Nippon Kagaku Zasshi* **63**, 634 (1942), *Chem. Abstr.* **41**, 2975; (h) T. Suzuki and T. Kwan, *Nippon Kagaku Zasshi* **87**, 395 (1966).
211. L. Simandi and F. Nagy, *Acta Chim. Acad. Sci. Hung.* **46**, 137 (1965).

co-workers[210(d)] have shown that butadiene is probably hydrogenated through the reaction sequence

$$2Co(CN)_5^{3-} + H_2 \rightleftarrows 2[HCo(CN)_5]^{3-}$$
$$[HCo(CN)_5]^{3-} + C_4H_6 \rightleftarrows [H, Co(CN)_5^{3-}, C_4H_6]$$
$$[H, Co(CN)_5^{3-}, C_4H_6] + [HCo(CN)_5]^{3-} \rightarrow 2Co(CN)_5^{3-} + C_4H_8 \text{ (slow)}$$

They isolated the intermediate complex given above as $[H, Co(CN)_5^{3-}, C_4H_6]$ The formation of such a *stable* intermediate is not a *necessary* condition for such hydrogenation processes, however. Simandi and Nagy[211] found that the hydrogenation of cinnamic acid involved two slow successive hydrogen atom transfers from $[HCo(CN)_5]^{3-}$ to the substrate.

$$2Co(CN)_5^{3-} + H_2 \rightleftarrows 2HCo(CN)_5^{3-}$$
$$HCo(CN)_5^{3-} + C_6H_5—CH{=}CH—COO^- \rightarrow Co(CN)_5^{3-} + C_6H_5\overset{\cdot}{C}H—CH_2—COO^- \text{ (slow)}$$
$$HCo(CN)_5^{3-} + C_6H_5\overset{\cdot}{C}H—CH_2COO^- \rightarrow Co(CN)_5^{3-} + C_6H_5CH_2—CH_2—COO^- \text{ (slow)}$$

The structure of the adduct of perfluoroethylene and hydridopentacyano-cobaltate(III) has been determined.[212] Here there are six octahedrally arranged bonds about the cobalt, all to single carbon atoms. The formula of the ion can be given succinctly as $[(CN)_5CoCF_2CF_2H]^{3-}$.

The cyanide complex containing hydrogen has been written above as $[HCo(CN)_5]^{3-}$, though there is evidence to suggest that the cobalt(II)–cyanide–hydrogen system is actually more complex than this.[210(a,c), 213] The direct, reversible reaction of molecular hydrogen with $[Co(CN)_5]^{3-}$ gives a colorless complex, but the sequence of steps may well involve

$$Co(CN)_5^{3-} + H_2 \underset{\longleftarrow}{\overset{Slow}{\longrightarrow}} [H_2Co(CN)_5]^{3-}$$

followed by

$$[H_2Co(CN)_5]^{3-} + Co(CN)_5^{3-} \rightleftarrows 2[HCo(CN)_5]^{3-}$$

Alternatively, the existence of an appreciable salt effect on the hydrogen absorption rate led Mills et al.[210(c)] to propose that the activation of hydrogen could proceed in part by a *heterolytic* scission

$$[Co(CN)_5]^{3-} + H:H + X^- \rightleftarrows [HCo(CN)_5]^{4-} + H^+ + X^-$$

followed by

$$[HCo(CN)_5]^{4-} + [Co(CN)_5]^{3-} \rightarrow 2[Co(CN)_5]^{4-} + H^+$$

with the cobalt(I) species also being catalytically active. These workers found that solutions of cobalt(II) cyanide aged (probably via dimerization) and lost their ability to undergo facile reduction by hydrogen. Subsequent work has favored a hydride complex of cobalt(II) rather than a cobalt(I) cyanide as the active catalyst. The reaction of cobalt(II) cyanide with hydrogen at 1 atm has a half-life of about 1 minute.

212. R. Mason and D. R. Russell, *Chem. Commun.* p. 182 (1965).
213. C. K. Jorgensen, "Inorganic Complexes," p. 147. Academic Press, New York, 1963.

This hydride complex, $[HCo(CN)_5]^{3-}$, is formed very readily in aqueous solution, even at $0°C$, and provides a convenient and practical way to activate molecular hydrogen for subsequent reduction processes. The application of this system for the reduction of many types of organic compounds has been studied over a period of years by Murakami and his co-workers.[214] The complex is effective in at least two types of hydrogenation reactions. The first consists of the hydrogenation of some unsaturated compounds. The second type is the reductive amination of α-oxo acids and their esters in the presence of 6% ammonia. The preparation of phenylalanine using this catalyst may be effected by the reduction of the oxime of phenylpyruvic acid or by the reduction of phenylpyruvic acid itself in the presence of ammonia

$$
\begin{array}{ccc}
C_6H_5CH_2{-}\underset{\displaystyle \underset{O}{\|}}{C}{-}C\!\!\diagup_{OH}^{O} & \xrightarrow[\substack{H_2,\,40°C \\ 50\ kg/cm^2}]{\substack{NH_3 \\ CoCl_2,\,KCN}} & C_6H_5CH_2{-}\underset{\displaystyle \underset{NH}{\|}}{C}{-}C\!\!\diagup_{OH}^{O} \\
\Big\downarrow NH_2OH & & \searrow Reduction \\
C_6H_5CH_2{-}\underset{\displaystyle \underset{NOH}{\|}}{C}{-}C\!\!\diagup_{OH}^{O} & \xrightarrow[40{-}70°C;\ 100\ kg/cm^2]{CoCl_2,\,KCN,\,H_2} & C_6H_5CH_2{-}\underset{\displaystyle \underset{NH_2}{|}}{\overset{\displaystyle \overset{H}{|}}{C}}{-}C\!\!\diagup_{OH}^{O}
\end{array}
$$

With unsaturated hydrocarbons it was found that they are reduced only when they are capable of coordination to the cobalt. Cinnamic acid gave dihydro-cinnamic acid and sorbic acid gave γ,δ-hexenoic acid. Other reductions that have been carried out with this type of catalyst include the reduction of aromatic nitro compounds to amines (e.g., $C_6H_5NO_2$ to $C_6H_5NH_2$) or azines (e.g., $C_6H_5NO_2$ to $C_6H_5N{=}NC_6H_5$).[215] In earlier studies,[216] this group had established that unsaturated ligands in cobalt complexes were more readily reduced with hydrogen than were the free ligands. $C_6H_5CH_2CH(NH_2)COOH$ was obtained in about 65% yield when $[Co(pn)_2O_2CC(:NO){-}CH_2C_6H_5]^+$ was hydrogenated in methanol at $95°{-}100°C$ under pressure of $150\ kg/cm^2$. The addition of cyanide (as KCN) to systems such as this was found to facilitate the reduction process very considerably, presumably because this would assist

214. M. Murakami and J. W. Kang, *Bull. Chem. Soc. Japan* **36**, 763 (1963) is paper VIII in a series on the homogeneous hydrogenation of organic compounds using complexes of cobalt as catalysts.

215. M. Murakami, R. Kawai, and K. Suzuki, *Nippon Kagaku Zasshi* **84**, 669 (1963); *Chem. Abstr.* **60**, 4053.

216. M. Murakami, J.-W. Kang, H. Itani, S. Senoh, and N. Matsusato, *Nippon Kagaku Zasshi* **84**, 48, 51, 53 (1963); *Chem. Abstr.* **59**, 15207. J.-W. Kang, *Nippon Kagaku Zasshi* **84** 56 (1963); *Chem. Abstr.* **59**, 15208.

in the formation of $HCo(CN)_5^{3-}$. When the cobalt(II) cyanide complex was used as a catalyst for the reduction of $HOOCC{\equiv}CCOOH$, the product consisted of $HOOCCH_2CH_2COOH$ and fumaric acid, and fumaric acid was also obtained as the principal product when the reduction catalyst was a mixture of $[Co(NH_3)_5Cl]Cl_2$ and KCN in a 1:5 ratio.[217] This indicates that the addition of hydrogen occurs in a trans fashion. When ammonia is present the process involved is a reductive amination. Thus in the reduction of $C_6H_5COCOC_6H_5$ with $[Co(CN)_5]^{3-}$ in 6% aqueous ammonia, the products in this case are 38% $C_6H_5COCH(OH)C_6H_5$; 24% *erythro*-$C_6H_5CH(OH)$ $CH(NH_2)C_6H_5$, and 4% *erythro*-$C_6H_5CH(NH_2)CH(NH_2)C_6H_5$. The compounds whose reduction by this catalyst have been examined by other workers include styrenes,[210(d)] cyclohexadiene,[210(a)] cyclopentadiene,[210(d)] butadiene,[210(d)] benzoquinone,[210(d)] ferricyanide,[210(c)] and sorbic acid[210(b)] among others.

The use of other transition metal hydride complexes (in aqueous or alcoholic solutions) as intermediates in hydrogenation and hydrogen transfer reactions is successful in many cases. A typical hydrogen transfer reaction of this sort is[218]

3-*tert*-butylcyclohexanone + CH$_3$—CH—CH$_3$ $\xrightarrow[(CH_3O)_3P]{H_2IrCl_6}$
                               |
                               OH

$\qquad$ 3-*tert*-butylcyclohexanol (axial) + CH$_3$—C—CH$_3$
$\qquad\qquad\qquad\qquad\qquad\qquad\qquad\qquad\qquad\qquad\qquad$ ‖
$\qquad\qquad\qquad\qquad\qquad\qquad\qquad\qquad\qquad\qquad\qquad$ O

The use of rhodium(III) complexes as catalysts for homogeneous hydrogenations is also very well established. Rhodium(III) complexes catalyze the reduction of ferric ions to ferrous ions by hydrogen in aqueous solutions at 80°C,[219] and an intermediate $[HRhCl_5]^{3-}$ was suggested as the reductant. Subsequently[220] it was shown that 1,2,6-trichlorotripyridinerhodium(III) catalyzes the hydrogenation of 1-hexene in ethanolic solution. Since rhodium(III) complexes are also capable of isomerizing olefins,[221] it was found that this reaction involves the initial isomerization of the 1-hexene, followed by hydrogenation. In later work, rhodium complexes which were much more effective catalysts were discovered.[222] Thus, 1,2,3-tris(triphenylphosphine)trichlororhodium(III) and its dimethylphenylarsine analogue very

217. M. Murakami, K. Suzuki, and J.-W. Kang, *Nippon Kagaku Zasshi* **83**, 1226 (1962); *Chem. Abstr.* **59**, 13868.
218. Y. M. Y. Haddad, M. B. Henbest, J. Husbands, and T. R. B. Mitchell, *Proc. Chem. Soc.* p. 361 (1964).
219. J. F. Harrod and J. Halpern, *Can. J. Chem.* **37**, 1933 (1959).
220. R. D. Gillard, J. A. Osburn, P. B. Stockwell, and G. Wilkinson, *Proc. Chem. Soc.* p. 284 (1964).
221. J. F. Harrod and A. J. Chalk, *J. Am. Chem. Soc.* **86**, 1776 (1964).
222. J. A. Osburn, G. Wilkinson, and J. F. Young, *Chem. Commun.* p. 17 (1965).

effectively catalyze the hydrogenation of 1-hexene. These complexes are also catalysts for hydroformylation reactions.

$RhCl(PPh_3)_3$ is also a very efficient catalyst for the homogeneous hydrogenation of olefins and acetylenes under very mild conditions (25°C and hydrogen pressures less than 1 atm).[223,224] Here benzene is used as the solvent and enters into an intermediate complex of lower coordination number, $RhCl(PPh_3)_2S$, that is responsible for some of the activity. For example, 1-hexene in ethanol–benzene solutions is quantitatively reduced to n-hexane by hydrogen at 20°C with a catalyst concentration of 5×10^{-3} M. Using $RhCl(PPh_3)_2$ and similar conditions with 2 M 1-hexyne, n-hexane was also formed quantitatively. This complex is also a catalyst for hydroformylation:

1-hexyne $\xrightarrow[\substack{H_2, CO_2, 110°C \\ 120\ atm}]{\substack{RhCl(PPh_3)_3\ in \\ ethanol-benzene}}$ $CH_3CH_2CH_2CH_2CH_2CH_2CHO$ + $CH_3CH_2CH_2CH_2\underset{\underset{H}{|}}{\overset{\overset{CH_3}{|}}{C}}HC{=}O$

The related ruthenium complexes $RuCl_2(PPh_3)_4$ and $RuCl_2(PPh_3)_3$ can also catalyze the hydrogenation of olefins and alkynes in benzene–ethanol mixtures. Here the ethanol plays an important role as the reactions are much slower in its absence.[225] In both of these cases an intermediate hydrido complex is involved.

4.8.1. PLATINUM(II)–TIN CHLORIDE COMPLEXES

The interaction of aqueous solutions of platinum salts with stannous chloride leads to complexes which are capable of catalyzing the homogeneous hydrogenation of ethylene at room temperature and 1 atm pressure of hydrogen.[226] The same complex had previously[227] been shown to be an effective catalyst for the carbonylation of unsaturated compounds. Stannous chloride facilitates the addition of ethylene to platinum(II) to form $KPtCl_3 \cdot C_2H_4 \cdot H_2O$ (Zeise's salt) and in this reaction there is evidently the formation of an intermediate complex containing coordinated $SnCl_3^-$ groups.[227] Stannous tin has a so-called "lone pair" and $SnCl_3^-$ has also, so $SnCl_3^-$ has all the requirements needed to act as a donor in complexes.

223. J. F. Young, J. A. Osburn, F. H. Jardine, and G. Wilkinson, *Chem. Commun.* p. 131 (1965).

224. J. F. Young, J. A. Osburn, F. H. Jardine, and G. Wilkinson, *Chem. Ind.* (*London*) p. 560 (1965).

225. D. Evans, J. A. Osburn, F. H. Jardine, and G. Wilkinson, *Nature* **208**, 1203 (1965).

226. R. D. Cremer, E. L. Jenner, R. V. Lindsey, Jr., and U. G. Stolberg, *J. Am. Chem. Soc.* **85**, 1691 (1963).

227. E. L. Jenner and R. V. Lindsey, Jr., U.S. Patent 2,876,254, March 3, 1959.

Actually it functions as a weak σ-donor and a strong π-acceptor[228,229]; it is similar to carbon monoxide in this respect.

The reaction of $PtCl_6^{2-}$ and $SnCl_2$ in methanol gives the five-coordinate platinum(II) complex anion, $Pt(SnCl_3)_5^{3-}$ by the reaction

$$3Cl^- + PtCl_6^{2-} + 6SnCl_2 \xrightarrow{CH_3OH} Pt(SnCl_3)_5^{3-} + SnCl_6^{2-}$$

The $SnCl_3^-$ ligands have a number of unusual effects on the platinum(II). They stabilize it against reduction to the metal by hydrogen; they have a strong trans effect (between SCN^- and CN^-); and they facilitate the formation of complexes with hydride, ethylene, and carbon monoxide. The complexes isolated from such reaction mixtures include both four- and five-coordinated platinum(II), i.e., derivatives of $Pt(SnCl_3)_5^{3-}$, $\{Pt(SnCl_3)_2[P(C_6H_5)_3]_2\}$, $[Pt(Cl)_2(SnCl_3)_2]^{2-}$, $[HPt(SnCl_3)_4]^{3-}$, and $\{HPt(SnCl_3)_2[(C_2H_5)_3P]_2\}^-$. The $Pt(SnCl_3)_5^{3-}$ ion is a trigonal bipyramid.[230]

The stannous chloride–platinum(II) complexes become poorer hydrogenation catalysts as the molecular weight of the olefin becomes progressively larger, so the ease of hydrogenation is apparently related to the ease with which the platinum–olefin complex can be formed. A number of analogous complexes, all of the type $(R_3Q)_2MX_2$ (where R = organic group; Q = P, As, or Sb; and M = Ni, Pd, or Pt) have been prepared and shown to be effective catalysts for the hydrogenation of olefins.[231]

An analogous rhodium complex, $[Rh_2Cl_2(SnCl_2,C_2H_5OH)_4]$, has also been reported and is a catalyst for both hydrogenation and hydroformylation reactions.[232]

4.8.2. RELATED WORK

A series of papers by V. A. Tulupov[233] investigated the catalysis of hydrogenations of carbon–carbon double bonds, using stearates of the transition elements and their neighbors from scandium(III) to zinc(II). The compounds hydrogenated included cyclopentene, cyclohexene, and 1-pentene. This work of Tulupov's is one of the first in which a clear distinction is made between catalytic *reductions* and catalytic *hydrogenations*. Tulupov proposed that the hydrogen may react with a coordinated, activated olefin in these systems.

228. R. V. Lindsey, Jr., G. W. Parshall, and U. G. Stolberg, *J. Am. Chem. Soc.* **87**, 658 (1965).
229. G. W. Parshall, *J. Am. Chem. Soc.* **88**, 704 (1966).
230. R. D. Cremer, R. V. Lindsey, Jr., C. T. Prewitt, and U. G. Stolberg, *J. Am. Chem. Soc.* **87**, 658 (1965).
231. J. C. Bailar, Jr., and H. Itatani, *J. Am. Chem. Soc.* **89**, 1592 (1967).
232. A. G. Davies, G. Wilkinson, and J. F. Young, *J. Am. Chem. Soc.* **85**, 1692 (1963).
233. V. A. Tulupov, *Russ. J. Phys. Chem.* (*English Transl.*) **39**, 1251 (1965) summarizes most of the previous work.

Chapter V *THEORETICAL AND PHYSICAL STUDIES ON COORDINATED LIGANDS*

5.1. Theoretical Studies

The coordination process results in very definite changes in many of the properties of the ligand. The most immediate cause of these is the change in the electronic density patterns of the ligands. This results from the polarization due to the proximity of the acceptor, an electron-poor species. This acceptor may be a positive ion, a neutral species, or rarely, a negative ion. The analogy of the coordination act to protonation is only a very crude one, since most of the acceptor species do not introduce such a high potential into the neighborhood of the electron cloud of the ligand. The formation of coordinate bonds with π-, as well as σ-components makes *a priori* predictions of the changes in electron density patterns reasonably difficult. It is necessary to have some understanding of the theoretical approaches to this problem before the interpretation of experimental data bearing on this point can be put on a systematic basis.

5.1.1. CHARGE REDISTRIBUTION

In recent years the interests of theoreticians working on the quantum mechanics of coordination compounds have been centered on the variations in the properties of the metal ions. The valence bond theory and the crystal field theory, in their simplest forms, both make reasonably definite statements about the ligand charge density in the complex in comparison with that in the free state. The valence bond theory considers that the electron pair of the coordinate bond is shared equally between the two atoms participating in it. This corresponds approximately to the transfer of an electron from the donor atom to the acceptor atom and this increases the formal charge of the donor atom by a unit positive charge.

$$M^+ + :B \rightarrow M:B^+$$

From such evidence as is available, this represents an *overestimate* of the charge redistribution. The crystal field theory considers that no ligand electron pairs are shared with the central acceptor atom in a complex and that, to a first approximation, the electronic distribution in the ligand does not change upon coordination. This represents an underestimate of the charge redistribution. The molecular orbital theory is formulated in a much more flexible manner in this respect. It allows the electrons to be distributed in orbitals made up of varying contributions from the central atom orbitals and the ligand orbitals. In some cases a direct experimental estimate of the relative contribution of the ligand and the metal orbitals to the complex orbitals can be made, e.g., from electron spin resonance spectra.

The number of instances in which theoretical calculations have been carried out on ligand electron densities is rather small. Of these, one of the most thoroughly studied appears to be the rather atypical complex, pyridine N-oxide. This may be represented as a coordination compound between pyridine and an oxygen atom.

This compound has been the subject of theoretical[1-6] and experimental[7-9] studies and the related pyridinium and pyridine systems have also been examined. The electronic charge densities (for the π-electron system) at the various atoms in these ring systems have been calculated and somewhat

1. H. Jaffe, *J. Am. Chem. Soc.* **76**, 3527 (1954).
2. R. A. Barnes, *J. Am. Chem. Soc.* **81**, 1935 (1959).
3. R. D. Brown and M. L. Heffernan, *Australian J. Chem.* **12**, 554 (1959).
4. R. McWeeny and T. E. Peacock, *Proc. Phys. Soc.* (*London*) **A70**, 41 (1957). (Self-consistent M.O. theory with configuration interaction.)
5. S. Mataga and N. Mataga, *Bull. Chem. Soc. Japan* **32**, 521 (1959).
6. N. Mataga and K. Kinoshita, *Z. Phys. Chem. N.F.* **13**, 140 (1957).
7. G. Tsoucaris, *J. Chim. Phys.* **31**, 619 (1961).
8. C. M. Box, A. R. Katritzky, and L. E. Sutton, *J. Chem. Soc.* p. 1254 (1958); p. 1258 has py:BF_3.
9. A. R. Katritzky, A. M. Munro, J. A. T. Beard, D. P. Dearnaley, and N. J. Earl, *J. Chem. Soc.* p. 2182 (1958).

different values have been obtained by different authors. Some of the typical results are as follows:

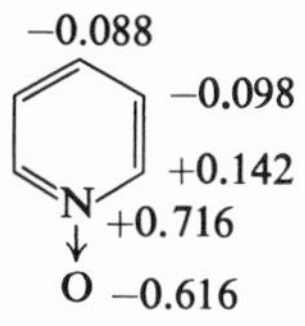

$$-0.088$$
$$-0.098$$
$$+0.142$$
$$N +0.716$$
$$\downarrow$$
$$O -0.616$$

Jaffe[1]

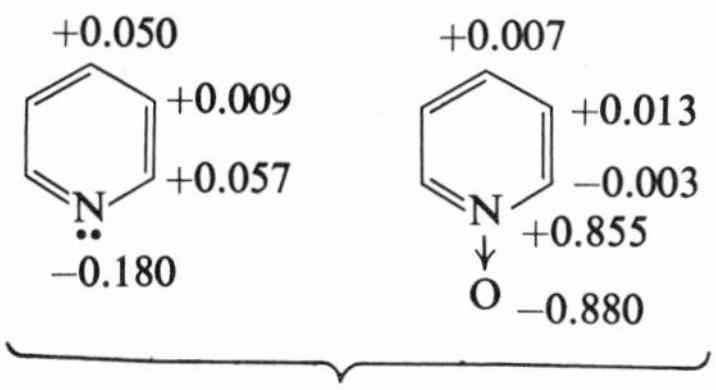

$$+0.050$$
$$+0.009$$
$$+0.057$$
$$N \ddots$$
$$-0.180$$

$$+0.007$$
$$+0.013$$
$$-0.003$$
$$N +0.855$$
$$\downarrow$$
$$O -0.880$$

Barnes[2]

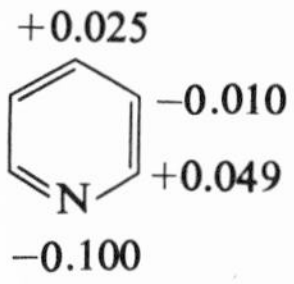

$$+0.025$$
$$-0.010$$
$$N +0.049$$
$$-0.100$$

McWeeny
and Peacock[4]

Here the numbers on the carbon atoms give the excess or deficiency, in electrons, in comparison with a system in which there is an even distribution (i.e., pyridine is compared to benzene).

Brown and Heffernan give several alternative methods for obtaining the π-electron density of pyridine and conclude that the following two sets probably bracket the *true* values, with these being closer to structure (B) than to structure (A).

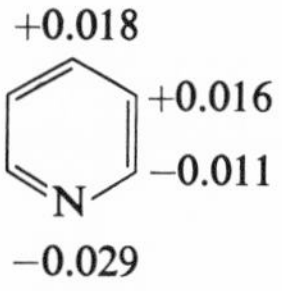

$$+0.018$$
$$+0.016$$
$$N -0.011$$
$$-0.029$$

(A)

$$+0.019$$
$$-0.004$$
$$N +0.048$$
$$-0.107$$

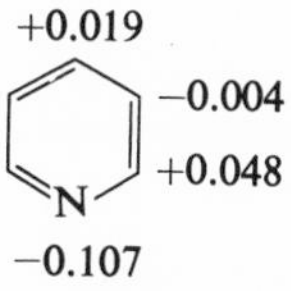

(B)

For the pyridinium ion such a treatment leads to the following two π-electron distributions:

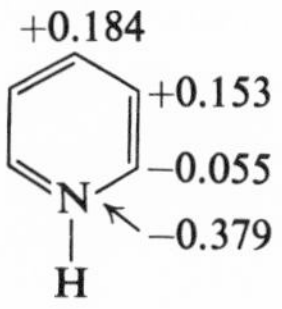

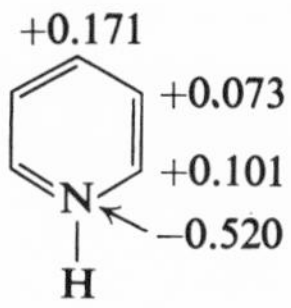

$$+0.184$$
$$+0.153$$
$$N -0.055$$
$$-0.379$$
$$H$$

$$+0.171$$
$$+0.073$$
$$N +0.101$$
$$-0.520$$
$$H$$

Jaffe showed that a "static" method of calculation (which corresponds to either the starting molecule or some point on the reaction path prior to the transition state) could not predict the order of reactivity toward both electrophilic and nucleophilic attack in the case of pyridine *N*-oxide. The method of localization (which corresponds more closely to a point on the reaction path beyond the transition state) was more successful. A comparison of the results obtained so far shows a considerable variation in their ability to predict the site of attack by electrophilic species. In the case of the results of Jaffe and Barnes, it would appear that they are consistent with the observation that the position of attack of pyridine by electrophilic reagents (normally the 3-position) is changed to the 4-position (or 2-position) in pyridine N-oxide. According to Jaffe,[1] pyridine N-oxide undergoes nucleophilic attack at these same two positions. The results of Barnes and of Brown and Heffernan show that this result is actually critically dependent upon the assumptions used to evaluate the integrals, specifically, the values assumed for the resonance integrals, β, between the carbon and nitrogen of the ring. Barnes used $\beta_{CN}{=}\beta_{CC}$ as suggested by Brown.[10] Brown and Heffernan used $\beta_{CN} = 2.470$ electron volts for pyridine and the values 2.30 and 2.50 electron volts for the pyridinium ion. (These values were derived by fitting the calculated energies of spectral transitions of the species involved to the experimental values.) The value of β_{NO} for pyridine N-oxide is similarly critical in the calculation of electron density of that compound. In an earlier paper, Brown[11] had pointed out many of the problems involved in the correlations of such MO calculations with chemical behavior.

In addition to the π-electron densities, there are a number of other theoretically accessible parameters which are related to the ease of attack of a given position by an electrophilic or nucleophilic species. Because the positions for electrophilic and nucleophilic substitutions in pyridine N-oxide are the *same*, it is obvious that any procedure that considers only the π-electron density will fail to be useful for both types of reaction.[1] This procedure can be considerably improved by the calculation of the *localization* energies for electrophilic and nucleophilic attack. These are carried out on the basis of a suitable model for the molecule in some state beyond the transition state *toward* the products. Localization energies of this sort were calculated for pyridine and for pyridine N-oxide by Jaffe[1] and are summarized in Table IX.

These result in the 4-position being the most active in pyridine N-oxide for both electrophilic and nucleophilic attack, the 3-position being the position in pyridine preferred for attack by electrophilic reagents, and the 2-position the one preferred by nucleophilic reagents. The localization energy, as used here, may be defined as

$$L = E^r - E$$

10. R. D. Brown, *J. Chem. Soc.* p. 272 (1956). This choice produced calculated reactivities which agreed with experimentally obtained rate factors for the attack of the phenyl radical on the pyridine nucleus.

11. R. D. Brown, *Quart. Rev. (London)* 6, 63 (1952).

TABLE IX

Localization Energies[a]

Compound	Position	Electrophilic substitution	Nucleophilic substitution
Pyridine	2	2.712	2.312
	3	2.487	2.378
	4	2.637	2.228
Pyridine N-oxide	2	2.634	2.689
	3	3.218	2.357
	4	2.474	1.714

[a] All energies are given in units of β, the resonance integral for the carbon–carbon bond.

where E^r is the π-electron energy of the molecule after some of the π-electrons have been localized in a certain portion of the aromatic system. When this localization energy is removed, the π-electron energy of the system is E. This localization energy, L, is essentially the same as a term ΔW introduced by Wheland in an earlier treatment of aromatic substitution.[12] An example of the type of model used here can be seen in the one used by Barnes[2] in the calculation of the localization energy for electrophilic attack at the 3-position of pyridine. Here the π-electron system, which originally extends over all six atoms (for calculation of E), is restricted to the five atoms other than the one being attacked. An electron pair is localized on this position, in readiness to form a bond with the electron-pair-deficient, attacking electrophilic reagent. In this state we can represent the molecule as

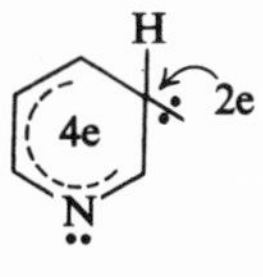

It must be noted that the introduction of heteroatoms into an aromatic system (i.e., the transformation of benzene into pyridine in which a carbon atom is replaced by a nitrogen atom) results in charge shifts that are not consistent with the assumptions of the Hückel molecular orbital treatment of conjugated systems.[4, 13]

12. G. W. Wheland, *J. Am. Chem. Soc.* **64**, 901 (1942).
13. R. McWeeny, *Proc. Roy. Soc. (London)* **A237**, 355 (1956).

A related, but simpler, set of theoretical studies has been carried out on 8-hydroxyquinoline and some of its derivatives.[14] Here, three species were considered, the form protonated on both oxygen and nitrogen (A), which is present in acidic solution, the form protonated only on the oxygen (B) that is

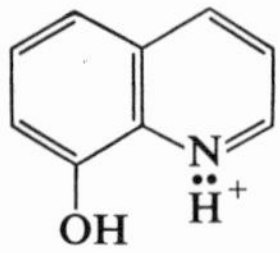

(A) 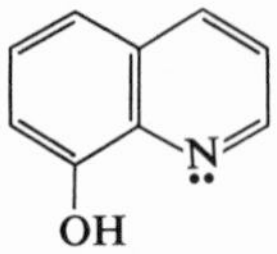   (B) 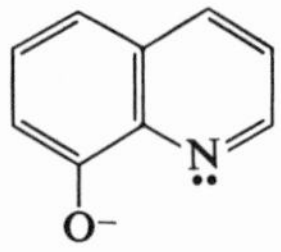   (C)

present in neutral solution, and the phenolate anion form (C) that is present in basic solution. These calculations were carried out using the Hückel LCAO procedure and the usual[15, 16] variation method. This leads to a secular determinant of the form

$$|H_{ij} - S_{ij}E| = 0$$

H_{ij} is defined as

$$H_{ij} = \int \Phi_i H \Phi_j d\tau$$

where i and j represent the nuclei with which the Φ are associated, while S_{ij} is the overlap integral, defined as

$$S_{ij} = \int \Phi_i \Phi_j d\tau$$

where Φ_i and Φ_j are the orbitals involved. For the π-electron systems under consideration, these orbitals are the atomic p orbitals of the atoms involved. In order to obtain numerical answers, it is customary to introduce certain assumptions. Thus H_{ii} for all the carbon-based p orbitals are assumed to be the same, as are all the H_{ij} terms where both of the orbitals involved are centered on carbon atoms. When a heteroatom is present, the terms that involve its orbitals will certainly be different from those for carbon. Such terms, which involve a carbon atom orbital and a heteroatom orbital or only

14. R. E. Burton and W. J. Davis, *J. Chem. Soc.* p. 1766 (1964).
15. R. Daudel, R. Lefebvre, and C. Moser, "Quantum Chemistry," pp. 49 ff. Wiley (Interscience), New York, 1959.
16. A. Streitwieser, "Molecular Orbital Theory for Organic Chemistry." Wiley, New York, 1961.

heteroatom orbitals, must be evaluated on some reasonable basis. In the treatment of 8-hydroxyquinoline, these parameters were expressed as follows:

$$H(N_{p\pi}, N_{p\pi}) = H_{CC} + m\beta_{CC}$$

$$H(O_{p\pi}, O_{p\pi}) = H_{CC} + n\beta_{CC}$$

$$H(N_{p\pi}, C_{p\pi}) = x\beta_{CC}$$

$$H(O_{p\pi}, C_{p\pi}) = y\beta_{CC}$$

where

$$H_{CC} = H(C_{p\pi}, C_{p\pi})$$

and β_{CC} is the bond integral term for carbon–carbon bonds. (The value of β_{CC} can be estimated from the resonance energy of benzene to be $(-)18$ kcal. From other data, values ranging from less than 18 kcal up to 76 kcal have been obtained, so these parameters are difficult to fix with certainty. A discussion may be found in the text by Streitwieser.[16]) The parameters m, n, x, and y must then be assigned fixed values by some procedure. The methods used by various authors to do this differ in a nontrivial way. Burton and Davis used the value $H(N_{p\pi}, C_{p\pi}) = 1.0 \beta_{CC}$ for their calculations on 8-hydroxyquinoline (this is the same as that used by Brown and Harcourt[17]) and carried out calculations on the protonated species, the neutral molecules, and the anion. They used the values $m = 0.5$ for nitrogen with a core charge of $+1$, and $m = 2.0$ for nitrogen with a core charge of $+2$ (these were selected on the basis of previous, more detailed theoretical studies). The evaluation of the relevant terms for the carbon-to-oxygen bond introduced a similar problem. This was solved by allowing n and y to vary to obtain the best fit (lowest energy). The best fit for the neutral molecule was obtained with $n = 1.5$ and $y = 0.8$; for the anion the corresponding values were $n = 0.75$ and $y = 0.8$. Using this procedure, the localization energies for electrophilic, nucleophilic, and radical attack were calculated for the anion, neutral molecule, and cation found in the 8-hydroxyquinoline system. In the case of electrophilic reagents, the preferred position of attack is the 5-position in each case.

This Hückel-type calculation is one potentially capable of dealing with such questions as the kind of coordination center which must be used with aniline or pyridine to effect a change in their orientation patterns towards electrophilic reagents. The treatment of such examples can be carried out with a considerable degree of thoroughness as the method allows the inclusion of the metal orbitals which can participate in the aromatic π-electron system.

17. R. D. Brown and R. D. Harcourt, *J. Chem. Soc.* p. 3451 (1959).

It should be noted that there is some experimental evidence for the presence of π-bonding involving pyridine and Ag^{+}[18], for substituted benzoic acids and $Cu(II)$[19], and for various ligands and their influence on the equilibrium[20]

$$[Co\ (py)_2\ X_2] + 2\ py \rightleftharpoons [Co\ (py)_4\ X_2]$$

Tetrahedra   Octahedra

In these cases the presence of electron-withdrawing groups results in an increase in the stability of the complex because of the presumed increased involvement of the metal d electrons in a π bond. These arguments, however, have been questioned.[21]

Although molecular orbital calculations are available on some other systems, the majority of these are ones with simple inorganic ligands that do not lend themselves to interpretations of the sort necessary in discussions of ligand reactivity.

The interaction of various substituents (X) in the compounds X—C_6H_5—$Cr(CO)_3$ with the rest of the molecule has been examined using a molecular orbital approach.[22] Here both the σ- and π-portions of the coordinate bond were considered and the net charge transferred found to be dependent upon the nature of X. Here again the exact calculation of such effects is determined by the parameters assigned to the integrals involving X.

Other calculations of a related type that have been carried out include those on the following systems: the ferrous and ferric complexes of porphyrin,[23, 24] acetylacetone complexes,[25] pyridine complexes,[26] α,α-dipyridyl complexes,[27] tetraphenylporphin and its zinc complex,[28] a perturbation method calculation on some pyridine complexes,[29] and related calculations on some catalytic systems.[30] The basic feature of the results of these calculations bears on the manner in which interaction of the metal ion orbitals perturb the orbitals of the ligand. The most immediate way in which this is expected to reveal itself is in the absorption (or fluorescence) spectra involving ligand electronic transitions. In the case of α,α-dipyridyl complexes a perturbation calculation, in which the perturbation is the neighboring cation, has been carried out. The

18. H. Irving and J. J. R. F. da Silva, *Proc. Chem. Soc.* p. 250 (1962).
19. W. R. May and M. M. Jones, *J. Inorg. Nucl. Chem.* **25**, 507 (1963).
20. H. C. A. King, E. Koros, and S. M. Nelson, *Nature* **169**, 572 (1962).
21. A. Yingst and D. H. McDaniel, *J. Inorg. Nucl. Chem.* **28**, 2919 (1966).
22. D. A. Brown and H. Sloan, *J. Chem. Soc.* p. 3849 (1962).
23. C. Spanjaard and G. Berthier, *J. Chim. Phys.* **58**, 169 (1961).
24. K. Ohno, Y. Tanabe, and F. Sasaki, *Theoret. Chim. Acta* **1**, 378 (1963).
25. D. W. Barnum, *J. Inorg. Nucl. Chem.* **22**, 183 (1961).
26. S. Mataga and N. Mataga, *Z. Physik. Chem. (Frankfurt)* **33**, 374 (1962).
27. R. Taube and S. Herzog, *Z. Chem.* **2**, 225 (1962).
28. M. Gouterman and P. E. Stevensen, *J. Chem. Phys.* **37**, 2266 (1962).
29. H. L. Schlafer and E. Konig, *Z. Physik. Chem. (Frankfurt)* **30**, 143 (1961).
30. A. Goudot, *Compt. Rend.* **252**, 125 (1961); *Zh. Fiz. Khim.* **34**, 2137 (1960).

effects upon the spectra of the α,α-dipyridyl have been calculated in this manner with reasonable success,[29] and this can also be said for calculations of the effect of coordination on the fluorescent spectra.[28] The same types of problems arise in the treatment of ferrocene and related compounds; in these cases also the results obtained have depended upon the values used for the integrals where metal and carbon orbitals are both present.

Before proceeding to other topics it is valuable to consider two fairly simple problems in greater detail. These are the orientation problems for pyridine and for aniline and their complexes. It is known for both of these molecules that coordination *can* result in an altered orientation for electrophilic substituents if the pyridine is coordinated to an oxygen atom and the aniline shares its lone pair with a proton. In the case of pyridine, as was seen earlier in this section, the critical factor determining orientation was the delocalization energy. The same would appear to be true of aniline also, though in a somewhat different manner. Coordination to the nitrogen atom in this latter case decreases, but does not wholly prevent, the participation of the lone pair in the aromatic system. As a result, tying up the electron pair by a variety of agents, R, of differing effectiveness leads to a situation in which the relative delocalization energies must be evaluated for the alternative situations

(A)   and   (B)

It is known empirically that the relative importance of (B) increases as the electronegativity of R increases. Unfortunately this cannot be placed on a firm theoretical basis until the localization of the electron pair between R and N can be predicted with greater assurance by some *a priori* method.

5.2. Experimental Studies

5.2.1. INTERATOMIC DISTANCES AND BOND ANGLES

The coordination act can be expected to produce changes in bond distances and bond angles of other species bound to either the donor or the acceptor center. This is obvious in cases where the number of groups bound to a coordination center changes in the process. An example is the reaction

$$BF_3 + F^- \rightarrow BF_4^-$$

Here the change is from a trigonal planar arrangement of groups about the boron to a tetrahedral one. Such changes are characteristic of the coordination process in many cases, and *even* when the coordination number of the central species is unaltered, we may expect changes in the interatomic distances and the bond angles of the species introduced. A salient feature of such reactions is the transformation of a lone pair into a bond pair and the consequent reduction of the repulsive forces between it and the other bond pairs of the donor atom (as in H_2O, NH_3, H_2S, and similar species). The most comprehensive survey of such changes is that given by Lindqvist.[31] In agreement with an earlier observation of Bauer,[32] it is considered by Lindqvist that the donor species undergoes relatively minor changes in comparison with those which occur with the acceptor species. In order to examine such effects, X-ray structural data of a high order of precision are required. A paucity of such data of the desired degree of accuracy existed until 1960. Since then a very large number of examples have become available. The acceptor changes are those resulting from an increase in the coordination number and its attendant changes in stereochemistry and hybridization. An illustration of the kind of changes which ensue upon coordination may be seen by comparing internuclear distances in $(CH_3)_2O:BF_3$[33] and $(CH_3)_2O$.[34] As mentioned previously, in BF_3 one has a planar molecule with bond angles of 120°; upon coordination to dimethyl ether the bond angles become approximately those characteristic of a tetrahedral stereochemistry. The bond distances and their changes upon coordination may be seen in the following table:

Bond	Length in complex (Å)	Length in free species (Å)
B—F	1.43	1.30
B—O	1.50	—
C—O	1.45	1.44
C—H	1.09	1.09

The B—F bond in BF_3 is unexpectedly short, a fact ascribed to the occurrence of π-bonding in addition to the σ-bonding.[35]

31. I. Lindqvist, "Inorganic Adduct Molecules of Oxo-Compounds," pp. 11 ff., 63 ff. Academic Press, New York, 1963. See also I. Lindqvist, *Nova Acta Regiae Soc. Sci. Upsalien.* Ser. IV, Vol. 17, No. 11 (1956).

32. S. H. Bauer, *Advan. Chem. Ser.* **32**, 89 (1961).

33. S. H. Bauer, G. R. Finlay, and A. W. Laubengayer, *J. Am. Chem. Soc.* **65**, 889 (1943); *J. Am. Chem. Soc.* **67**, 339 (1945).

34. L. E. Sutton and L. O. Brockway, *J. Am. Chem. Soc.* **57**, 473 (1935).

35. F. A. Cotton and J. R. Leto, *J. Chem. Phys.* **30**, 993 (1959).

In the metal carbonyls, the C—O distances are longer than in carbon monoxide itself.[36] In most of the simple carbonyls this distance is about 1.15 Å. In CO itself, the internuclear distance is 1.13078 Å; in H_3BCO it is 1.131 Å; while in compounds containing normal carbon–oxygen double bonds it is longer than this. In CO_2 it is 1.1632 Å; in COS, 1.1637 Å; and in CH_2CO, 1.16 Å. Some additional data of this sort are listed in Table X.

TABLE X

EFFECT OF COORDINATION ON INTERNUCLEAR DISTANCES

Bond	Internuclear distances[37] (Å)
Si—F	1.560 in SiF_4; 1.71 in SiF_6^{2-}
Sn—Cl	2.33 in $SnCl_4$; 2.4 in $SnCl_4^{2-}$
Al—Cl	2.06 (nonbridging) and 2.21 (bridging) in Al_2Cl_6; 2.13 in $NaAlCl_4$
Ge—F	1.67 in GeF_4; 1.77 in GeF_6^{2-}
P—Cl	1.98 in PCl_4^+; 2.04(eq) & 2.19(ax) in PCl_5, 2.07 in PCl_6^-
P—F	1.55 in PF_5; 1.73 in PF_6^-
As—F	1.74 in AsF_5; 1.85 in AsF_6^-
In—Cl	2.46 in In_2Cl_6; 2.58 in $[InCl_5 \cdot H_2O]^{2-}$
Ti—Cl	2.20 in $TiCl_4$; 2.35 in $TiCl_6^{2-}$
Zr—Cl	2.33 in $ZrCl_4$; 2.45 in $ZrCl_6^{2-}$
Ge—Cl	2.10 in $GeCl_4$; 2.35 in $GeCl_6^{2-}$
Sn—Br	2.44 in $SnBr_4$; 2.60 in $SnBr_6^{2-}$
Sn—I	2.64 in SnI_4; 2.85 in SnI_6^{2-}
Pb—Cl	2.43 in $PbCl_4$; 2.49 in $PbCl_6^{2-}$
Bi—Cl	2.48 in $BiCl_3$; 2.52 in $[BiCl_6]^{3-}$
N—O	1.236 in $NaNO_2$; 1.26 in $[Co(NH_3)_3(NO_2)_3]$; 1.14(est.) in $K_2[Pd(NO_2)_4]$

5.2.2. ULTRAVIOLET SPECTRA

In many cases ultraviolet spectra arise from transitions involving electrons that are also important in determining chemical reactivity, for example, those involving the π-electron systems of aromatic compounds. In such cases it would be expected that much chemically useful information could be obtainable from the study of such spectra for pairs of systems containing the free and the coordinated species. The amount of experimental information of this sort that is available is not large because of the very common overlapping of bands characteristic of the ligand spectra with the absorption bands characteristic of the central metal ions. For example, ultraviolet absorption maxima for aliphatic ketones, aldehydes, oximes, nitro groups, and other functional

36. J. W. Cable and R. K. Sheline, *Chem. Rev.* **56**, 1 (1956).
37. "Interatomic Distances," Spec. Publ. No. 11. Chem. Soc., London, 1958.

groups containing double bonds fall in the range up to 295 mμ. Unfortunately, almost all transition metals ions also have absorption bands in this region. By and large, such studies must accordingly be restricted to complexes of the nontransition elements or to those transition ions that have no d electrons. The question which must then be examined experimentally is the following: How does coordination affect the electronic transitions which can be ascribed to n–π, π–π^*, n–π^* or related processes?

This has been examined in detail in the case of a considerable group of complexes with β-diketones as ligands.[38-44] In the case of acetylacetone, the main ultraviolet absorption band, which occurs at 280 mμ (ϵ_{max} = 9500) (solvent-dependent), is intensified in the chelate and split to give peaks at 254 mμ (ϵ_{max} = 18,000) and 304 mμ (ϵ_{max} = 26,000). The main band of the acetyl-acetonate peak is thus shifted to a higher wavelength (lower frequency by about 2800 cm^{-1}) when H$^+$ is replaced by Cu^{2+}. A molecular orbital treatment was used to calculate a theoretical shift of -3200 cm^{-1}, which is very good agreement. The calculation was based upon the relative electrostatic effects of one and two positive charges on the ground and first excited state of the acetylacetonate anion.[38] The copper(II) and calcium(II) chelates were found to have ultraviolet spectra that resemble each other in both intensity and band placement. Although these calculations have been criticized,[39] they have also been defended.[40] The band discussed, for which ν_{max} = 34,000 cm^{-1} in the anion, is found to shift to both lower and higher energies on coordination, but a shift to higher energies is more commonly encountered.[39, 40] The treatment of this system is complicated by the fact that the energy of the d orbitals falls in between the energies of the highest occupied π-orbital of the anion and its lowest unoccupied π-orbital. A reasonably complete theoretical treatment has been developed by Barnum,[40] who concluded that the importance of π-bonding increased throughout the series Ti(acac)$_3$, V(acac)$_3$, Cr(acac)$_3$, Mn(acac)$_3$, Fe(acac)$_3$, and Co(acac)$_3$ (where acac is CH$_3$CO=CH—CO—CH$_3$$^-$).

A perturbation treatment of this same general sort has been used to develop a theoretical model for pyridine and orthophenanthroline complexes.[45, 46] It should be noted that the ammonio group, —NH$_3$$^+$, is known to have an

38. R. L. Belford, A. E. Martell, and M. Calvin, *J. Inorg. Nucl. Chem.* **2**, 11 (1956).
39. R. H. Holm and F. A. Cotton, *J. Am. Chem. Soc.* **80**, 5658 (1958).
40. D. W. Barnum, *J. Inorg. Nucl. Chem.* **21**, 221 (1961); **22**, 183 (1961).
41. T. S. Piper and R. L. Belford, *Mol. Phys.* **5**, 169 (1962).
42. J. P. Fackler, Jr., F. A. Cotton, and D. W. Barnum, *Inorg. Chem.* **2**, 97 (1963).
43. J. P. Fackler, Jr. and F. A. Cotton, *Inorg. Chem.* **2**, 102 (1963).
44. L. S. Foster, *J. Am. Chem. Soc.* **86**, 3001 (1964).
45. H. L. Schläfer, *Z. Physik. Chem. (Frankfurt)* **8**, 373 (1956).
46. H. L. Schläfer and E. Konig, *Z. Physik. Chem. (Frankfurt)* **19**, 265 (1959).

enormous effect on the reactivity of a benzene ring to which it is attached, but has *no* effect on the 2600 Å region of the ultraviolet spectrum of benzene.[47]

In Schläfer's studies,[45, 46] he considers that the absorption spectrum of an electrostatically bonded complex ion consists of two parts, that resulting from the central ion and that from the ligand. The model used by Schläfer in his initial work was the electron-gas model of H. Kuhn, which reduces the problem of dipyridyl to one of three simple potential well problems. This is then reformulated as a perturbation problem to solve the case in which a metal ion approaches the dipyridyl and perturbs it with its charge. The results of these calculations are in surprisingly good accord with the experimental data in spite of the simplicity of the model and the general attribution of considerable covalent character to the bonds in dipyridyl complexes. A similar calculation on pyridine and its complexes[46] gave equally satisfactory results.

From these studies it can be appreciated that the gross features of the ultra-violet spectra of free and bound ligands can be interpreted on the basis of fairly simple models. It is also true that a complete analysis of the ultraviolet spectrum of the free ligand species is not available in most cases. When such an analysis is available, it will be possible to obtain much more detailed information from experimental studies of the ultraviolet spectra of complexes.

5.2.3.   INFRARED AND RAMAN SPECTRA

The infrared spectra of an enormous number of complexes have been obtained and studied in great detail.[48, 49] From these we may obtain information on the changes in the characteristic ligand vibrations which arise upon coordination. Coordination changes the symmetry of the ligand and hence would be expected to have an effect on the intensities of the various bonds. Although this is generally true, the effects are not always large. The *gross* infrared absorption pattern consists of the frequencies resulting from the ligand plus those from the metal–ligand bond. The detailed pattern will show both shifts and new bands. The extent of the change is strongly dependent upon the changes that coordination induces in the ligand. With some ligands, e.g., pyridine, the infrared spectrum is but slightly changed on coordination and in this case the changes resulting from coordination are much less pronounced than those resulting from protonation to give the pyridinium ion.[50] With other ligands the changes are often considerably more striking.

47. D. M. Bishop and D. P. Craig, *Mol. Phys.* 6, 139 (1963).
48. F. A. Cotton, *in* "Modern Coordination Chemistry" (J. S. Lewis and D. H. Wilkins, eds.), Chapt. V. Wiley (Interscience), New York, 1960.
49. K. Nakamoto, "Infrared Spectra of Inorganic and Coordination Compounds." Wiley, New York, 1963.
50. N. S. Gill, R. H. Nuttall, D. E. Scaife, and D. W. A. Sharp, *J. Inorg. Nucl. Chem.* 18, 79 (1961).

When a donor atom, D, in a ligand, R—D, forms a coordinate bond with a metal, M, the R—D bond will almost always be weakened and ν_{R-D} in the complex will occur at a lower frequency than it does in the free ligand.[51] Unfortunately other factors operating simultaneously tend to lead to an increase in the observed frequency. The observed shift is a composite of these and is usually a shift to lower frequency.[52]

These effects must be experimentally distinguished from the shifts which result from interactions with a solvent. A study of one of the stretching fundamentals of the C≡O group in Ni(CO)$_4$ showed that it occurred at 2057.6 cm^{-1} in the vapor phase, but was shifted to lower frequencies in solvents, being 2040.1 cm^{-1} in dioxane, for example.[53] These solvent effects are generally smaller than the shifts of either donor or acceptor which arise on coordination. In BF$_3$, there is a symmetric B—F stretching frequency at 888 cm^{-1} which is shifted to 804 cm^{-1} in BF$_3$:O(CH$_3$)$_2$ and to 769 cm^{-1} in BF$_4^-$.[54]

The variations in the infrared spectra of the ligand moiety that arise on coordination can sometimes be attributed to changes in the conformation of the ligand. This can be seen in work on the complexes of 1,5-hexadiene[55] and 1,5-cyclooctadiene.[56] The free ligand in the first case is predominantly trans, but the complexed form exists in a gauche or cis configuration. For the second ligand a more rigid "tub" form is found that persists in the complexes CuCl·C$_8$H$_{12}$ and PdCl$_2$·C$_8$H$_{12}$, whose infrared spectra show strong resemblances to that of the free ligand. The infrared spectra of complexes of ethylenediamine have been utilized in a similar way to show that the conformation of this ligand in many complexes is the gauche one,[57] as is the case with 1,2-dithiocyanatoethane.[58]

A study of the infrared spectra of various adducts of ethyl acetate[59] showed that the change in the C=O bond stretching frequency could be used as an indication of the strength of the donor–acceptor interaction, and that it was in very good agreement with the other measurements on these systems, specifically, dipole moment data and enthalpies of formation. Here the donor oxygen is the carbonyl oxygen, and the C=O bond will be weakened as the acceptor interaction with this oxygen increases. The absorption of this bond

51. I. Lindqvist, "Inorganic Adduct Molecules of Oxo-Compounds," p. 11. Academic Press, New York, 1963.
52. M. F. Lappert, *J. Chem. Soc.* p. 817 (1961).
53. G. Bor, *Spectrochim. Acta* **18**, 817 (1962).
54. G. M. Begun, W. H. Fletcher, and A. A. Palko, *Spectrochim. Acta* **18**, 655 (1962).
55. P. J. Hendra and D. B. Powell, *Spectrochim. Acta* **17**, 909 (1961).
56. P. J. Hendra and D. B. Powell, *Spectrochim. Acta* **17**, 913 (1961).
57. S. Mizushima, "Structure of Molecules and Internal Rotation," p. 76. Academic Press, New York, 1954.
58. J. V. Quagliano and S. Mizushima, *J. Am. Chem. Soc.* **75**, 6084 (1953).
59. M. F. Lappert, *J. Chem. Soc.* p. 542 (1962).

in the free ester occurs at 1741 cm^{-1}; in the complexes this is shifted to lower values by 100 to 200 cm^{-1}. The shifts for some typical acceptors are as follows: BF_3, 119 cm^{-1}; BCl_3, 176 cm^{-1}; BBr_3, 191 cm^{-1}; $AlCl_3$, 117 cm^{-1}; and $AlBr_3$, 138 cm^{-1}. These shifts to lower frequencies would be greater were it not for the kinematic coupling of the oscillators C=O and O—B or O—Al, which, by itself, would result in an increase in the C=O frequency.[60] In the case of complexes of aromatic and aliphatic nitriles, it is found that coordination to boron trichloride actually *increases* the C≡N stretching frequency from values near 2225–2250 cm^{-1} by 75–89 cm^{-1}.[61]

Of direct interest are the shifts in the other frequencies attributed to other donor atom bonds. These generally follow the pattern given above: the stronger the donor–acceptor bond, the weaker the other bonds of the donor atom and the greater the decrease in their characteristic infrared spectra frequencies. This is found in the relation of the N—H stretching frequency and the stability of complexes with β-alanine.[62] The complexes with Pd^{2+}, Cu^{2+}, Ni^{2+}, and Co^{2+} have N—H frequencies of 3240, 3270, 3333, and 3338 cm^{-1}, respectively. The corresponding frequency for the sodium salt is 3413 cm^{-1}. Here it should be noted that the infrared spectra of the different alkali metal salts of an acid are often not *identical*, but rather show a systematic (but incompletely explained) dependence upon the cation involved. The differences found are of the order of magnitude of 10 cm^{-1}.[63]

A comparison of protonation and coordination is of direct interest, though the number of cases where such data have been analyzed is not large. The protonation of the sulfur atom in thioacetamide results in a greater shift of the highest fundamental frequency than is found for coordination to copper(I). This frequency is at 1482 cm^{-1} in thioacetamide, at 1515 cm^{-1} in the copper(I) complex, and at 1548 cm^{-1} in the protonated species.[64]

The metal–donor atom bonds give rise to vibrations which should give valuable information. These are at a relatively low frequency, however, that has only become readily accessible with commercial infrared instrumentation in recent years. In the case of the acetylacetonates of aluminum, gallium, and indium, the infrared spectra are almost identical in the region 3000–650 cm^{-1}, since the bands in this region arise from the ligand and are relatively little affected by chelation to different metals. In the region from 650 to 400 cm^{-1}, there are important differences. Bands here have been assigned to the M—O stretching frequency as follows: Al—O, 496 cm^{-1}; Ga—O, 446 cm^{-1}; and In—O, 434 cm^{-1}. The force constants are 1.45×10^5, 1.53×10^5, and

60. F. A. Cotton, R. D. Barnes, and E. Bannister, *J. Chem. Soc.* p. 2201 (1960).
61. W. Gerrard, M. F. Lappert, H. Pyszora, and J. W. Wallis, *J. Chem. Soc.* p. 2182 (1960).
62. V. S. Sharma, H. B. Mathur, and A. B. Biswas, *Spectrochim. Acta* **17**, 895 (1961).
63. J. H. S. Green, W. Kynaston, and A. S. Lindsey, *Spectrochim. Acta* **17**, 486 (1961).
64. W. Kutzelnigg and R. Mecke, *Spectrochim. Acta* **17**, 530 (1961).

1.56×10^5 dynes/cm, respectively, compared with 1.24×10^5 dynes/cm for the copper complex.[65] Similar results were obtained in a more extensive study of this type of compound.[66] The frequency shift of the C=O frequency in β-diketone complexes is related to the stability constants of the complexes by the expression:

$$\tfrac{1}{2}\log K_1 K_2 = c \log \varDelta \nu$$

The C=C vibration is lowered drastically in its frequency when the proton of the enol is replaced by a metal cation.[67]

Where back-donation from the metal to the ligand may be important, the situation may be much more complicated. Thus, in a comparison of $Ni(CO)_4$ and $Ni(PF_3)_4$, back-donation is presumably very important. That the degree of back-donation is very critically dependent on the ligand, may be seen in the variation of stretching force constants in the ligands. The stretching force constant for the C=O linkage in the complex is lower ($16.01 \times 10^{+5}$ dyne/cm) than that in the free ligand ($18.55 \times 10^{+5}$ dyne/cm), but that for the P—F linkage is higher ($7.73 \times 10^{+5}$ dyne/cm) for the coordinated ligand than for the free PF_3 molecule ($5.38 \times 10^{+5}$ dyne/cm).[68]

The decrease of the phosphoryl $\left(\underset{\diagdown}{\overset{\diagup}{}}P{=}O \right)$ stretching frequency that occurs when the oxygen coordinates to an acceptor species has been examined by several investigators.[60, 69] One interesting result is that $\varDelta \nu$, the shift of the frequency in the complex, increases in absolute magnitude (takes on greater negative values) in the order $ZnCl_2$ complex $<$ $ZnBr_2$ complex $<$ ZnI_2 complex. Here the factors which would tend to increase this stretching frequency (metal–oxygen π-bonding and enhanced phosphorous–oxygen σ-bonding) are overcome by the decrease of $p_\pi \rightarrow d_\pi$ back-bonding from oxygen to phosphorous. (Some of this change may result from the enormous increase in polarizability in going from chloride to iodide.)

If infrared spectra of complexes are to be used as guides to ligand reactivity, some direct relationship must be established between observable features of the spectra and experimental rate behavior.

5.2.4. Nuclear Magnetic Resonance Spectra

Nuclear magnetic resonance (NMR) spectra[70] can furnish a great deal of information on the interaction of the various groups in a molecule with each other. It also can provide indirect evidence on the electron density patterns

65. C. Djordjevic, *Spectrochim. Acta* **17**, 448 (1961).
66. K. E. Lawson, *Spectrochim. Acta* **17**, 248 (1961).
67. J. Charette and P. Teyssie, *Spectrochim. Acta* **16**, 689 (1960).
68. L. A. Woodward and J. R. Hall, *Spectrochim. Acta* **16**, 654 (1960).
69. M. J. Frazer, W. Gerrard, and R. Twaits, *J. Inorg. Nucl. Chem.* **25**, 637 (1963).
70. H. Sillescu, *Fortschr. Chem. Forsch.* **5**, 569 (1966).

of ligands. There is now a sufficient amount of data that it should be possible to show some of the patterns of correlation between the NMR spectra and changes in ligand reactivity.

The NMR spectra of a large number of simple and partially substituted acetylacetonates have been studied by Collman,[71,72] Piper,[73,74] and their co-workers. Fackler has summarized this work.[75] The unsubstituted acetylacetonates show two signals from protons at 7.8 and 4.4 τ, which have relative intensities of 6:1. For these tris(acetylacetonates), this represents the ratio of the methyl to the ring hydrogens. Replacement of the ring hydrogens by nitro groups gives chelates which exhibit only one proton resonance in the region 7.43–7.59 τ. The shift to lower frequencies is characteristic of electronegative substituents on the central carbon atom and is related to the *withdrawal* of electrons from the ring systems and their adjacent methyl groups. When tris complexes with two rings of one kind and one of another are examined, e.g., $[(XC_5H_6O_2)_2M(O_2H_6C_5Z)]$, these are found to give three signals for proton resonances. The two methyl groups in the X rings have different chemical environments because one is over another X ring and the other is over a Z ring. If the chelate rings are aromatic in the sense that they contain delocalized π-electrons, then the long range magnetic anisotropic shielding from these different kinds of rings will be different and the observed splittings can be interpreted in terms of such a chemical shift effect. The extent of delocalization of the π-electrons can presumably be estimated from a qualitative model of such a system.

There is a certain amount of controversy about the extent of the aromaticity of the rings in metal chelates of acetylacetone. The substitution reactions of these chelate rings do not seem to depend very much upon the nature of the metal involved and there is good reason to believe that electron delocalization occurs at least over the organic portion of such metal chelate rings. The involvement of filled or empty metal orbitals in such an unsaturated system is certainly a distinct possibility, and in some cases, e.g., $VO(C_5H_7O_2)_2$, the electron spin resonance spectra of the unpaired electron on the central vanadium indicates that it *is* delocalized, in part, over the chelate system as a whole. The NMR spectra of diamagnetic acetylacetonate complexes showed that the shifts of the proton resonances were close to that observed for the characteristic olefinic protons. Similarly the ultraviolet spectra were found

71. J. P. Collman, R. L. Marshall, W. L. Young, III, and S. D. Goldby, *Inorg. Chem.* **1**, 704 (1962).

72. J. P. Collman, R. L. Marshall, and W. L. Young, III, *Chem. Ind. (London)* p. 1380 (1962).

73. R. C. Fay and T. S. Piper, *J. Am. Chem. Soc.* **84**, 2303 (1962); **85**, 500 (1963); *Inorg. Chem.* **3**, 348 (1964).

74. R. A. Palmer, R. C. Fay, and T. S. Piper, *Inorg. Chem.* **3**, 875 (1964).

75. J. P. Fackler, *Progr. Inorg. Chem.* **7**, 374 (1966).

not to require a heteroaromatic ring for the diamagnetic chelates.[39] Chelates of Cr(III), Rh(III), Pd(II), and Pt(II) were found to have more complex spectra. The possible types of π-bonding with acetylacetone are restricted by the fact that the acetylacetonate anion does not have any vacant bonding orbitals of π-symmetry so d_π–p_π bonding between the metal and the ligand must involve donation of the oxygen lone pairs to the metal. A final aspect of this that has not been considered adequately is the possibility of perpendicular conjugation among the different chelate rings. Although the theoretical interpretation of these rings may be in doubt, their chemical behavior is not—the carbon–hydrogen bond on the central carbon atom undergoes those electrophilic substitution reactions typical of an aromatic C—H bond.

A different kind of system has been examined by Phillips and his collaborators.[76-79] They have used NMR studies to determine π-electron spin densities on the conjugated ligands of some paramagnetic nickel(II) chelates of various substituted aminotroponeiminates. In these cases the ligands had structures related to

where the hydrogen on the nitrogen atom is acidic and is replaced in the reaction with Ni^{2+} to give chelates of the type

In these chelates the spin densities at the various carbon atoms in the system have been evaluated for various R groups (phenyl, methyl, ethyl). Subsequently,[79] a more extensive study of this class of compounds showed that such

76. W. D. Phillips and R. E. Benson, J. Chem. Phys. 33, 607 (1960).
77. R. E. Benson, D. R. Eaton, A. D. Josey, and W. D. Phillips, J. Am. Chem. Soc. 83, 3714 (1961); W. R. Brasen, H. E. Holmquist, and R. E. Benson, J. Am. Chem. Soc. 82, 995 (1960).
78. D. R. Eaton, A. D. Josey, W. D. Phillips, and R. E. Benson, J. Chem. Phys. 37, 347 (1962).
79. D. R. Eaton, A. D. Josey, R. E. Benson, W. D. Phillips, and T. L. Cairns, J. Am. Chem. Soc. 84, 4100 (1962).

studies could be used to estimate changes in the favored position for attack in the unsubstituted ring of 2-naphthyl derivatives.

$$Z = \begin{array}{c} \text{[naphthalene ring structure with positions labeled 8, 1 at top; 7, 2 at middle; 6, 3; 5, 4 at bottom; with N attached at position 2]} \end{array}$$

Studies showed that a substituent at C_2 had a greater effect on the spin densities at C_6 than at any of the other carbons of this second ring. On this basis it was proposed that electron-releasing groups at C_2 direct electrophilic reagents to C_6 while an electron-withdrawing group at C_2 should deactivate C_6 and C_8 and direct electrophilic reagents to C_5 or C_7. Such data as were used by the authors supported this proposal.[80] The zinc and nickel chelates used in this study were all reasonably soluble in organic solvents, a factor that made their direct comparison with the free ligand straightforward. The extension of analogous techniques to other nickel(II) complexes leads to some serious problems.[81]

The use of NMR to investigate details of the mechanisms of metal-catalyzed reactions has been very successful in a number of cases.[82] Thus studies utilizing the ^{31}P nuclear spin (natural abundance 100%) have been used to obtain information on the positions of bonding to metal ions in ATP and ADP. Other studies that examined enzymatic sites showed that this technique could be used to determine equilibrium constants for the bonding of Mn^{2+} to bovine serum albumin and also to provide information on the nature of the bonding sites and their number.

When aromatic fluoro derivatives are present as ligands, it is possible to use the ^{19}F NMR shielding parameters to get information on the relative importance of σ- and π-bonding in diamagnetic complexes.[83,84] A comparison of the ^{19}F NMR shielding parameters for complexes of the types

$$\begin{array}{ccc}
\text{(A)} & \text{and} & \text{(B)}
\end{array}$$

(A) [phenyl ring with F at meta position, bonded to Pt with two P(Et)$_3$ ligands and X] (B) [phenyl ring with F at para position, bonded to Pt with two P(Et)$_3$ ligands and X]

80. L. Fieser and M. Fieser, "Organic Chemistry," 3rd Ed., pp. 743–746. Reinhold, New York, 1956.
81. R. W. Kluiber and W. DeW. Harrocks, *Inorg. Chem.* **6**, 430 (1967).
82. A. Kowalsky and M. Cohn, *Ann. Rev. Biochem.* **33**, 481 (1964).
83. G. W. Parshall, *J. Am. Chem. Soc.* **86**, 5367 (1964); **88**, 704 (1966).
84. M. G. Hogben, R. S. Gay, and W. A. G. Graham, *J. Am. Chem. Soc.* **88**, 3457 (1966).

allows this to be established. The shielding parameter for the meta-substituted compound (A) varies with the σ-donor character of X, and that for the para-substituted compound (B) varies with the π-acceptor/donor properties of X. For compounds of these types, there is a considerable displacement of electronic charge from the platinum into the aromatic ring. The shifts in the shielding parameter for the meta-substituted compound parallels the basicity of the X groups. The shifts in the parameters for compounds of type (B) are larger than those of type (A), and can be correlated very closely with the π-donor or π-acceptor character of X. The extension of this method to related systems has been carried out[84] and it is now possible to determine the relative importance of π-withdrawal or π-donation for any ligand which can be incorporated into suitable complexes.

5.2.5. ELECTRON SPIN RESONANCE SPECTRA

Electron spin resonance (ESR) is a procedure for determining the interaction of the unpaired electronic spins in a molecule with its molecular environment. It is thus possible to determine the degree of mobility of such electrons in their molecules. Since a large number of transition element complexes contain a central ion with unpaired electrons, this technique has been widely used to examine these complexes. The ESR spectra are composites of two sorts of effects. The first or fine structure results from the fact that one will have $n + 1$ Zeeman levels for n unpaired electrons under the conditions of observing the spectra. The selection rules allow n transitions between the $n + 1$ levels and this gives the fine structure. Hyperfine structure for these lines arises from the interaction between the electronic spin and the magnetic moment of the nuclei (nuclear spin) of the atom with the unpaired electron. For a nucleus of spin I one splits each Zeeman line into $2I + 1$ components. If the electrons that are unpaired can spread out over two or more different kinds of nuclei with different values of I, this will be revealed in the hyperfine spectra and one can assign the unpaired electrons to spend various percentages of their time in the orbitals of the different atoms.[85] From this it is possible to evaluate the actual atomic orbital coefficients in the molecular orbital in which the electron is present.

An example that is relevant to the discussion of acetylacetonate complexes is that of Ti(acac)$_3^{3+}$, which was examined by McGarvey.[86] In this case the results were interpreted as favoring the presence of π-bonding between the Ti^{3+} and the ligand. Similar evidence for π-bonding in bis(2,4-pentanediono)-copper(II) had been presented earlier.[87]

85. A. MacCragh and W. S. Koski, *J. Am. Chem. Soc.* **85**, 2375 (1963).
86. B. R. McGarvey, *J. Chem. Phys.* **38**, 388 (1963).
87. A. H. Maki and B. R. McGarvey, *J. Chem. Phys.* **29**, 31 (1958).

A rather comprehensive survey of the ESR spectra of metal chelates, as well as those of the closely related organometallic compounds, has been presented by Robertson.[88] The utility of this method is potentially great, but its application is normally restricted to molecules of known crystal structure, which can be prepared as a dilute "admixture" in an isomorphous diamagnetic compound. This is necessary because the examination of the paramagnetic molecule must be carried out in an environment that has only a very low concentration of paramagnetic species and these must be separated from each other by a sufficient distance to insure the absence of their interaction with each other.

5.2.6. DIPOLE MOMENTS

The changes in dipole moment that arise as a result of coordination *should* give valuable information on the charge distribution in the coordinate bond. These, in turn, should be of considerable assistance in formulating predictions of changes in ligand reactivity. The number of complexes whose dipole moments have been measured is not too large, but in most of these cases rather sizeable dipole moments are found. The interpretation of the data is subject to some uncertainty, as most of the measurements have been carried out at only a single temperature. This requires the use of various assumptions to estimate the temperature-independent part of the electronic polarization, and these, in turn, have a validity of an uncertain nature.

There have been very comprehensive collections of the literature in this field.[89] An early example of the use of dipole moments with complexes may be seen in the data on the α- and β-forms of $\{PtCl_2[P(C_2H_5)_3]_2\}$, which have dipole moments of 0 and 10.7 D, respectively.[90] This shows that the β-form is the cis isomer and that the bonds in the complex may have a considerable polarity.

The major problem involved in the interpretation of the dipole moments is the calculation of the moment of the coordinate bond. This requires a knowledge of the moments of the other bonds in the complex as well as the contributions of any lone pairs which may be present. This problem has been studied by several groups of investigators and several solutions to it have been proposed.

88. R. E. Robertson, *in* "Determination of Organic Structures by Physical Methods" (F. C. Nachod and W. D. Phillips, eds.), Vol. 2, pp. 617–660. Academic Press, New York, 1962.
89. A. L. McClellan, "Tables of Experimental Dipole Moments." Freeman, San Francisco, California, 1963, is one which gives references to comprehensive treatments of the relevant experimental and theoretical aspects of dipole moment determinations.
90. K. A. Jensen, *Z. Anorg. Allgem. Chem.* **225**, 97 (1935).

The first of these is based upon the changes in dipole moment (designated $\Delta\mu_{xy}$) which occur when a given kind of coordinate bond is formed.[91] This change involves a number of separate terms, including one from the change in the stereochemistry of the acceptor bonds. For example, the dipole moment of trimethylamine is 0.74 D; trimethylamine complexes with oxygen, boron trichloride, and boron trifluoride have moments of 4.87, 6.23, and 5.76 D, respectively. From these we calculate

$$\Delta\mu_{NO} = 4.87 - 0.74 = 4.13 \text{ D}$$

$$\Delta\mu_{NBCl_3} = 6.23 - 0.74 = 5.49 \text{ D}$$

$$\Delta\mu_{NBF_3} = 5.76 - 0.74 = 5.02 \text{ D}$$

The degree of sharing of the electron pair can be calculated if we use these $\Delta\mu_{xy}$ values to obtain the bond moments μ_{xy}. For the amine oxide, $\Delta\mu_{NO} \approx \mu_{NO}$; for the adducts with BCl_3 and BF_3, $\Delta\mu_{NB} = \mu_{NB} + \mu_{BX_3}$, where μ_{BX_3} is the moment of the BX_3 part of the adduct. If these are assumed to be equal to the moments of chloroform and fluoroform (1.2 and 1.6 D, respectively), then

$$\mu_{NB} = 5.49 - 1.2 = 4.3 \text{ D for the } BCl_3 \text{ adduct}$$

$$\mu_{NB} = 5.02 - 1.6 = 3.4 \text{ D for the } BF_3 \text{ adduct}$$

If the shared electron pair is symmetrically located between the acceptor and donor atoms, the bond moment is $4.80l$ where l is the internuclear distance in Ångstroms. For a moment of only $4.80l/x$, the center of the electron cloud is at a distance of only $(x/2)l$ from the donor atom. For several of the compounds studied, x values were estimated. These are summarized below.

Bond:	N—O	N—B	P—O	P—S	P—B	O—B	S—B	S—O	S—C
x:	0.65	0.58–0.46	0.36	0.33	0.45–0.49	0.56–0.41	0.42	0.36–0.44	0.58

These are only approximate values, but they do show that the transfer of charge is less than that predicted by the simple "equal-sharing" picture of the coordinate bond used in most valence bond discussions of these complexes.

The N—S bond moment is much smaller than the N—O bond moment; it is 2.7 ± 0.4 in amine–SO_2 adducts.[92] This was attributed to resonance involving, as canonical structures, the normal coordinate bond structure, R_3N^+—SO_2, in which the electrons are equally shared, and one in which the compound is held together by dipole–dipole interactions $R_3N\cdot\cdot SO_2$. This

91. G. M. Phillips, J. S. Hunter, and L. E. Sutton, *J. Chem. Soc.* p. 146 (1945).
92. J. A. Moede and C. Curran, *J. Am. Chem. Soc.* **71**, 855 (1949).

bond moment in $(C_2H_5)_3N:SO_3$ is increased to 3.6 D and this probably results from an increased contribution from the R_3N^+—$^-SO_3$ form. For tetrahedral metal complexes, the breakdown of the measured dipole moments into individual bond moments is usually not possible. For such complexes which have the composition $MX_2 \cdot 2B$, it is possible to obtain the sum of the $B \rightarrow M \rightarrow X$ dipoles by dividing the total dipole moment by 1.16 $(2\cos54°44')$.[93] The fact that such zinc(II) complexes having B equal to pyridine show an increasing dipole moment in the series $Cl < Br < I$, shows that the polarizability of the X group may be important in fixing the order. Analogous relationships found with some nickel complexes have been attributed to a decreasing angle between the two bonds to the halide anions.[94]

The basic flaws in using published dipole moments to determine bond moments and electron distributions in complexes are (1) bond moments for a given type of coordinate bond are not constants and (2) most of the dipole moments in the literature have been determined from measurements at a single temperature. This last has had the result that considerable dipole moments are often ascribed to highly symmetrical molecules. For example, the tris(acetylacetonates) of the type $M(acac)_3$[95] have been treated in this manner. A thorough study of many anomalous compounds in this second class has been carried out.[96] Measurements of the Kerr constants, dipole moments, and dielectric absorptions revealed that the complexes are, in fact, nonpolar and each of them has a center of symmetry. The problem that arises here is caused by unexpectedly large *atomic* polarizations, so that the difference between the polarization determined at long wavelengths (P) and that for optical wavelengths (R) cannot be ascribed to contributions from a permanent dipole. The role of lone pairs in determining base strength and how this is affected by a change in hybridization has been examined in detail for some typical bases.[97] Since the degree of hybridization is determined by the nature of the substituents on the donor atom, one may expect that coordinate bond moments will not be constant nor will the contributions of the lone pair to the total moment be constant, even for a series of rather closely related ligands.

In summary, it seems safe to say that dipole moment studies, when derived from studies covering a reasonable temperature range, may furnish valuable information about coordinate bond moments and the electronic distributions that are their cause, in some favorable circumstances. The variability of most

93. M. Schafer and C. Curran, *Inorg. Chem.* **4**, 623 (1965).
94. M. C. Browning, R. F. B. Davies, D. J. Morgan, L. E. Sutton, and L. M. Venanzi, *J. Chem. Soc.* p. 4816 (1961).
95. J. W. Smith, "Electric Dipole Moments," p. 278. Butterworth, London and Washington, D.C., 1955.
96. R. S. Armstrong, C. G. LeFevre, and R. J. W. LeFevre, *J. Chem. Soc.* p. 371 (1957).
97. J. H. Gibbs, *J. Chem. Phys.* **22**, 1460 (1954).

bond moments, however, and the difficulties that arise in assigning the total moment of a complex of high molecular weight into contributions from the constituent bond moments, make the method one which must be applied with considerable caution.

5.2.7. ELECTRICAL CONDUCTIVITY

The electrical conductance of a reaction medium can be used to detect the presence or absence of ions. In the case of ligand reactions with Lewis bases, it can often be used to detect the presence of rearrangements to give conducting species, or the presence of species in which the ligand polarization has proceeded to the extent that ionization occurs. Thus, the 1:1 complexes of pyridine or piperidine with gallium halides exhibit a conductivity in excess of that anticipated for neutral complexes. This has been interpreted[98] in terms of a small proportion of a charged species in equilibrium with the principal component, the neutral 1:1 complex.

$$2L + 2GaX_3 \rightleftarrows GaX_2L_2^+ + GaX_4^-$$

The appreciable conductivity of compounds such as $C_6H_5COCl \cdot AlCl_3$ is generally interpreted in terms of an equilibrium of the sort[99]

$$C_6H_5COCl \cdot AlCl_3 \rightleftarrows C_6H_5CO^+ + AlCl_4^-$$

The active species in the Friedel-Crafts benzoylation of aromatic compounds in the $C_6H_5CO^+$ ion, or the ion pair $C_6H_5CO^+, AlCl_4^-$.

It can be seen that the electrical conductivity of a system is useful only in cases in which a rearrangement or extreme polarization occurs. Where the rate of reaction, rather than the nature of the complexes, is desired, the generation of conducting species may be followed by such measurements. In cases in which such conducting species are not found, dielectric constant or dielectric relaxation measurements can generally be used to obtain qualitative information on the extent of polarization.

One additional type of information which can often be obtained from conductivity measurements is the extent of labilization of hydrogen atoms that are bonded directly to a donor atom. These become more acidic, and hence more readily ionized. Because of the very high conductivity of the solvated hydrogen ion in most solvents, this behavior can be studied quantitatively by measurements of electrical conductivity. From the equilibrium constants obtained in this manner, an estimation of the relative extent of the polarization (in related donor systems) may be obtained.

98. N. N. Greenwood, in "Coordination Chemistry," Plenary Lectures, 7th Intern. Conf. Coordination Chem. 1962 p. 91. Butterworth, London and Washington, D.C., 1963.
99. G. Olah, "Einfuhrung in die Theoretische Organische Chemie," Bd. I, p. 191. Akademie Verlag, Berlin, 1960.

5.2.8. Nuclear Quadrupole Measurements

For nuclei of spin greater than unity the mean distribution of nuclear charge may depart from one of spherical symmetry. The quadrupole moment of the nucleus is a measure of this departure.[100–104] The interaction between this nuclear quadrupole moment and the electrical field gradient at the nucleus then leads to quantized energy levels. The transitions among these levels are observed in nuclear quadrupole spectra; they are in the microwave range. From the energies of these transitions one can determine the factor $|eQq|$, where e is the electronic charge, Q is the quadrupole moment of the nucleus, and q is the field gradient ($\partial^2 V/\partial Z^2$) where V is the electric potential. Since eQ is often known from other measurements $|q|$ can be determined from $|eQq|$. The sign of eQq can often be obtained from the hyperfine splitting in pure rotation spectra.[100] For a polyatomic system the contributions of charges in the molecule to q are proportional to the inverse *cube* of the distance separating them from the nucleus with the quadrupole moment.

The nuclei of most interest are nitrogen and the halogens. The electronic configurations that give rise to a field gradient are those that are *not* spherically symmetrical. For comparative purposes, it is customary to select reasonable reference standards for q. Thus for chlorine, gaseous Cl_2 is taken as having a purely covalent bond with equal sharing of the bonding electrons, and gaseous KCl is taken as 100% ionic with a spherical electron cloud about the chlorine nucleus. This leads to the relation

Fractional Ionic Character $= \{1 - [(eQq)/(eQq)_{atom}]\}$

Alternatively one may use the "p electron defects" defined as

$$-f = \frac{-(eQq)_{mol}}{(eQq)_{atomic}}$$

This has led to the estimates of ionic character given in Table XI.

This kind of information has also been used to estimate the double bond character of the C—Cl bond in vinyl chloride.[102] Of greater interest are the studies on nitrogen compounds. Here a direct comparison of the absorption in the free ligand and in the complex ligand would appear to be possible, though such data appear to be presently unavailable. There can be little doubt

100. J. C. D. Brand and J. C. Speakman, "Molecular Structure," p. 115. Arnold, London, 1960.
101. R. Livingston, *in* "Molecular Physics" (D. Williams, ed.), Vol. 3, p. 501. Academic Press, New York, 1962.
102. C. T. O'Konski, *in* "Determination of Organic Structures by Physical Methods" (F. C. Nachod and W. D. Phillips, eds.), Vol. 2, p. 661. Academic Press, New York, 1962.
103. W. Orville Thomas, *Quart. Rev. (London)* **11**, 167 (1957).
104. M. Kubo and D. Nakamura, *Advan. Inorg. Chem. Radiochem.* **8**, 257 (1966).

TABLE XI

ESTIMATES OF FRACTIONAL IONIC CHARACTER IN
BONDS FROM NUCLEAR QUADRUPOLE MEASUREMENTS

Compound	Fractional ionic character
Cl_2	0
KCl	1.00
CsCl	0.97
FCl	0.26
ClBr	0.110
CH_3Cl	0.31

that this will become an important tool for the elucidation of the reactions of coordinated ligands in the future.

5.2.9. THE MÖSSBAUER EFFECT

The Mössbauer effect[105] is based upon the discovery that when a nucleus emitting a γ-ray (in the general range of 10–100 kiloelectron volts) is embedded in a suitable solid at low temperature, there is a good probability that the recoil momentum of the γ-ray is taken up by the crystal lattice as a whole rather than the single nucleus from which it comes. As a result the natural line width for such a process is extremely small, with $\delta\nu/\nu$ about 10^{-12}. Unless the special precautions enumerated by Mössbauer are taken, however, this resolution is lost because of the Doppler broadening arising from thermal agitation and because of the recoil of the emitting nucleus.[106, 107] Mössbauer showed that by giving *small* Doppler velocities to the source one can annul the absorption. Mössbauer spectra are obtained by measuring the absorption of energy from an incident beam of γ-rays as the source and absorbers are given various small relative velocities. Since this is a resonance fluorescence process as far as the absorber is concerned, one may also measure the energy emitted in a direction at right angles to the original beam. Examination of such spectra (Mössbauer or velocity spectra) has revealed that they show important variations as the chemical environment of the absorbing species is changed. A schematic Mössbauer curve is shown in Fig. 7.

105. E. Fluck, *Advan. Inorg. Chem. Radiochem.* 6, 433 (1964); E. Fluck, *Fortschr. Chem. Forsch.* 5, 3 (1966); K. Burger, L. Korecz, I. B. A. Manuaba, and P. May, *J. Inorg. Nucl. Chem.* 28, 1673 (1966).
106. A. J. F. Boyle and H. E. Hall, *Rept. Progr. Phys.* 25, 441 (1962).
107. E. Fluck, W. Kerler, and W. Neuwirth, *Angew. Chem.* 75, 461 (1963).

The requirements on the nuclei are that suitable γ-ray absorption and emission processes be accessible. This has had the effect of limiting the possible absorbers, a list of which is given by Boyle and Hall.[106] Much of the work of interest here has been done with excited ^{57}Co which can emit γ-rays suitable for absorption by ^{57}Fe; or ^{119}Sn which has been used as both source and absorber. There is a very specific effect of the s electron density on this particular aspect of nuclear behavior. This has its origin in the interaction of the s electrons with the nuclear charge distribution in the excited and the ground

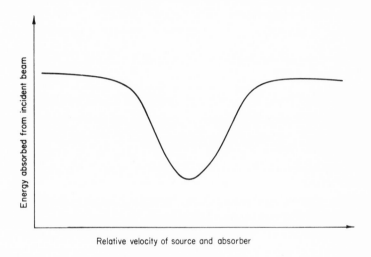

FIG. 7. An idealized Mössbauer spectrum.

state. The velocity with which the source must be moved toward the absorber (when both are the same nuclei) is directly proportional to the difference in s electron density between the absorber and the source. This is called the isomer shift S and is thus

$$S = \text{Factor } [|\Psi_s(0)|_A{}^2 - |\Psi_s(0)|_s{}^2]$$

Some typical values of S obtained for compounds of tin are[106] given in Table XII. (A positive velocity has the source moving toward the absorber.) Thus, the s electron density can be probed rather directly via the Mössbauer spectra.

The data observed with iron compounds are somewhat more difficult to interpret as the 3d electrons and their variations have an effect on the s electron density. There can also be rather complex splitting of the lines of such spectra. In the case of iron compounds there are generally two lines. The displacement,

TABLE XII
S Values for Tin Compounds

Compound	S (mm/sec)
Sn, white	0 (standard)
$SnCl_2 \cdot 2H_2O$	+2.1
$SnCl_2$	+2.1
SnF_2	+1.0
SnS	+0.7
SnS_2	−1.5
SnI_4	−0.8
$SnCl_4 \cdot 5H_2O$	−2.5
SnF_4	−3.1

S, is dependent on the formal oxidation state of the metal, but also on other factors, such as the nature of the bonding. Thus Fe^{2+} should show absorption at larger positive values than Fe^{3+} and this is generally true of simple compounds, but not of complexes, especially those in which π-bonding is involved.

In complexes in which all the ligands but one are identical it is possible to obtain some detailed information on π-bonding where there is a back-donation from the metal to the ligand. The data[104] in Table XIII show this (all at 25°C).

TABLE XIII
S Values for Some Iron Complexes

Complex	S (mm/sec)
$K_4[Fe(CN)_6]$	−0.394
$Na_2[Fe(CN)_5NO] \cdot 2H_2O$	−0.607
$Na_3[Fe(CN)_5NH_3] \cdot H_2O$	−0.340
$Na_4[Fe(CN)_5NO_2]$	−0.342
$Na_5[Fe(CN)_5SO_3]$	−0.378

Inasmuch as the six-coordinated cyanide groups in $Fe(CN)_6^{4-}$ can all participate in such π-bonding and so reduce the electron density around the iron, one would expect that replacing one of these groups by another ligand could have two different results. If the ligand is better able to accept back-donated electrons, the S value should be shifted towards more negative values. If the ligand cannot form such π-bonds at all, or if it can do so only more poorly than the cyanide ion, then the electron density on the iron will be greater and the shift will be toward less negative values of S. From the values given above it can be seen that the ligands can be arranged in the order of increasing S or decreasing strength of the π-bonds as follows:

$$NO^+ > CN^- > SO_3^{2-} > NO_2^- = NH_3$$

This analysis of Fluck and his co-workers has not yet been extended to analogous complexes containing only σ-bonds. As can be seen it should ultimately be capable of providing detailed information on the charge distribution in the neighborhood of the metal–ligand bond.

An examination of the Mössbauer effect in organometallic complexes of iron[108] allowed some estimate to be made of the relative importance of donation to the iron and donation from the iron. These shifts, for complexes of the type $(diene)Fe(CO)_3$, are in the range -0.140 to -0.218 mm/sec. For cationic complexes of the type $(dienyl)Fe(CO)_3^+, BF_4^-$ the shifts are in the range -0.098 to -0.126 mm/sec. For these compounds both types of bonding seem to be important but the dominance of forward-coordination over back-donation seems to be reasonably general. This can be seen in the comparison of the values of bis(triphenylphosphine)iron tricarbonyl ($S = -0.324$) and that of iron pentacarbonyl ($S = -0.282$); the greater donation of electrons to the iron results in a more *negative* shift for the phosphine complex.

5.2.10. THERMOCHEMICAL DATA

Thermochemical data can be used to determine if coordination has a dominant or significant influence on the course of a reaction by its effect on the thermodynamics of the over-all reaction. It can also be used to determine the strengths of coordinate bonds when the complications found in treating the condensed phase can be eliminated. The chief problem here is the estimation of the thermodynamic changes accompanying the formation of coordinate bonds in the gaseous state. This can be done directly by measurements of the heat of vaporization (where the complex is a volatile one), or by means of a suitable theoretical model.

It is obvious that equilibria in a reaction system should be displaced in favor of the products when these can form coordinate bonds with an added coordination center and the initial reactants are incapable of such a reaction. It would be anticipated that products which can form one or more chelated rings would be even more favored. Unfortunately, there is very little thermochemical information available on such systems.

One other problem which thermochemical data can solve is the estimation of effects on the enthalpy changes in a ligand reaction in which the reaction does not involve that portion of the ligand in the immediate neighborhood of the metal. Here again, there is only sparse information, but this indicates that

108. R. L. Collins and R. Pettit, *J. Am. Chem. Soc.* **85**, 2332 (1963).

the enthalpy changes are not greatly dependent upon whether the metal is present or not. A study of the bromination of 8-hydroxyquinoline and its chelates with iron(III), chromium(III), and cobalt(III) showed that the enthalpy changes were the same in all cases, within experimental error.[109]

In the case of the Gatterman-Koch reaction, Eley and Dilke have provided thermodynamic data showing quantitatively how helpful the coordination of the product is in altering the free energy change of the reaction to favor the formation of the products.[110]

In organic reactions, especially those involving aromatic systems and a Lewis acid such as aluminum chloride, the Lewis acid is often found to be capable of isomerizing the products to give those thermodynamically favored, rather than those expected on the basis of kinetic factors. One of the results of this is the abnormal orientation often reported for the products in such aromatic systems. Thus meta orientation is often found when ortho or para orientation would be anticipated from the nature of the initial substituents. These have been studied in great detail insofar as product composition is concerned, and for many cases the thermodynamic aspects are fairly well understood.[111]

5.2.11. CONCLUSION

From such studies as have already been carried out it is apparent that physical studies should, in the near future, provide us with those kinds of information on the electronic patterns of coordinated ligands that are presently believed to hold the clue to the explanation of their reactivity patterns. Whether this will still be believed when such information is amply available is doubtful. These methods normally give us information only on initial and final states of a reaction. They do not necessarily provide direct information on the ease of attainment of transition states for the reactions. However, they do allow us to approach a more detailed knowledge of these problems in a way which is impossible by any other means.

109. J. E. Hix, Jr. and M. M. Jones, *J. Inorg. Nucl. Chem.* **26**, 781 (1964).
110. M. H. Dilke and D. D. Eley, *J. Chem. Soc.* p. 2613 (1949). See Sections 4.2 and 6.1.
111. D. R. Stull, *in* "Friedel-Crafts and Related Reactions" (G. A. Olah, ed.), Vol. I, p. 937 Wiley (Interscience), New York, 1963.

Chapter VI THE PREDICTION OF THE EFFECTS OF COORDINATION ON LIGAND REACTIVITY

The goal of detailed studies of reactions of ligands can be nothing less than a *quantitative* understanding that will allow predictions to be made for both the kinetic and thermodynamic factors governing the behavior of ligands in complexes. The analogies with physical organic chemistry are obvious and the study of such ligand reactions is enormously assisted by the use of concepts borrowed from this field. The peculiarly inorganic aspects are, however, inescapable. An appreciation of the various theoretical approaches to the electronic configuration of metal ions must be used to provide an understanding of the basis of metal ion specificity in these reactions.

Because of the difference of methods used, it is convenient to separate the thermodynamic aspects of the problems from the kinetic ones. In a very real sense the use of models in the treatment of these two aspects is quite different, since the thermodynamic aspects are fruitfully discussed only for systems in which the rates of the reactions under consideration can be assumed to be reasonably rapid.

6.1. Thermodynamic Effects

The basic equation to be examined in formulating any predictions of changes in the thermodynamics of a reaction is

$$\Delta G = \Delta H - T\Delta S$$

By considering the enthalpy and entropy variations in turn it is possible to estimate how coordination changes each of these and then these may be combined to obtain an estimate of the changes in ΔG.

231

We can estimate alterations in ΔH by considering the three principal contributions. These are changes in the bond energies, changes in ΔH resulting from changes of state, and crystal field stabilization energy (CFSE) factors. Consider the very general reaction

$$A + B \rightarrow C + D \tag{1}$$

This can be run in the presence of a metal or metallic compound, M, to give the same products, which are then usually coordinated to the metal to at least a certain extent.

$$A + B + M \rightarrow MC + D \tag{2}$$

The enthalpy changes in *these* reactions may be estimated from the bond energies of the participants as

$$\Delta H_1 = \sum E(C) + \sum E(D) - \sum E(A) - \sum E(B)$$

and

$$\Delta H_2 = \sum E(MC) + \sum E(D) - \sum E(A) - \sum E(B) - \sum E(M)$$

Here $\sum E(C)$ is the summation over all the bond energies in C and the other terms have an analogous meaning. The change in the enthalpy of the reaction is then

$$\Delta\Delta H = \Delta H_2 - \Delta H_1$$

If any changes in state are introduced by the introduction of M into the system, these must be included in the corresponding ΔH term. For the case examined $\Delta\Delta H$ can be given as

$$\Delta\Delta H = \sum E(MC) - \sum E(M) - \sum E(C)$$

This can be evaluated for specific cases without great difficulty. Thus if M is a coordination center (such as BF_3) that merely forms an additional bond with one of the products the resulting equation is

$$\Delta\Delta H \approx E(M\text{—}C)$$

where $E(M\text{—}C)$ is the energy of the new coordinate bond. In a number of cases M is initially present as a hydrated cation and ends up in the product in which it forms two coordinate bonds to C, one of which is through an atom from which a hydrogen ion has been removed. In such a case

$$\Delta\Delta H \approx E(M\text{—}C_1) + E(M\text{—}C_2) - 2E(M\text{—}OH_2) - 2E(C\text{—}H)$$

An expression of this sort is a reasonable approximation to $\Delta\Delta H$, i.e., one involving only the bond energies related to the coordination process. Thus coordinate bond energies are very useful in obtaining a more detailed understanding of such catalytic processes. Unfortunately they are available in only a relatively few cases. Crystal field stabilization energy differences of a series of cations may be expected to have an effect through $\Delta\Delta H$ that arises in many cases because of the small "crystal field" provided by water in the $E(M—OH_2)$ term and the large "crystal field" provided by other ligands. This *difference* will increase in the same order as the general order of CFSE's for the *cations* themselves. Thus the term

$$E(M—C_1) + E(M—C_2) - 2[E(M—OH_2)]$$

will be expected to vary for the transition metal divalent ions as

$$Mn^{2+} < Fe^{2+} < Co^{2+} < Ni^{2+} < Cu^{2+} > Zn^{2+}.$$

Predictions of the alterations in ΔS for a reaction that arises as a direct result of coordination must include the following factors:

(1) Changes in the total number of particles.

(2) Changes from restrictions placed upon the motion of products or reactants related to either simple coordination or chelation.

(3) Changes in state or precipitation reactions.

(4) Special entropy changes resulting from great differences in the solvent structure-making or -breaking characteristics of the reactants and the products.

(5) Entropy changes arising from changes in the symmetry of the products or reactants.

(6) Entropy changes arising from changes in the charges on the reactants.

Entropy changes arising from a change in the total number of particles are sufficiently dependent on the state of the system that the phase must be indicated. For each mole of a new gaseous particle produced, ΔS increases by about 22 cal mole^{-1} deg^{-1}; when a gaseous neutral species is hydrated the entropy change is -22 cal mole^{-1} deg^{-1}. The standard entropy of a monatomic ion (of mass M) may be estimated from the relation

$$S^\circ = \tfrac{3}{2}R \ln M + 25.992$$

Entropy changes arising from restrictions upon the motion of products resulting from simple coordination or chelation may be estimated from experimental values on similar systems. These changes show up most clearly when chelation is involved and their magnitudes are definitely determined by the standard states used.[1,2] Although such changes tend to vanish as the standard state becomes a more concentrated one (e.g., as it approaches unit mole fraction), it has also been emphasized[1] that they become *more* important as the standard state becomes a less concentrated one. In short, the chelate

1. A. E. Martell, *in* "Essays in Coordination Chemistry" (W. Schneider, G. Anderegg, and R. Gut, eds.), pp. 52–64. Birkhäuser, Basel, 1964; G. Schwarzenbach, *Helv. Chim. Acta* **35**, 2344 (1952).

2. A. W. Adamson, *J. Am. Chem. Soc.* **76**, 1578 (1954).

effect will generally be found to *assist* reactions in which a chelate ring is formed in dilute solutions. Adamson[2] suggested a figure of 7.9 eu as the entropy increase associated with chelate ring formation, though a value of 4–5 eu has also been proposed for a five-membered ring.[1] This effect is superimposed on the general tendency of large complex ions to have the higher entropy values that result from the neutralization or isolation of the charge and the consequent reduction in solvation that occurs. The presence of this size factor makes the comparison of data on ammonia complexes with data on ethylenediamine complexes rather inexact. Thus the entropy of solvation of an ion as estimated from arguments based upon the Born equation or its related expressions contains a factor *inversely* proportional to some function of the ionic radius, i.e , of the sort

$$S_{298}^{\circ} = \tfrac{3}{2}R \ln \text{(formula weight)} - \frac{\text{ionic charge factor}}{\text{ionic radius factor}} + \text{constant}$$

Such dependence is generally *not* factored out in discussions of the chelate effect.

Rather detailed discussions of the contributions of other sorts to the entropies of chelation have been presented.[3–5] For example, the greater relative stability of five-membered chelate rings, opposed to that of rings with six or more members, is established by a considerable amount of data.[4,5] Some useful data of the sort required include

$$Cd(H_2NCH_3)_2^{2+}(aq) + en(aq) \rightleftarrows Cd(en)^{2+}(aq) + 2CH_3NH_2(aq)$$

for which $\Delta S^{\circ} \approx 4.7$ eu[6] and thus allow an estimate of ΔS° to be made for open and closed ring systems with related geometry, and

$$Cu(en)^{2+}(aq) + tn(aq) = Cu(tn)^{2+}(aq) + en(aq)$$

for which $\Delta S = -7 \pm 4$ eu (tn = trimethylenediamine). This indicates that the difference between no ring and a five-membered ring is offset to a considerable extent when one goes from a five-membered ring to a six-membered ring. A more complete analysis of the entropy changes in ring-closing reactions has been given.[7]

Changes in entropy resulting from changes in state or precipitation reactions can generally be estimated from data on previously studied systems. Thus for vaporization one may use Trouton's rule or tables such as that given by Moelwyn-Hughes.[8] Entropies of solution of neutral complexes are markedly

3. F. H. Westheimer and L. L. Ingraham, *J. Phys. Chem.* **60**, 1668 (1956).
4. F. A. Cotton and F. E. Harris, *J. Phys. Chem.* **59**, 1203 (1955).
5. H. Irving, R. J. P. Williams, D. J. Ferrett, and A. E. Williams, *J. Chem. Soc.* p. 3494 (1954).
6. C. G. Spike and R. W. Parry, *J. Am. Chem. Soc.* **75**, 2726 (1953).
7. F. A. Cotton and F. E. Harris, *J. Phys. Chem.* **60**, 1451 (1956).
8. E. A. Moelwyn-Hughes, "Physical Chemistry," p. 267 (fusion), p. 270 (vaporization). Macmillan (Pergamon), New York, 1957.

dependent upon both the solute and the solvent.[9] For ionic solutions a guide is available in the very comprehensive study of Noyes.[10] Noyes argued that the *effective* dielectric constant in the immediate neighborhood of the solvent was much *less* than the macroscopic dielectric constant as a result of the electrostatic potential gradient at the surface of an ion (of the order of millions of volts per centimeter) that causes the solvent molecules there to undergo an extreme polarization. Noyes wrote the free energy of hydration of an ion as the sum of two terms

$$\Delta G_{hyd}^{\circ} = \Delta G_{neut}^{\circ} + \Delta G_{el}^{\circ}$$

where ΔG_{neut}° is the free energy change resulting from the hydration of a neutral species (otherwise identical with the ion) and ΔG_{el}° is the free energy change resulting from the electrostatic interaction as the charge is built up on the species. ΔG_{el}° is given by

$$\Delta G_{el}^{\circ} = -\frac{q^2}{2r}\left(1 - \frac{1}{\epsilon}\right)$$

where q is the charge, r is the radius of the (spherical) species, and ϵ is the dielectric constant of the medium. For "experimental" values of the thermodynamic properties of hydrated ions, Noyes showed that the effective dielectric constants were indeed quite small (~ 1.2 to 3.5) and that they increased with the ionic radius. Noyes proposed the relationship

$$\epsilon_{eff} = 1.000 + 1.376(r - 0.054)$$

for estimating ϵ to calculate ΔG_{el}°. The ΔS_{el}° term can be obtained from

$$\Delta S_{el}^{\circ} = -\left(\frac{\partial \Delta G_{el}^{\circ}}{\partial T}\right)_P = \frac{q^2}{2rT\epsilon}\left(\frac{\partial \ln \epsilon}{\partial \ln T}\right)_P$$

From values given by Noyes for $(\partial \ln \epsilon/\partial \ln T)_P$ for large ions it would appear that this procedure can be used with reasonable confidence with *large* complex ions. The terms relating to the hydration of the hypothetical "neutral" species are given by Noyes as

$$\Delta G_{neut}^{\circ} = 0.16 + (6.76/r) \text{ kcal/mole}$$

$$\Delta H_{neut}^{\circ} = -10.83 + (14.13/r) \text{ kcal/mole}$$

and

$$\Delta S_{neut}^{\circ} = -36.86 + (24.70/r) \text{ cal/mole deg}$$

Estimates of ΔG_{hyd}°, ΔH_{hyd}°, and ΔS_{hyd}° can thus be made by adding the "neutral" contribution to the "electrical" one. This method of Noyes does

9. M. M. Jones, A. T. Davila, J. E. Hix, Jr., and R. V. Dilts, *J. Inorg. Nucl. Chem.* **25**, 374 (1963).
10. R. M. Noyes, *J. Am. Chem. Soc.* **84**, 513 (1962).

make some allowance for the structure-breaking characteristics of large ions but it may not do this with a great deal of precision.

The entropy changes arising from changes in the symmetry of the reactants or products can be estimated in a straightforward manner by the use of the relationship

$$\Delta S^\circ = R \ln(\sigma_P/\sigma_R)$$

where σ_P and σ_R are the symmetry numbers of the product and the reactant.[11,12] Use of this relationship allows the evaluation of this contribution to ΔS° found with different routes for a given reaction. The symmetry number is defined as the number of equivalent orientations of the molecule which can be obtained by simple rotation. A simple example will show how this can be evaluated. Consider the two reactions

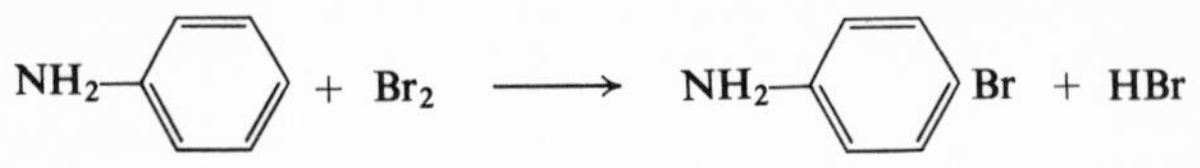

$$NH_2-\text{⟨⟩} + Br_2 \longrightarrow NH_2-\text{⟨⟩} Br + HBr$$

and

$$M\left(NH_2\text{⟨⟩}\right)_4 + 4Br_2 \longrightarrow M\left(NH_2\text{⟨⟩}Br\right)_4 + 4HBr$$

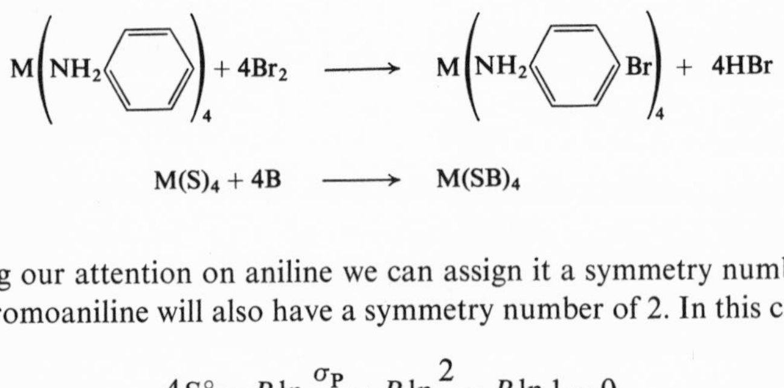

$$M(S)_4 + 4B \longrightarrow M(SB)_4$$

Centering our attention on aniline we can assign it a symmetry number of 2, then p-bromoaniline will also have a symmetry number of 2. In this case

$$\Delta S^\circ = R \ln \frac{\sigma_P}{\sigma_R} = R \ln \frac{2}{2} = R \ln 1 = 0$$

If the product here is m-bromoaniline ($\sigma_P = 1$) then

$$\Delta S^\circ = R \ln \tfrac{1}{2} = R \ln 0.5 = 1.98(-0.693) = -1.37 \text{ eu.}$$

In the case of the tetrahedral complex $\sigma_R = (4 \cdot 3 \cdot 2 \cdot 1)2 = 48$ and $\sigma_P = 48$, so ΔS° is again 0. If the product is complexed m-bromoaniline $\sigma_R = 48$ and $\sigma_P = 24$ so

$$\Delta S^\circ = R \ln \tfrac{1}{2} = -1.37 \text{ eu}$$

11. S. Glasstone, "Theoretical Chemistry," p. 386. Van Nostrand, Princeton, New Jersey, 1944.
12. J. R. Partington, "An Advanced Treatise on Physical Chemistry," Vol. 1, p. 346. Longmans, Green, New York, 1949.

This factor will assist in cases where the reaction itself generates a symmetry in the complex which is not present in the free reacted ligand. Only in exceptional circumstances will this be a term of importance.

As an example of a reaction in which the formation of chelate rings *and* an insoluble product facilitates a reaction, consider the following:

Here, $\Delta(\Delta G) = \Delta(\Delta H) - T\Delta(\Delta S)$, and $\Delta(\Delta H)$ consists of contributions from the bond energy terms and from the heat of precipitation (the reverse of the heat of solution) of the complex. It can be estimated as follows[13]:

$$\Delta(\Delta H) = \Delta(\Delta H)_{bonds} - \Delta(\Delta H)_{soln}$$

where

$$\Delta(\Delta H)_{bonds} = 2E(Ni-N) + 2E(Ni-O) - 2E(O-H) - \Delta H_{hydr}(Ni^{2+})$$
$$+2\Delta H_{hydr}(H^+)$$

and

$$\Delta(\Delta H)_{soln} \approx 10 \text{ kcal/mole}$$

The bond energies and other terms in $\Delta(\Delta H)_{bonds}$ are as follows: $E(Ni-N) = 57$ kcal,[14] $E(Ni-O) = 60.3$ kcal,[14] $E(O-H) = 110$ kcal, $\Delta H_{hydr}(H^+) = -267.9$ kcal/mole,[10] $\Delta H_{hydr}(Ni^{2+}) = -519.5$ kcal. From these figures (remembering that bond energies represent energies evolved)

$$\Delta(\Delta H)_{bonds} = -234.6 + 220 + 519.5 - 535.6$$

$$= -30.7 \text{ kcal}$$

and $\Delta(\Delta H) = -30.7 - 10 = -40.7$ kcal/mole. The entropy change can be estimated as

$$\Delta(\Delta S) = 2S^{\circ}_{H^+} - S^{\circ}_{Ni^{2+}} - (\Delta H_{soln}/T) + S^{\circ}_{Ni \, chel}$$

13. The heats of solution of such inner complex salts are of the order of 10 kcal/mole or less: M. M. Jones, J. L. Wood, and W. R. May, *J. Inorg. Nucl. Chem.* **23**, 305 (1961).
14. J. L. Wood and M. M. Jones, *J. Phys. Chem.* **67**, 1049 (1963).

From   Noyes,[10] $2S_{H^+}^{\circ} - S_{Ni^{2+}}^{\circ} = +29.5$ eu; $(-\Delta H_{soln}/T) \approx -33$ eu;   and $S_{Ni\,chel}^{\circ} \approx +15$ eu, so

$$\Delta(\Delta S) \approx 12 \text{ eu}$$

It is then possible to obtain $\Delta(\Delta G)$ as

$$\Delta(\Delta G) = -40{,}700 \text{ cal} - (298)(12) = -44{,}300$$

Since $\Delta(\Delta G) = -2.303 RT (\Delta \log K)$

$$\Delta \log K = \frac{-\Delta(\Delta G)}{2.303 RT} = \frac{+44{,}300}{(2.303)(1.98)(298)}$$

$$= +32.7$$

The formation of the complex is thus expected to alter the equilibrium constant in the direction favoring the products by a factor of approximately 10^{33}. This is certainly too large, but the calculation does show the factors responsible for an increase in the yield of the product. These are (1) large bond energies for the coordinate bonds, (2) a small hydration energy for the ion used as a coordination center, (3) a large positive heat of solution of the complex formed. The chelate effect will uniformly assist in making the free energy change more favorable to the formation of chelate rings, but can be easily overridden by other effects.

The analysis of the Gatterman-Koch reaction by Dilke and Eley[15] has been referred to previously. In this study the heats of formation of the complex formed between the product (benzaldehyde) and the catalyst (a metal halide such as aluminum chloride) were determined. They formulated the reaction as consisting of either one or two steps, depending upon the presence of a catalyst, viz.,

$$C_6H_6(l) + CO(g) \rightleftarrows C_6H_5CHO(l); \Delta G_1^{\circ}$$

$$C_6H_5CHO(l) + \tfrac{1}{2}Al_2Cl_6(s) \rightleftarrows C_6H_5CHO \cdot AlCl_3(s); \Delta G_2^{\circ}$$

An estimate of ΔG_2° was obtained from the value of the equilibrium constant for the reaction and ΔH_2° was measured calorimetrically. Combination of these allowed ΔS_2° to be obtained. The values of ΔG_2° were much smaller than those of ΔH_2°, though they fall in the same order. In this case formation of the complex resulted in a change of ΔG_1° from a positive value ($+2050$ cal at $298^{\circ}K$) that did not favor a very substantial yield, to a situation in which $\Delta G_1^{\circ} + \Delta G_2^{\circ}$ was *negative* (as much as -7600 cal for the complex with $SnCl_4$) and a situation in which the equilibrium yield of (complexed) product was essentially quantitative.

15. M. H. Dilke and D. D. Eley, *J. Chem. Soc.* p. 2601, 2613 (1949).

6.2. Kinetic Effects

The most attractive potential uses of coordination as an aid to synthesis lie in the kinetic effects which metal ions can produce. There are many cases where these are known to speed up reactions which are otherwise too slow to be fully exploited. However, when a comparison is made with the field of physical organic chemistry, where the predictions of analogous effects on purely organic systems can often be made with an amazing (and often quantitative) accuracy, some problems are immediately obvious. The first, and most serious, is the extreme (relative) scarcity of quantitative data on the rates of synthetic reactions involving metal ions or complexes as catalysts. A second problem, closely related to the first, is the rudimentary stage of our understanding of the *mechanisms* of most such reactions. A third problem is the fact that understanding of some of these processes is retarded by a lack of understanding of the nature of some of the reactions in the absence of metal ions. All in all, the shortcomings and problems are sufficient to provide considerable disappointment for those attempting to put present knowledge to immediate use; on the other hand this area provides an abundance of unsolved problems to those interested in such an underdeveloped field.

With these remarks in mind, it is possible to begin to sort out the *types* of reactions which have been examined on the basis of reasonable *models* which can serve as a starting point for more detailed discussions. The types that demand separate consideration are the following:

(1) Reactions in which an electrophilic or nucleophilic species attacks an aromatic ligand.

(2) Polar reactions of aliphatic systems.

(3) Polar reactions of ethylenic systems.

(4) Reactions in which a free radical attacks an organic ligand.

(5) Reactions in which the metal ion or complex assists in the generation of a free radical.

(6) Reactions in which the metal ion or complex assists in the generation of a polar attacking species.

6.2.1. REACTIONS IN WHICH AN ELECTROPHILIC OR NUCLEOPHILIC SPECIES ATTACKS AN ORGANIC LIGAND

These reactions can be represented by either an electrostatic model or by calculation of the localization energies required to form suitable transition states. In the first case the attacking species is considered to be either an ion or a dipole, and the substrate–complex difference is interpreted as caused by a difference in *charge* arising from the addition of the metal ion to the ligand. The relevant equations have been derived earlier (Section 4.1). The result is conveniently expressed in terms of the ratio of the rate constants for the complex (k_c) and the free ligand (k_f).

$$\ln\left(\frac{k_c}{k_f}\right) = \left\{\frac{-Z_M Z_B e^2}{\epsilon d_{AB} kT}\right\}$$

Here the increase in charge on the substrate from its reaction with the metal ion of charge Z_M will increase its rate of reaction with oppositely charged ions (nucleophiles) and decrease its rate with similarly charged ions (electrophiles). Although the general trends predicted here are observed the equation does not adequately distinguish the great qualitative differences between a ligand combined with a proton and one combined with a metal ion of the same charge. The derivation of this equation can be refined to a considerable degree but this requires that the transition state be specified much more exactly. (See Section 4.1.)

The treatment of this problem through the calculation of localization energies can be formally brought to an analogous equation

$$\ln(k_c/k_f) = \ln(A_c/A_f) + \{E_{L,f} - E_{L,c}\}$$

where $E_{L,c}$ and $E_{L,f}$ are the localization energies for substitution with the complex and the free ligand respectively, and A_c and A_f are the corresponding pre-exponential factors.

In a comparison of these models with experimental data, it should be noted that coordination can affect the rates of such reactions via changes in both the activation energy *and* the pre-exponential factor (or entropy of activation). The model based on the calculation of localization energies does not allow the estimation of changes in the pre-exponential factors and will be useful primarily where these are not altered greatly by coordination. The electrostatic model allows changes in both A and E_a to be estimated. A comparison of the theory with experiment can be carried out if a model of the transition state (to give d_{AB}) is constructed. Unfortunately, ϵ is also a variable as it cannot be equated to the macroscopic value of the dielectric constant.[16] The shortcomings of the simple electrostatic theory can be appreciated from the data obtained on the iodination of 8-hydroxyquinoline-5-sulfonic acid and some of its chelates with tervalent metal ions.[17, 18] These are given in Table XIV. From this it is obvious that the variation among complexes is greater than the difference between the ligand and the most rapidly reacting of the complexes. Other studies of this same reaction, but with labile complexes of divalent species[18] revealed a ratio of k_c/k_f of about 10^{-2}. From the electrostatic model

16. K. J. Laidler, "Chemical Kinetics," 2nd Ed., pp. 222–230. McGraw-Hill, New York, 1965.
17. R. C. McNutt, Ph.D. Thesis, p. 77. Vanderbilt University, Nashville, Tennessee, 1967.
18. C. Bostic, Q. Fernando, and H. Freiser, *Inorg. Chem.* 4, 602 (1965).

TABLE XIV

RATE CONSTANTS FOR THE IODINATION OF 8-HYDROXYQUINOLINE-5-SULFONIC ACID AND ITS
COMPLEXES

Compound	Rate constant at pH 7 and 40°C
8-Hydroxyquinoline-5-sulfonic acid	6.94×10^1 lm^{-1} s^{-1}
Iron(III) 1:3 chelate	1.75×10^1
Chromium(III) 1:1 chelate	4.22×10^{-4}
Palladium(II) 1:1 chelate	8.79×10^{-4}
Rhodium(III) 1:1 chelate	1.37×10^{-4}

(using $Z_A = -1$), this gives a value of (ϵd_{AB}) of 160×10^{-8}; if $\epsilon = 80$, then d_{AB} for this reaction is 2×10^{-8} cm. If one now reverses this process to estimate a k_c for a typical 1:1 complex with a tervalent ion, one obtains $k_c/k_f = 3 \times 10^{-5}$; the actual ratio from the tabulated data is 2×10^{-6}. This shows that the crude electrostatic model is not without some merit. The data for the iron(III) 1:3 complex shows that in such a case, the effect of the positive charge of the iron is spread over *three* ligands, with a corresponding reduction in the deactivation suffered by each. A more detailed analysis of this case cannot be presented until more detailed rate constants are available for *all* of the reacting species present in solution.

6.2.2. POLAR REACTIONS OF ALIPHATIC SYSTEMS

There are a number of ways in which the relative rates for ligand and complex may be estimated for these systems including: (1) an electrostatic model, (2) a model, based on extensions of the Hammett equation to such systems, that considers the metal ion as a "substituent" in the system, and, (3) more formal quantum mechanical treatments based upon particular models for the reaction.

The treatment of such systems is often complicated by the fact that the literal ligand involved is the conjugate base of the parent organic compound. For most of these reactions it is possible to set up an electrostatic model based upon the treatment of Branch and Calvin.[19] Where a reasonable electrostatic model of the reaction can be formulated, such a treatment will at least allow an estimate to be made of relative rates and may furnish more detailed information. In such cases a problem of some importance is the estimation of a microscopic dielectric constant, and this will generally frustrate efforts to develop a completely *a priori* treatment of a given reaction. The estimation of suitable microscopic dielectric constants has been studied in some detail,[16]

19. G. E. K. Branch and M. Calvin, "The Theory of Organic Chemistry," p. 216. Prentice-Hall, Englewood Cliffs, New Jersey, 1939.

but such refinements introduce additional parameters which can be adjusted to give a fit of experimental data. Changes of this sort do not facilitate the use of such a model to predict the behavior anticipated in other systems.

The extension of the Hammett equation (or more accurately linear free energy relationships) to aliphatic systems has met with reasonable success.[20] Although such a treatment may work quite well in assessing a constant characteristic of the steric and electronic properties of a complex involving a donor group that did not participate directly in the reaction, it might be expected to be unsatisfactory when a chelate ring involving the reactive group is formed. The normal linear free energy relationships may be expected to be useful in comparing the free ligand and complex reactivities for structures of the type

$$M:D—CH_2—CH_2—R$$

where M is a metal ion, D the donor group, and R the reactive group in a reaction that does not involve D.

One way in which the Taft treatment can be *formally* extended to systems which contain metal ions is to estimate values of σ^* (the polar substituent constants) from the data available on the rate constants of the reactions of such complexes. The equation used to define σ^* values is

$$\sigma^* = \left(\frac{1}{2.48}\right)\left[\log\frac{k_B}{k_A} - \log\frac{k_{0B}}{k_{0A}}\right]$$

Here k_{0B} and k_{0A} are the rate constants for the base- and acid-catalyzed reactions of the reference substance, in this case the hydrolysis of the reference compound ethyl acetate; k_B and k_A are the corresponding rate constants for the compound under consideration for which σ^* is to be defined. Typical values of σ^* are $H = 0.490$; $Cl_3C— = 2.65$, and $tert\text{-}C_4H_9 = -0.300$. For a preliminary test of such a procedure, it is necessary to *ignore* the fact that metal ions are usually not present in the complex under the acidic conditions required to obtain k_A values. Because of this problem, and the resultant simplifications introduced, we will designate our "polar substituent constants" by the symbol σ_M^*. The data on the hydrolysis of ethyl glycinate and its complexes provide one set of data which allow σ_M^* to be estimated. These are given in Table XV. In order to obtain the σ_M^* values, k_A for the complexes was taken to be the same as that for ethyl glycinate, a rather drastic assumption. The use of the k_A value for the parent ligand rather than the metal complex is unfortunate in that it does not allow the direct comparison desired between

20. R. W. Taft, Jr., *in* "Steric Effects in Organic Chemistry" (M. Newman, ed.), p. 556. Wiley, New York, 1956. J. E. Leffler and E. Grunwald, "Rates and Equilibria of Organic Reactions," pp. 216–235. Wiley, New York, 1963.

TABLE XV

ESTIMATION OF $\sigma_M{}^*$ VALUES

Compound	k_A	k_B	$\sigma_M{}^*$	Reference
Ethyl acetate	4.51×10^{-5a}	4.65×10^{-2a}	0	21
Ethyl glycinate	2×10^{-2b}	38.1	$H_2N—CH_2— = +0.107$	22
Ni^{2+} complex of ethyl glycinate	"2×10^{-2}"	3.98×10^3	$Ni^{2+}NH_2—CH_2— = +0.523$	23
Co^{2+} complex of ethyl glycinate	"2×10^{-2}"	9.9×10^3	$Co^{2+}NH_2—CH_2— = +0.678$	23
Zn^{2+} complex of ethyl glycinate	"2×10^{-2}"	23.3×10^3	$Zn^{2+}NH_2CH_2— = +0.832$	23

[a] Data at 25°C; units on rate constants; liter mole^{-1} sec^{-1}.

[b] For acid-catalyzed hydrolysis of protonated form $\overset{+}{H_3N}—CH_2COOC_2H_5$. The corresponding values cannot be determined for labile complexes of the sort listed. Such a value might be obtained by direct measurement on a complex ion such as

$$[PtCl_3(NH_2CH_2COOC_2H_5)]^-.$$

the ligand and its complexes. The more rigorous comparison would restrict such estimates to systems [such as the complexes with Pt(II) and Pd(II)] in which the complex possesses sufficient stability to exist in acidic media and undergo the acid-catalyzed hydrolysis in preference to a ligand substitution reaction. The definition used in the table has the enormous advantage that it can be used for the comparison of ligands with their complexes, both labile and inert. Use of the same limited data allows a corresponding $\rho_M{}^*$ value to be obtained for the basic hydrolysis of this compound from the relationship

$$\log(k_{B,1}/k_{B,2}) = \rho_M{}^*(\sigma_{M,1}^* - \sigma_{M,2}^*)$$

From the data on the metal-catalyzed reactions a $\rho_M{}^*$ value of about 2.5 is obtained (this does not allow the uncatalyzed reaction to be suitably accommodated). The constants resulting from such a crude analysis are only indicative; they can only be put on a secure basis when the standards for the definition of $\sigma_M{}^*$ can be more exactly specified. Alternatively this can be done when a sufficient number of metal-catalyzed reactions have been examined kinetically so that an internally consistent set of $\sigma_M{}^*$ values can be obtained.

21. "Tables of Chemical Kinetics—Homogeneous Reactions," *Nat. Bur. St.* (*U.S.*), *Circ.* **510**, 101 (1951).
22. R. W. Hay, L. J. Porter, and P. J. Morris, *Australian J. Chem.* **19**, 1197 (1966).
23. J. E. Hix, Jr. and M. M. Jones, *Inorg. Chem.* **5**, 1863 (1966).

6.2.3. Polar Reactions of Ethylenic Systems

For these reactions it is again possible to set up an electrostatic model, though the polarity generated in the ethylenic bond by coordination may be slight. Such complexes are very similar to the π-complexes of olefins with protons that have been invoked as intermediates in many addition reactions.[24] The theoretical work on conjugated systems allows some of these reactions to be put on a basis similar to that used for aromatic systems.[25] Although the theoretical relationship of olefin–metal complexes to protonated aromatic systems has been recognized,[26] it has not been exploited. The known effects of coordination in accelerating the reactions of olefins with water, hydrogen halides, and nucleophiles, in general presumably go by a path in which the complex provides a high concentration of olefin in a state favorable to the formation of an incipient carbonium ion. In the catalytic processes involving olefins, it is often more profitable to focus on the catalyst. Halpern has outlined the analogies that exist between such transition metal catalysts and the reactant types of carbon species.[27] Halpern starts from the viewpoint that a saturated carbon atom with a coordination number of four and no nonbonding electrons is analogous to a transition metal complex with a coordination number of *six* and six nonbonding electrons. Such species have as their characteristic reactions, *substitution* processes, e.g.,

$$R_3C—Cl + OH^- \rightarrow R_3COH + Cl^-$$

and by analogy

$$RhCl_6^{3-} + H_2O \rightarrow RhCl_5(OH_2)^{2-} + Cl^-$$

and

$$RhCl_6^{3-} + H_2 \rightleftarrows RhHCl_5^{3-} + HCl$$

Species that have a coordination number of five with seven nonbonding electrons are analogous to the free radicals of organic chemistry. The corresponding reactions of such species are dimerization, abstraction, and addition. The best-characterized transition metal complex of this sort is $Co(CN)_5^{3-}$. It dimerizes to form $[Co_2(CN)_{10}]^{6-}$, can abstract an iodine atom from methyl iodide, and can undergo an addition reaction with acetylene.

$$2Co(CN)_5^{3-} + HC≡CH \rightarrow [(CN)_5CoCH=CHCo(CN)_5]^{6-}$$

Carbene (R_2C:) compounds have their analogs in transition metal complexes which have a coordination number of four with eight nonbonding

24. E. S. Gould, "Mechanism and Structure in Organic Chemistry," Chapt. 13. Holt, New York, 1959.
25. (a) L. Salem, "The Molecular Orbital Theory of Conjugated Systems." Benjamin, New York, 1966. See especially Chapt. 6; (b) H. H. Greenwood and R. McWeeny, *Advan. Phys. Org. Chem.* **4**, 73–145 (1966).
26. H. H. Perkampus, *Advan. Phys. Org. Chem.* **4**, 256, 267 (1966).
27. J. Halpern, *Chem. Eng. News* Oct. 31, p. 68 (1966).

electrons. The characteristic reactions found in both cases are addition and insertion. A complex in this category is $IrI(CO)(PPh_3)_2$, which undergoes the reactions

$$IrI(CO)(PPh_3)_2 + C_2H_4 \rightleftarrows IrI(CO)(PPh_3)_2(C_2H_4)$$

$$IrI(CO)(PPh_3)_2 + H_2 \rightleftarrows IrH_2I(CO)(PPh_3)_2$$

The electronic analog of the carbonium ion (R_3C^+) is the species with a coordination number of five and six nonbonding electrons [e.g., $Co(CN)_5^{2-}$] which undergoes the anticipated reaction to add nucleophiles. Finally, the carbanion $(R_3C:^-)$ has its analog in species with a coordination number of five and eight nonbonding electrons. An example is seen in $Mn(CO)_5^-$ and the characteristic reaction is the addition of an electrophile.

$$Mn(CO)_5^- + H^+ \rightleftarrows HMn(CO)_5$$

The basic notion here is that the six-coordinate transition metal complex with six nonbonding electrons is similar to the four-covalent carbon compound. The act of removing a given number of attached groups or changing the number of nonbonding electrons leads to similar reactant species. This is summarized in the following table.

Change in coordination number	Change in *number* of nonbonding electrons	Examples
-1	0	R_3C^+, $Co(CN)_5^{2-}$
-1	$+1$	$R_3C\cdot$, $Co(CN)_5^{3-}$
-1	$+2$	$R_3C:^-$, $Mn(CO)_5^{2-}$
-2	$+2$	$R_2C:$, $IrI(CO)(PPh_3)_2$

6.2.4. REACTIONS IN WHICH A FREE RADICAL ATTACKS AN ORGANIC LIGAND

This group of reactions is one for which an apparent theoretical basis is already on hand in the various treatments which have been developed for the parent organic systems,[28] e.g., the free valence index of Coulson. Unfortunately, this group of reactions may well prove to be one of the most difficult to incorporate into a qualitative scheme for a very simple reason: The point of attack of such reagents has been found to vary not only between the ligand and a given complex, but also among complexes with various metals.[29]

28. Ref. 25(a); A. Streitwieser, "Molecular Orbital Theory," pp. 289–290, 398–407. Wiley, New York, 1961.
29. E. L. Patmore, Ph.D. Thesis, Univ. of Connecticut, Storrs, Connecticut, 1963. Univ. Microfilms No. 64–3553.

6.2.5. REACTIONS IN WHICH THE METAL ION ASSISTS IN THE GENERATION OF A FREE RADICAL

In many of these cases the gross energy change involved in the reaction can be estimated from a knowledge of the energies of the bonds involved. When this can be done, it will be possible to select metal ions that are suitable as catalysts. The basis for such calculations is very similar to that used for this type of reaction in the gas phase.[30] Basically, the feasibility of such processes is determined by the magnitudes of the bond energies involved. The overall process must result in the formation of bonds that are stronger than those which are broken.

6.2.6. REACTIONS IN WHICH A METAL ASSISTS IN THE GENERATION OF A POLAR ATTACKING SPECIES

In these cases the usual reaction involved is one of the type

$$A:B: + M \rightarrow A:B:\overset{\delta+\,\delta-}{M}$$

The efficacy of M in activating A:B: is expected to be determined by the ease with which it forms a coordinate bond to B (which may be the same as A, as in Cl_2). The coordination preferences of various metal ions have been examined in detail.[31-33] One would thus anticipate that the platinum metal ions would be superior activators for the heavier halogens and that mercuric salts would activate iodine. When an insoluble salt MB can result, this assists the activation process as in the use of silver sulfate and iodine as an iodinating agent. In this latter case one does *not* have a catalyst and the difference that sets off catalysts from the general run of activators is worth noting. For a coordination center to act as a catalyst in such reactions it must be continually regenerated, as in

$$FeBr_3 + Br_2 \rightleftarrows \overset{\delta-}{Br_3FeBr}:\overset{\delta+}{Br}$$
$$\overset{\delta-}{Br_3FeBr}:\overset{\delta+}{Br} + ArH \rightarrow Br_3FeBr^- + ArBr + H^+$$
$$H^+ + Br_3FeBr^- \rightarrow FeBr_3 + HBr\uparrow$$

When a stable complex is formed, as with the platinum metals, or an insoluble salt results, as with Ag^+, a stoichiometric amount of activator is needed and

30. (a) V. N. Kondrat'ev, "Chemical Kinetics of Gas Reactions," p. 151 ff. Macmillan (Pergamon), New York, 1964. (b) E. W. R. Steacie, "Atomic and Free Radical Reactions," 2nd Ed. Reinhold, New York, 1954. (c) S. Glasstone, K. J. Laidler, and H. Eyring, "The Theory of Rate Processes," pp. 141 ff. McGraw-Hill, New York, 1941. (d) P. G. Ashmore, "Catalysis and Inhibition oɩ Chemical Reactions." Butterworth, London and Washington, D.C., 1963.
31. G. Schwarzenbach, *Experientia Suppl.* 5, 162 (1956).
32. S. Ahrland, J. Chatt, and N. R. Davies, *Quart. Rev. (London)* 12, 265 (1958).
33. R. G. Pearson, *J. Am. Chem. Soc.* 85, 3533 (1963).

the reaction simply cannot be referred to as a catalytic one. It is easy to see that if the parent acid that results from the activation is stable in the system, one will not have a catalyst—so the coordination center cannot bind the anion resulting from the activation process too tightly if it is to serve a catalytic function. A corollary of this has the result that the presence of a large cation in such a system (which may be generated *in situ*) will often lead to the formation of a stable solid containing the activating species as an anion and greatly lower the efficiency of the catalytic process.

6.3. Conclusion

Several decades ago,[34] one of the theoretical physicists most influential in the development of quantum mechanics surveyed the progress up to that time and concluded:

> The underlying physical laws necessary for the mathematical theory of a large part of physics and the whole of chemistry are thus completely known, and the difficulty is only that the exact application of these laws leads to equations much too complicated to be soluble. It therefore becomes desirable that approximate practical methods of applying quantum mechanics should be developed, which can lead to an explanation of the main features of complex atomic systems without too much computation.

These much desired "practical methods" are still in a process of slow, piecemeal development. Because of the great effort that has been expended in the development of such methods in organic chemistry, there are a number of procedures which can be used for theoretical studies of ligand reactivity after the perturbation caused by the introduction of a charged metal ion has been satisfactorily incorporated. The general problem of formulating a theoretical treatment for such systems is now recognized as different in character from that imagined by earlier investigators. It is a *dynamic* problem and must deal with transition states. Here again physical organic chemistry can furnish many guidelines if we are willing to work with the *differences* in the behavior of systems, rather than demand complete *a priori* calculations on a single reaction. There is every reason to believe that such theoretical treatments of ligand reactivity will become available in the near future.

34. P. A. M. Dirac, *Proc. Roy. Soc.* (*London*) **123**, 714 (1929).

Envoi

In any book of this sort, it is inevitable that the author's opinions and prejudices will play a dominant role in the determination of the material to be presented *and* how it will be interpreted. Because this is a field in which opinions differ widely, it is important for the reader to appreciate just how drastic this difference of outlook and opinion is. For this purpose, there is given below, a list of references (many of them reviews) whose perusal will *enormously* benefit the interested reader.

J. Halpern, *Ann. Rev. Phys. Chem.* **16**, 103 (1965); *Chem. Eng. News* Oct. 31, pp. 68 ff. (1966) (Homogeneous catalysis, especially via transition metal complexes of unusual types.)

D. H. Busch, *Record Chem. Progr.* (*Kresge-Hooker Sci. Lib.*) **25**, 107 (1964); *Advan. Chem. Ser.* **37**, 1 (1963) (general review with emphasis on template reactions).

M. T. Beck, *Record Chem. Progr.* (*Kresge-Hooker Sci. Lib.*) **27**, 37 (1966) (a broad survey).

M. Bender, *Advan. Chem. Ser.* **37**, 19 (1963) (Nucleophilic attack on coordinated ligands).

R. J. P. Williams, *in* "Enzymes" (H. Lardy and K. Myrback, eds.), 2nd Ed., Vol. 1, pp. 391–441. Academic Press, New York, 1958 (emphasis on biochemical aspects); A. E. Dennard and R. J. P. Williams, *in* "Transition Metal Chemistry" (R. L. Carlin, ed.), Vol. 2, pp. 115 ff. Dekker, New York, 1966.

R. W. Hay, *Rev. Pure Appl. Chem.* **13**, 157 (1963); *J. Chem. Educ.* **42**, 413 (1965) (Nucleophilic attack on coordinated ligands and homogeneous catalysis of decarboxylation).

F. P. Dwyer, *in* "Chelating Agents and Metal Chelates" (F. P. Dwyer and D. P. Mellor, eds.). Academic Press, New York, 1964 (a general survey).

J. Chatt, *Proc. Chem. Soc.* p. 318 (1962) (emphasis on platinum metal complexes).

Q. Fernando, *Advan. Inorg. Chem. Radiochem.* **7**, 185 (1965) (reactions of metal chelates).

G. Eichhorn, *in* "The Chemistry of the Coordination Compounds" (J. C. Bailar, Jr. and D. H. Busch, eds.), p. 698. Reinhold, New York, 1956; *Advan. Chem. Ser.* **37**, 37 (1963); *in* "Chelation Therapy" (A. Soffer, ed.), pp. 133 ff. Thomas, Springfield, Illinois, 1964 (biochemical aspects).

J. P. Collman, *in* "Transition Metal Chemistry" (R. Carlin, ed.), Vol. 2, pp. 1 ff. Dekker, New York, 1965 (a broad survey, emphasis on preparative reactions); *Angew. Chem. Intern. Ed. English* **4**, 132 (1965).

W. Tochtermann, *Angew. Chem. Intern. Ed. English* **5**, 351 (1966) (work of G. Wittig).

R. Criegee, *Angew. Chem. Intern. Ed. English* **5**, 333 (1966); K. Dimroth, *Angew. Chem. Intern. Ed. English* **5**, 338 (1966) (work of H. Meerwein).

G. N. Schrauzer, *Advan. Organometal. Chem.* **2**, 1 (1964); *Angew. Chem.* **76**, 28 (1964) (Cyclooctatetraene/Reppe chemistry).

W. Langenbeck, *Fortschr. Chem. Forsch.* **6**, 301 (1966) (a broad survey which includes metal-chelate catalysis as one part).

G. Hesse, *in* "Handbuch der Katalyse" (G. M. Schwab, ed.), Vol. VI, pp. 68 ff. Springer, Vienna, 1943; *in* "Methoden der Organischen Chemie (Houben-Weyl)" (E. Miller, ed.), Vol. IV, Pt. 2, pp. 61–136. Thieme, Stuttgart, 1955.

G. Wilke *et al.*, *Angew. Chem.* **75**, 10 (1963); *Angew. Chem. Intern. Ed. English* **2**, 105 (1963); *Angew. Chem.* **78**, 157 (1966) (Transition metal-allyl compounds).

M. Orchin and I. Wender, *in* "Catalysis" (P. H. Emmett, ed.), Vol. V. Reinhold, New York, 1957.

I. Wender, H. W. Sternberg, and M. Orchin, *in* "Catalysis" (P. H. Emmett, ed.), Vol. V. Reinhold, New York, 1957.

J.-C. Lauer, *Ann. Chim. (Paris)* **10**, 301 (1965) (Homogeneously catalyzed hydrogenations).

O. A. Chaltykyan, "Copper-Catalytic Reactions," transl. by A. E. Stubbs. Consultants Bur., New York, 1966 (Homogeneous catalysts involving cuprous complexes).

J. P. Candlin, K. A. Taylor, and D. T. Thompson, "Reactions of Transition-Metal Complexes." Elsevier, Amsterdam, 1968 (notice of the existence of this book was obtained after the present manuscript was completed).

E. W. Stern, *Catalysis Revs.* **1**, 73 (1967) (Reactions of unsaturated ligands in Pd(II) complexes).

C. W. Bird, "Transition Metal Intermediates in Organic Synthesis." Academic Press, New York (1967).

AUTHOR INDEX

Numbers in parentheses are reference numbers and indicate that an author's work is referred to, although his name is not cited in the text.

Adamson, A. W., (166), 186, 187, (179), 189, (2), 233, 234
Aguilo, A., (71), 162
Ahrland, S., 86, (32), 246
Akabori, S., (160), 85, (322), (323), (324), 122
Alexander, M. D., (19), 38, (19), 39, (27), 154
Allen, A. D., (93), 167
Allen, A. O., (184), 189
Allinger, N. L., (134), 174
Amma, E. L., (384), 137
Anderson, A. W., (141), 177
Anderson, J. S., 103
Andrews, L. J., (44), 158
Ang, K. P., (307), 118
Angelici, R. J., (22a), 41
Angyal, S. J., (134), 174
Arbusov, A. E., (11), 3
Arlman, E. J., (142), 177
Armstrong, R. S., (96), 223
Arro, L., (162), 86
Ashby, C. E., (141), 177
Ashford, T. A., (344), 126
Audrieth, L. F., (213), 96
Axelrod, J., (101), 168

Baaz, M., (53), 159
Babaeva, G. V., (379), 135
Babbitt, J. M., (176), 90
Bacon, R. G. R., (275), 106
Badar-Ud-Din, (374), 134
Baddeley, G., (106), 65
Bag, S. P., (14), 15
Bailar, J. C., Jr., 29, (31), 46, (330), 124, (374), 134, (127), 172, (136), 174, (231), 200
Baker, W. A., (36), 47

Bakore, G. V., (170), 187
Bamann, E., (23), 42, (24), (25), (26), 43, 44, (29), 45, 49, 50, (59), 51
Banks, C. V., (335), 125
Bannister, E., (60), 215, (60), 216
Barbeau, C., (176), 189
Barker, M. F., (45), 9, (333), 125
Barnes, R. A., (2), 202, 205
Barnes, R. D., (60), 215, (60), 216
Barnett, C. J., (305), 118
Barnum, D. W., (25), 208, 212
Barry, W. J., (32), 20
Barsh, M. K., (267), 104, (193), (194), (196), 193
Barth, A., (206), 95
Bartlett, P. D., (137), 74
Barton, D. H. R., (137), 174
Basolo, F., 14, (10), 15, (20), (21), 16, (364), 133, (159), 186
Basu, S., (121), 70
Bates, H. G. C., (183), 189
Bath, S. S., (145), 179
Baudisch, O., (36), (37), (38), (40), (41), 7, (202), 95, (241), 100
Bauer, H., (46), 9
Bauer, H. F., (330), 124
Bauer, S. H., 210
Bawn, C. E. H., (168), 89. (140), 175
Baxendale, J. H., (240), 100, (182), 189
Bayston, J., (210), 195
Beard, J. A. T., (9), 202
Beck, M. T., 10 (170), 89, (302), 117, (304a), 118, (121), 170, (155), 182
Beevers, R. B., (140), 175
Begun, G. M., (54), 214
Belford, R. L., (164), 186, (38), (41), 212
Belfry, H. M., (345), 127

251

SUBJECT INDEX